THE SOCIAL RELATIONS OF SCIENCE

J. G. CROWTHER

THE
SOCIAL RELATIONS
OF SCIENCE

DUFOUR
1967

Library of Congress Catalog Card Number 67-20333

Printed in Great Britain
by Ebenezer Baylis and Son, Limited
The Trinity Press, Worcester, and London

Preface

THE aim of this book, completed in 1939 and first published in 1941, was to conceive the Social Relations of Science as a new discipline, to be distinguished from the history and philosophy of science on the one hand, and political and economic history on the other. It was a response to the knowledge and experience of the 1930s. This new edition is slightly shorter than the original, and contains a number of corrections.

Since 1939 much research on the history of science has been published. A great deal of it has been directed to the elucidation of the logic of scientific discovery, which has its own special importance. In its bearing on the social relations of science, it has led to modifications in knowledge of facts and dates, attributions and emphases, but not of the general picture.

The most important contribution, from the perspective of this book, is Dr. Joseph Needham's treatise on *Science and Civilization in China*. The researches of Dr. Needham have demonstrated that the comparative contribution of China to science and technology is much greater than had been previously understood, enhancing still further the importance of the transmission of scientific and technical knowledge from East to West.

I have dealt with the development of the social relations of science since 1939 in my forthcoming *Science in Modern Society*, due to appear in 1967.

Prefatory Note to the First Edition

THE present crisis of civilization shows that science is a determining factor in the destiny of mankind, so scientists and other members of the community have now the decisive responsibility of seeing that it is used for good and not for evil. The beneficence of science has not been seriously doubted during the last three centuries, and the majority of scientists have plodded happily along with their problems, taking the justification of their work for granted. The danger in this detachment has now become evident. Scientists and other responsible citizens must formulate a social policy for science. Some have repeated the view that science and scientists are above social conflict, and should pursue the promptings of curiosity without reference to contemporary affairs. The ease with which the exponents of this view have recently been brushed aside, ignored or exterminated shows that science will suffer severely unless its roots in social interest are consciously strengthened.

The creation of a durable social policy for science depends, therefore, on an understanding of the actual relations of science to society. These relations, and the nature of science itself, cannot be understood without an examination of how science came into existence. The elucidation of this problem is the first step towards the construction of an effective social policy for science. The first part of this book is therefore offered as a contribution to this problem.

The scientific and proto-scientific activities of man in prehistoric, classical, medieval and modern times are surveyed, in order to discover what social conditions are essential for the birth and growth of science.

It is concluded that the birth of modern science was completed in the seventeenth century. Since then, no fundamental innovation has been made in its method.

The rôles of freedom, class interest, national ambition, the repute of manual labour, and other social influences in the development of science are elucidated by attention to the history of science. But it should be understood that this book is not at all intended to be a history of science.

After the nature of science as a social product has been demonstrated, a few striking illustrations of the many events of the last three centuries which exhibit science in this light will suffice. The relations between navigation and Newtonian astronomy, Lavoisier's chemical theory and French social history, thermodynamics and the steam engine, and the general drive of a commercial civilization to discover the raw material of everything, which has culminated in modern electrical science, are among the illustrations chosen.

The reader then will wish to learn something of the conditions of science today. The scientist's personal motives, the nature of his scientific work, the conditions in which he works, the motives of those who set him to work, and many other influences to which he is subject are analysed.

Thus the reader will finally gain some conception of how science has come into existence, the sort of social developments and conditions that have actually stimulated science in the past, and the social and personal motives which influence science today. He can then begin to consider what can be done, in the light of this knowledge, to create an effective social policy for science.

This book is offered as a possible selection of the data which will assist all interested in science to work out the best policy for it.

Acknowledgments

THE views of B. Hessen and T. Veblen have provided much inspiration for this book. The works of J. D. Bernal, V. Gordon Childe, B. Farrington, C. H. Haskins, L. Hogben, T. E. Hulme, R. K. Merton, Lewis Mumford, H. Pirenne, G. Sarton, C. Singer, Bernard J. Stern and A. P. Usher have furnished valuable facts and suggestions.

The researches of O. Neugebauer and J. R. Partington have transformed conceptions of the evolution of science and technology during the early historical period.

To all these authors, and those mentioned in the lists of references given later in the book, grateful acknowledgment is made here.

J. G. CROWTHER

'In history nothing is improvised, and
here once more we can see how untrue it
is that little causes lead to great results'
— H. Pirenne, *A History of Europe*

Contents

Contents

Why Science Exists

SCIENCE is the system of behaviour by which man acquires mastery of his environment. His evolution from an animal into a man was accompanied by a new attitude towards nature, in which he began to study the contents of his environment in order to use them to his advantage. His initiation of this activity brought science into existence, and at the same time began the transformation of himself from an animal into a man. It follows that science in the fundamental sense is virtually indestructible, and attempts to arrest its growth are contrary to a biological movement at least five hundred thousand years old.

Archaeologists divide the history of man into a series of ages, known as the Old Stone Age, the New Stone Age, the Bronze Age and the Iron Age. During each of these ages species of man used implements of characteristic types. The implements, and the objects created with them, such as the foundations of dwellings, indicate the extent of the knowledge of nature possessed by their makers, and the economy by which they obtained a living, and multiplied. The size of the population in an age may be deduced from the number of burials that have survived. It has been found that the human population of the Old Stone Age, which lasted from about 500,000 until 25,000 years ago, was very sparse and its members belonged to species which have become extinct. These men could not stand erect. They had sharp teeth and powerful jaws more suitable than our own for fighting, and their brains were large compared with those of higher apes.

Men of anatomical type almost indistinguishable from our own appear in graves belonging to the New Stone Age. It seems probable that the beginning of the New Stone Age is associated with the emergence of our own particular species of man. The number of burials surviving from this age is far greater than from

the Old Stone Age, so it is concluded that the human population
had greatly increased. The next relatively sudden increase in the
number of surviving burials is associated with the beginning of
the Bronze Age, and not with any notable change in the anatomical constitution of man. Since the Bronze Age, there have
been only two major increases in human population, one associated with the invention of iron implements, and the other with
the numerous scientific and technical inventions of our own period,
of which steam and electrical power are particularly important.

It is not generally realized that the technical changes since the
Renaissance are comparable only with those of the four past ages
of man, and that we are living at the beginning of a fifth age as
distinctive as its four predecessors.

The earliest human species were better anatomically equipped
than we for fighting, but they were less well equipped than any
other higher animal with natural armaments, such as powerful
teeth and claws. They could overcome other animals possessing
these natural advantages only by artificial inventions. They could
use sharp-pointed poles and sharp broken stones as substitutes
for teeth and claws. Their ability to make tools depended on the
inheritance of binocular vision from animal ancestors. The two
different pictures of any object seen by the eyes are combined
into one picture through co-ordination by the eye muscles. The
brain derives from these muscular movements an impression of
solidity in the object, and a sense of distance. This faculty is
restricted to man and higher apes. It provides the nervous mechanism for the delicate judgment of distance requisite for the
control of the movements of the hand by the eye, upon which the
development of manual skill depends. Elliot Smith explained
that this nervous mechanism and its controlling centres in the
brain were in turn developed by the use of tools. This growth of
the brain through the use of tools led to the anatomical changes
by which species of animals became men. Experimenting with
instruments is not only the activity by which man advances after
he has evolved from the animal, but it is the cause of his biological
change from an animal into a man.

Modern experimental science, which is the source of the contemporary advance in knowledge, has evolved from the pre-
human experimentation with tools. There is no essential difference, though there has been a vast increase in subtlety, in the
method by which man advanced five hundred thousand years

ago, and that by which he advances today. The invention of tools is the product of an attitude which is essentially scientific. It is therefore the first great achievement of science in the broadest sense, and it has had the social effect of transforming animals into men.

2

Elemental Science: Tools

THE present geological era is about half a million years old, and has been characterized by four ice ages. Pieces of flint which appear to have been intelligently chipped have been found in deposits laid before the first of these ice ages. These rough implements show that lower species of man existed more than half a million years ago. No remains related to the human species have been found with these roughly shaped stones, scarcely distinguishable from pebbles split by natural agencies such as frost or fire.

The fossilized remains of a lower human species have been found in deposits laid shortly after the end of the second ice age, about 370,000 years ago. These remains, found in the cave of Chou-kou-tien, near Peking, are accompanied by very roughly shaped flakes of stone, and bones which have been burned. This discovery proves that lower species of man could make stone tools and control fire more than quarter of a million years ago.

The manufacture of the simplest flint implement involves considerable natural knowledge. The maker must be able to recognize the best sort of stone, and know where it may be found. This involves the first crude ideas of mineralogy and geology. The technique of making flint tools by striking one stone with another is difficult, and the early men who gradually developed it during hundreds of thousands of years must have learned through it much about the properties of stones, of their relative hardnesses and tendencies to cleavage. The impact of the stones will have given them crude ideas on elasticity and the inertia of moving bodies.

The first rough implements were probably for general use.

Implements for particular uses, such as scraping or boring, were made much later, after a traditional technique of flint-working had been created, and could be applied to achieve a desired design.

3
Fire

THE traces of fire left by the Peking man show that the control of fire was known at a very early date. It may have arisen from early human experiments with eternal fires provided by escapes of natural gas and petroleum which have been ignited by lightning. Natural fires of this sort have been known for thousands of years in Iran. Early man would have less difficulty in acquiring knowledge of fire from a static source than from a dynamic natural forest fire or a volcano. It would have been difficult to approach such alarming phenomena with the calmness of experimentation, but all kinds of experiments could be made with a small constant flame issuing from the ground. In particular, the experimenter could ignite sticks in the flame, and then carry them to other places to provide new fires.

The discovery of the preservation of a natural fire by feeding it with wood was probably made long before the manufacture of artificial fire. The rites for the preservation of sacred fires, such as the Vestal fire at Rome, are a survival from the times before the discovery of artificial fire.

The control of fire is second only to the invention of implements in the history of the achievements of man. The most usual manifestation of natural fire is the forest fire, and this is even more terrifying than an earthquake. The other common form of fire is lightning, and this also is frightening. The early man who first approached these terrifying phenomena with the intent of control and exploitation achieved a marvellous triumph which involved psychological and practical elements of equal importance. As Gordon Childe writes, he made a revolutionary departure from the behaviour of other animals, and was asserting his humanity, and making himself.

The psychological element of the triumph consisted of the courage found to approach fire objectively, and therefore without fear, and the boldness, no doubt at first unconscious, of the idea of exploiting not merely a great natural force but the most terrifying force in nature, whose reputation is preserved in the belief that fire is the most characteristic feature of hell.

Early man achieved a great extension of control over his environment through his mastery of fire. It provided him with artificial warmth, so that he could explore and survive in cold countries. The invention of cooking improved the variety of diet, and increased the available food supply by making inedible raw food edible. Part of the night could be turned to use by illumination from fire flames which removed the darkness. Caverns, which could be easily protected, made relatively comfortable homes when warmed and illumined by fire. He could unconsciously demonstrate his distinction from animals by frightening them away through their fear of fire, which they still had, but which he had subdued.

The properties of fire introduced him to a new world of change which is the basis of chemistry. It is said that the name of this science is derived from quem, which is the hieroglyphic for Egypt, and also means black land or charcoal. Chemistry is associated from the beginning of history with a product of fire. Fire produces swift and impressive changes in matter. It boils water, and reduces wood and flesh to charcoal and finally to ash. It splits stones and hardens clay. The observation of these changes extended early man's acquaintance with the properties of matter. The disappearance of matter in combustion showed that things can go out of existence almost instantaneously. This suggested that there is a principle of change behind the superficial phenomena of nature, and helped to suggest that he might himself be able to disappear and reappear by an analogous principle.

The discovery of the artificial production of fire was probably made much later. The oldest method consists of drawing sparks from iron pyrites or haematite by striking them with flint, and using the sparks to ignite inflammable material. Modern savages also produce fire by friction between two pieces of wood, and by the heat generated in air compressed in a bamboo tube. Archaeologists consider that the variety of methods indicates that the artificial production of fire may have been discovered late in human history when man was already widely scattered in isolated groups.

The ability to produce fire and heat increased early man's sense of initiative beyond the degree necessary for the mere preservation of a natural fire. It gave him the power to produce at will a fascinating and potent thing very different from the normal environment. As Gordon Childe remarks, the evocation of flame from flint and pyrites looks very much like making something out of nothing. It must have exhilarated early man and increased his sense of creative power.

The social effects of the second great achievement of the essential scientific attitude, the control and production of fire, permeate all aspects of human life. Cooking, pottery and metallurgy are three of its offspring. The process of cooking trains observation and attention and develops taste, and had a great humanizing influence on early man. Fire increased the stability of his life, besides his mobility. He could build a more permanent and developed life with its aid in any convenient place. These conditions would be followed by an increase in the population, and in the complexity of the social relations between its members.

The overwhelming social importance of fire is symbolized in the legend of Prometheus. According to this, the gods owe their superiority to man to the possession of secret knowledge. Prometheus stole this secret for man, to enable him to rise to a higher state. The myth is a recognition that the mastery of fire has transformed the status of man.

The early observations that heat may be produced by friction, and by adiabatic compression of air are highly abstract, and different from common phenomena. The modern analysis of them has provided a large part of the evidence for the dynamical theory of heat and the laws of thermodynamics.

4

Natural History

THROUGH nearly the whole period of his history man has obtained his food by gathering and hunting. It is assumed that early man lived on fruits, roots, shell-fish, eggs, and slain animals. The recognition of the sort and whereabouts of edible plants required the accumulation of considerable botanical knowledge. The successful hunting of large animals depended on exact observation of their behaviour, and this would reveal its relation to seasonal conditions. The appearance of eggs in spring and fruits in autumn would also attract attention to the phenomena of the seasons. The assistance of moonlight to hunting and fishing would inspire exact observation and forecasts of the phases of the moon.

Early man's mode of living was impossible without a considerable knowledge of elemental mineralogy, geology, zoology, botany and astronomy. Archaeologists believe that he must also have begun to learn the technique of the organization of social units larger than the family, as the capture of big wild animals could not have been done successfully by a unit as small as a family.

It is to be expected that early man was interested in elemental medical science, and this is definitely proved. The Neanderthal men, who had a brutish aspect, could not hold their heads erect, could not talk properly owing to chinless jaws, and could only shuffle along, flourished about fifty thousand years ago, before the onset of the last ice age. These men buried their dead in graves near the hearths in their caves. They protected them with stones from the pressure of the earth, and provided them with stone pillows for their heads, and tools and joints of meat. These facts suggest that the Neanderthalers associated life with warmth, and believed that the application of warmth would restore life in the dead. The process of planned burial suggests that systematic treatment of disease was already in existence. If the dead were tended, then the sick were also tended.

The ritual burial proves that the Neanderthalers were capable of imaginative thought, for they could conceive a life after death. They were prompted to this imaginative effort, so remarkable in such physically brutish men, by their feeling of utter helplessness and terror at death.

'The pathetic and futile tendance of the dead' became a habit of man before he emerged in his modern shape. The belief in the survival of the dead, which is the basis of religion, is reflected in these burials, and is therefore very old. This evidence for the early existence of religion may seem of the chief importance to many. Here, however, religious burial rites will be regarded as an illegitimate offspring of sound elemental medical science, and therefore a confirmation of its existence. The development of belief in survival was due to the lack of courage to face the failure of medical efforts to save life, and draw the correct conclusion from the absence of effects from burial near warmth. The lack of courage allowed the imagination to run beyond the facts, and entangle itself in the false world of magic.

The existence of ritual burials implies some sort of traditional burial service. As the actions in the service do not lead to a material result, they become divorced from medical technique and material reality and grow into imaginative make-believe. This is a source of the arts of poetry, fiction and drama.

5

Refined Hunting Technique Provides Leisure and Art

THE degree of culture rose to notable heights under the best conditions for gathering and hunting. Some men of the later old stone age established camps at strategic positions on mountain passes used by thousands of migrating animals at the appropriate season. They have left immense middens of bones. In one of these, the remains of more than one thousand mammoths have been recognized. These large sources of food could support a considerable population, who could employ their social organization and leisure for constructing buildings. Restriction to stone implements does not prevent complicated and permanent technical constructions; the Red Indians of British Columbia built elaborate wooden houses in the nineteenth century while they were still restricted to stone implements.

The crude Neanderthalers died out about seventeen thousand years ago, some thousands of years after the end of the last ice age, and were replaced by men of species very similar to our own. The climate improved steadily with the retreat of the ice, and Western Europe became richly stocked with game. The new men exploited these conditions with success. They invented a variety of tools, and devised special tools for making tools. They invented the bow, which is the first mechanical engine. It operates by storing human energy during a slow contraction. When the bow-string is released, the energy is suddenly discharged and used to propel an arrow with great speed.

The increased stock of game gave scope for these improved weapons, and the combination of circumstances gave the new men an easier life, and even some leisure. The human population increased far beyond that of earlier ages. As the mammoth disappeared in these times, its extinction may have been due to the improved hunting weapons, to the larger numbers of hunters, and superior zoological knowledge and organization in the chase.

These skilful and somewhat leisured hunters produced a realistic art. They have left some magnificent drawings and coloured paintings of animals on the walls of inaccessible caves. They reveal particular animals in active postures. It is thought that the artists believed that the life-like representations gave magical assistance in the hunting of the animals for food. The accuracy of the drawings shows that the artists, who were also among the hunters, had progressed in zoological knowledge and recognized various species of fish and deer. They were also familiar with the physiological importance of the heart, as they have left a picture of a bison with its heart exposed and pierced by a dart. This represents no doubt a hunter's wish.

6
Magic

ADVANCES in knowledge are always difficult. A slight improvement in technique may require the work of many men for a large part of their lives. When this has been achieved it benefits mankind for ever, so the social profit on invention is naturally infinite. But to the individual inventors, the slight advance seems a trifling return for years of toil. Kelvin said on the occasion of the jubilee of his great professorship at Glasgow that the recollection of his career left him with a sense of failure. His achievements had fallen so far below need and desire. The same feeling probably afflicted inventors among early men with far greater force. The disparity between their inventive achievements and their desperate needs tempted them to relieve their sense of failure by self-deception. They added large spurious claims to the real advantages of any piece of technique, to make it appear more potent and therefore more comforting.

The spurious accretion to a genuine process consisted of magical theories and operations. Magic was invented by early man to increase his sense of power and give him more confidence in solving the problem of living. He could not bear the plain facts of his helplessness, and he wanted something which gave quicker returns than technical invention. In his extremity, he convinced himself that magic could do this.

It was a product of his limitations, his difficulties, and the lack of a productive social system which could relieve them. It was invented by individualists, because it envisages the solution of the problems of life less by technical co-operation, than by the enhancement of the personal power of individuals.

The population of early men was small, and their social system was primitive. Under these conditions, they were individualistic, and looked for individualist solutions to their problems. The perception that the amelioration of man's condition does not come through the magical enhancement of the power of the individual, but through the accumulation of invention, occurs only after the evidence has been presented in the history of society over a long period.

The idea that man can best help himself by helping others is social, and arises after men have been organized in society for a long time. It is based on the observation that contribution of work and invention pays the individual, because in return for his single efforts he receives the benefits of the work and inventions of thousands of others. Isolated early man did not achieve this idea because he lacked the social experience and historical perspective from which it could be drawn.

He was not in a position to recognize the effective alternative to magic. Thus magic, born of the contrast between the magnitude of early man's fear and the triviality of his technique, became strongly established in the most ancient tradition, and persisted, as it still persists, long after the rational alternative had become plain.

It declines, on the whole, as the cumulative achievements of technique become more manifest. But when at any period the difficulty of gaining and organizing life increases faster than the discovery of the appropriate technical solutions, as in our own time, the practice of magic temporarily increases.

As magic became established so early, all genuine technical processes, until recent times, were covered with growths of magic, like large cancers on small but healthy organs. There is no space here to describe the magical accompaniments of the operation of the wonderful technical inventions made by prehistoric man. No doubt they appeared to him bigger and far more important than the genuine operation, and their existence should always be kept in mind when the genuine elements in any prehistoric technique are being described.

7

Early Applied Biology

THE accomplished hunters and gatherers of the last millennia of the Old Stone Age developed a discovery which brought that age to an end. Their ancestors for hundreds of thousands of years had included fruits and seeds in their diet. Some of these were wasted and scattered on the ground near caves where hunting families had lived for generations. They germinated and produced more seed, which was consumed as food. The cultivation of plants was probably used by the late hunters for augmenting the food supply for a long period before it began to approach hunting and gathering in importance. This occurred about eight thousand years ago.

The climate, which had been steadily ameliorating since the end of the last ice age, became notably milder and drier at that time, and more suitable for grass. The seeds of wild grasses, such as the ancestors of wheat and barley, became an increasingly important item of diet, and the auxiliary cultivation of them extended. Presently, in some communities, the cultivation of these grasses became more productive than hunting and gathering,

and the communal economy was gradually adapted to cultivation of grasses rather than hunting. Though the change from
gathering and hunting occurred recently and suddenly against
the background of half a million years of human history, it
probably took some thousands of years in absolute time.
The early agriculturalists who saved primitive wheats and
barleys year after year must have had difficulty through the
exhaustion of the fertility of the soil. They generally evaded this
by moving to new sites, as there was plenty of virgin soil.

The social effects of the development of agriculture were
enormous and comparable only with those produced by the
invention of implements and fire. Wheat and barley seeds are
very nutritious, compact and lasting. They provide more food
than almost any other means for equal amounts of labour, and
they need little attention while growing. The growers of grain
had more leisure than their predecessors, and much less difficulty
in storing food for the winter. Their new technique allowed an
indefinite increase in the population. Hitherto, the numbers of
men had been limited by the amount of game and edible wild
plants. These were relatively sparse. Increase in an agricultural
population was unlimited as long as virgin soil was still available,
for each extra member could support himself by acquiring a new
plot of land. Agriculture greatly increased the scope of women
and children, as many of its processes such as weeding, unlike
those of hunting, are not dangerous and do not require great
strength. It seems reasonable to suppose that agriculture brought
a big reduction in infanticide.

The surplus of plant food had another major effect. Food
surpluses in the hunting age were irregular and consisted of meat.
When they existed, they attracted dangerous animals. Plant surpluses attracted less harmful plant-eating animals. It is thought
that the progressive desiccation of Northern Africa, due to the
deflection of rain-bearing winds through the retreat of the
northern ice, forced more and more animals to concentrate
around the agricultural camps of men near lakes and rivers.

Numbers of animals came to depend on the agriculturalists for
food, and grew tame, and presently were domesticated. The
domestication of animals gave the agriculturalists a magnificent
new store of fresh, mobile food.

As they developed their technique they were led to invent plant
and animal breeding. The steady almost unconscious selection

of the biggest grains of wheat for seed presently produced plants much more fertile than their ancestors. The extermination of unruly cattle provided docile herds. The milk production of herds was improved by selecting good milkers. Wild sheep are covered with hairs separated by only a little woolly down, and wool-covered sheep without hair were produced by selection.

The climatic changes since the end of the last ice age have shaped man's environment and his destiny. The melting of the ice was followed by millennia of tundra, and as the climate improved this was converted into steppe, and then covered with pine forests, and these were superseded by oak forests. The Old Stone Age extended into a period of wood. Flaked flint implements are unsuitable for cutting wood, so there was a motive for inventing tools more suitable for dealing with the forest, which spread like a gigantic weed and hampered hunting. The invention of agriculture occurred while the forests were still predominant, and may have had something to do with the worsening conditions for hunting. It also stimulated the demand for better wood-cutting implements in order to clear the forest for new fields.

New stone implements were invented under these circumstances, which give the name to the New Stone Age, or Neolithic period. This age began about the same time as agriculture and therefore only about eight thousand years ago. It endured for a period very short compared with the half million years of the Old Stone Age. The new stone implements were characterized by smooth surfaces and straight sharp edges. Owing to these features they did not stick when driven into wood, but cut and cleaved through it. The smoothness was obtained by polishing, which is therefore typical. This process may have been suggested by the effect on stones used for grinding grain. It is suggested here, by the way, that the observation that warmth is produced in stones by grinding may have inspired the invention of fire-making by the friction of sticks.

The new smooth straight tools stimulated the development of carpentry, and the improvement of building and furniture.

Pottery was another great invention of the new epoch. The meat captured by the Old Stone Age hunters could be excellently roasted or grilled without vessels, but the cereals of the New Stone Age agriculturalists required baking at a milder and steadier temperature. Ovens were improved for this purpose, and the discovery that moulded clay would harden and preserve its shape after being baked may well have been made in connection with them.

Pot-making provides the first example of the use of a chemical change for a constructive purpose, and it involves a series of difficult technical processes. Clay cannot be moulded satisfactorily unless it has the correct consistency. If it is too wet it disintegrates into mud, and if too dry it crumbles. If it contains no grit it will stick to the fingers in moulding, and if the bits are too large they will interfere with the moulding and weaken the material.

If the damp moulded clay is immediately fired it will crack, so it must be dried first. Then it must be heated to 600° C. This produces the hardening, which is due to the expulsion of water chemically attached at lower temperatures to the aluminium silicate of which the clay is chiefly composed. The dried moulded vessel changes colour during the firing, and the resultant hue depends on the chemical constitution. If the clay contains iron oxide, and is exposed to air while heated, the oxide will be oxidized further into red ferric oxide and produce a reddish hue. If the pot is heated in glowing charcoal, so that the air is excluded, the iron oxide in the clay will be reduced to the black ferroso-ferric oxide, which will make it grey.

The New Stone Age potter, who was probably a woman, learned all these phenomena, and how to manipulate them.

The painting of pots involves further successful forecasting of colour-effects produced by chemical changes through heat. Paint which changes colour during heating must be prepared. This is applied to the unfired pot, and gives an artistic composition generally unlike that presented by the fired product. The patches of colour change, and the vessel shrinks. The potter must foresee all of these effects.

Owing to the existence of natural fuel which does not give a smoky flame, Asiatics solved these difficult technical problems earlier than Europeans.

The invention of pots had profound effects on human life. Cooking was transformed, and a variety of nourishing, economical and delicious new soups were invented. Jars could be used for preserving grain and oil, and for the preparation of fermented liquors. The observation of the changes which occur in mixtures of solids and liquids when heated in durable pots provided the data for an extensive development of elemental chemistry.

Again, the operations of pot-making provided a strong stimulus to the imagination. The moulding was a creative art, and the change from the dull damp moulded clay into the bright hard serviceable pot seemed not unlike a creation of life out of dust. The shape of the vessel was about the same before and after firing, but the material was quite different. This seemed to show that form persisted while matter changed.

The frequent use in the Bible and other ancient literature of the operations of pottery as similes for acts of creation shows the profound impression that their creative aspects made on the human mind.

The supplies of plant and animal fibres due to the inventions of agriculture and domestication provided the condition for the invention of the loom, another technical triumph of the New Stone Age. The simplest loom is a complex instrument, and weaving is a complex operation.

The new communities practising agriculture, stock-raising, pottery, weaving and the associated techniques sprang up from the Nile to the Indus and beyond. The human population of the world increased enormously. Though the New Stone Age did not last one hundredth of the period of the Old Stone Age, more than one hundred times as many skeletons have survived from it. The human population was therefore perhaps ten thousand times as dense. Even after this figure is pared down in various ways, the result still reflects the greatness of the new inventions. Yet the New Stone Age villages were small and none containing more than twenty graves has been found.

The women practised pottery and weaving around a fire on the village green, before the huts. They chatted as they worked in common, and mothers trained their daughters in the techniques by apprenticeship.

The village was completely self-supporting, and though it was in communication with the next, there was little trade. There is no definite evidence that the inhabitants of different villages engaged in warfare. The weapons which have survived are not distinctively for warfare, and were probably used for hunting.

The implements left in any particular village are usually of very uniform design. As they were made and used by communal groups, it seems probable that this reflects a strong control of tradition over social habits. The products of the innumerable independent villages nevertheless showed wide differences.

It seems that young persons of initiative could easily leave an old village and found a new one where they could do things in their own way, and introduce changes which occurred to them. An innovation made in a new village striking enough even to impress the conservatives in the older villages could come into existence and spread.

The New Stone Age was a period of great technical invention, immense increase in population, peace, and a combination of conservatism with initiative. Its members concluded their effort in a blaze of technical achievement which provided the means for the final supersession of the ages of stone.

8

Metallurgy

A S T H E few millennia of the New Stone Age passed, the climate in the Near East became drier, and large areas of fertile grass land became semi-arid. The agricultural communities in these regions found life more difficult, in spite of improving technique, and their members were driven to give particular attention to favoured sites with steady supplies of water. The land adjacent to rivers, such as the Nile, which seasonally overflow their banks, was doubly valuable because it was well-watered, and its fertility was renewed by the annual deposit of fresh silt. One crop could be continuously taken from the same plot, so the cultivators were encouraged to make their settlements permanent. This provided a favourable condition for large co-operative construction.

The original cultivable areas in the valleys of the Nile and the Euphrates were probably mounds surrounded by vast swamps. Though very fertile, they were small. The New Stone Age farmers who settled on them prospered, and gradually extended their size by draining from the surrounding swamp, until they had achieved the gigantic task of reclaiming the major parts of the valleys of these great rivers. In the valley of the Euphrates they created the land by covering the swamps with floating rafts of rushes, the method used by George Stephenson in laying the track across the Chat Moss swamp for his Manchester and Liverpool railway. The separation of the dry land from the water in the Biblical account of creation is a memory of the feat of the proto-Sumerians who raised the dry land of Mesopotamia out of the surrounding waters.

The accompaniment of all these technical achievements by magical practices has been mentioned in an earlier section. Unusual events and objects tend to acquire magical significance, because their rarity suggests that they are mysterious and therefore have unknown powers. Objects which possess similarity of shape and colour are supposed to have magic connections with the things they resemble. Thus coloured precious stones and rare minerals were regarded as magical. The colour of the brilliant green mineral malachite resembled the green of growing vegetation, so malachite became a magical symbol for fertility. The shape of cowrie shells resembles the female vulva, so they also are symbols for fertility. Farmers believed that they could guarantee the fertility of their land and animals and wives by decorating them with amulets made of these magical materials. Owing to the development of the technique of cultivation, the surplus production of cereals became considerable, and part of it could be exchanged for these supposedly potent objects. The demand for precious stones and other magical objects led to the invention of trade, after the prerequisite surpluses had been created through the advances in the technique of cultivation. Trade brings together in one place a variety of substances from different districts. The New Stone Age farmers lived on plains, whose soil was fertile but poor in precious stones. These are usually found in rocky, mountainous districts. Their invention of trade brought coloured stones to them from distant mountains. They already had a considerable knowledge of the technique of the production of high temperatures through their invention of pottery, and had the means to apply intense heat to the new coloured stones.

It happens that many brightly coloured minerals are metalliferous ores. Malachite is a form of copper carbonate. If a piece were dropped into a charcoal fire fanned by a strong wind, the carbonate might be reduced to metallic copper by the hot charcoal, and shining globules of copper might run out of the fire. This may well have happened many times in prehistoric Egypt, and when its significance was appreciated, the possibility of the science of metallurgy was discovered.

Pieces of native copper, gold and meteoric iron may have been known long before the invention of metallurgy. They would have been regarded merely as varieties of stone. The Red Indians of Lake Superior had many pieces of native copper from the local outcrops, but they failed to discover the possibilities of the metal.

Metallurgy was derived from the far more difficult discovery that metals may be obtained from certain stones by heating them with charcoal, or other materials. The phenomenon is in itself very remarkable, and must have seemed magical to the pre-historic men who first studied it. The complex change could not be appreciated without considerable knowledge of technical processes, probably acquired in making pottery. If this explanation of the discovery of metallurgy, which is advanced by authoritative archaeologists, is correct, the mode was typical of normal scientific discovery, where advance so often is made along a tortuous highly technical path, though an obvious one is found after the discovery is made. The discovery of radio waves in 1887 is an example. This followed from the pursuit by Hertz of the highly technical path suggested by the theoretical researches of Clerk Maxwell. After Hertz's success, it became evident that Henry in 1842, and Hughes in 1872 had observed effects due to radio waves, but had not perceived their full significance. So prehistoric men saw stones of native metal, and even beat them into implements, and no doubt saw some of them melt in fires, without discovering metallurgy.

Copper is tougher than stone and makes more durable tools, but its chief practical superiority is due to the possibility of casting it. From the perspective of a New Stone Age man, it is a reddish-brown stone that may be melted. A stone axe is soon blunted, and cannot be resharpened very often, because each resharpening reduces its size. A blunted copper axe may be melted and recast with little loss of material, so it lasts far longer.

The invention of metal casting, like that of moulding clay for pottery, provides fresh scope for the creative imagination. The maker of a stone implement is bound by the piece of stone with which he starts. He proceeds by taking away bits of the stone. He does not add any material. He attains the desired design by negative and not positive actions. When he moulds clay and casts metal he engages in positive creation, and consequently receives the higher psychological exaltation that comes from that sort of act. The invention of metallurgy stimulated the search for copper ore, which is not common, and not easily found. This extended the knowledge of geology, geography and natural history, and led to the discovery of silver, gold and tin as materials for metallurgical processes. The development of the technique of casting involved great accessions of skill. The oxidation of the molten metal must be prevented, and air bubbles must not be allowed to form in the cast. The invention and preparation of moulds which will resist high temperatures is in itself a whole branch of technique. Copper melts at a temperature of 1200° C., which cannot be obtained without an air blast. Men stepping out of the New Stone Age must have found these technical difficulties very great, and their success in solving them is a measure of their achievement in science.

The lodes of copper ore on the surface of Near Eastern countries were no doubt quickly exhausted. Copper is generally found in combination with sulphur in the form of copper pyrites, but when copper sulphide is exposed to the air at the earth's surface it is gradually converted into copper oxide. Surface lodes usually consist of copper oxide, which may be reduced by heating with charcoal, as described. But when the surface lodes are exhausted, the ore-collector must follow the vein down into the earth. He then finds that the ore below is sulphide. The extraction of copper from sulphide is more difficult than from oxide, and requires an additional process. The sulphide must be exposed to the atmosphere for weathering, so that the sulphur will gradually be removed by combination with the oxygen in the air.

Further, the ore-collector becomes a miner, and has to invent that technique which is a parent of so many advances in science. He must devise methods of boring hard rock, timbering of galleries, and preserving ventilation.

The bulky and heavy ores were rarely found near communities with a tradition of advanced technique, or in districts with copious supplies of fuel. They could not be utilized without improvements in the technique of transport.

9
Power

MAGIC stones could be carried effectively on the person of a traveller, but ores and bulk surpluses of food could not. Transporting agencies more powerful than the human frame were required, and these were found in the harnessing of domesticated animals, and in the exploitation of the wind for driving boats. The efficiency of sledges was increased by the invention of the wheel, which was also made by prehistoric man. Wheeled vehicles are depicted in Sumerian art already in 3500 B.C. They were not used until 1650 B.C. in Egypt, when they were introduced by the Hyksos conquerors.

As the technique of cultivation improved, more and more labour was required for its operations. To meet this, the ox-drawn plough was invented. The productivity of cultivation was increased, and the mode was changed from the tending of small plots into the working of fields, which is agriculture, according to the word's exact meaning. The numerous technical advances in these communities of cultivators provided the means for the support of a great increase in population. The operations of farming had become complex, and could not be conducted efficiently without an accurate solar calendar. Accordingly, one was worked out, and was probably in use in 4236 B.C. in Egypt.

The inventions of land cultivation and agriculture, domestication of animals, the wheel, the sailing boat and metallurgy were all made in the period 6000–3000 B.C. They involve the recognition of major principles in biology, mechanics, dynamics, chemistry and physics. This spate of fundamental achievement has not been approached in any other period, except the one which commenced about A.D. 1500, when science began to extend in a new way, and offers us visions as startling as those seen by the men of the New Stone Age, when they first conceived agriculture and metallurgy, and the possibility of transferring their burdens on to animals and the forces of nature.

Irrigation

THE good water supply and the sustained fertility of the soil made the valleys of the Euphrates, the Nile and the Indus exceptionally attractive after the technique of the cultivation of plants had been invented. Owing to the special conditions, the productivity of farming there outstripped that in the open countries. The surpluses were larger, and the trade for exploiting them was correspondingly more developed. The permanence of the fertility of the soil tended to make villages permanent. These circumstances favoured the growth of more complex technique, and this led to specialization. The extracting and working of metals cannot be done satisfactorily by any untrained member of a community. They require much knowledge and skill, acquired by specialization. The increasing surpluses of food provided the condition for the growth of specialization, as they could be used to feed specialists, and free them from the time and labour they would otherwise have to spend on farming.

The necessity for reclaiming land from the original swamps in those river valleys gave an extra spur to co-operation and discipline in work. Unlike the migrating farmers in open country, the farmers in the valleys repeated the same operations in the same place year after year. They acquired a new degree of regularity in working habits, which assisted specialization. The tremendous feats of land reclamation by co-operative social labour gave the social will of the community great authority. This was symbolized by gods, who represented the ancestors who had in fact created the land. Permanent residence was virtually a new social habit which strengthened affection for the site. Every feature had associations with parents and ancestors, and became a reminder of the idea of constructive achievement through social authority and organization.

The conduct of agriculture on land which is flooded seasonally demands the control of the flood waters. This entails the construction of drainage canals and banks, and the distribution of the flood water to the plots of every member of the community. The necessary engineering construction cannot be done by individuals, and the distribution of the water cannot be made without advances in the knowledge of hydraulics, and the development of a new degree of social foresight and organization.

The control of the distribution of flood waters created a new weapon of social discipline. If a farmer would not obey the rules of the society, or was obnoxious to the custodians of its traditions and therefore described by them as disrespectful to the gods, he could be instantly disciplined by the threat to cut off his water supply. Unlike an earlier farmer in the open plains, he could not leave the community if he was dissatisfied, and found a new farm elsewhere, because he could not undertake by himself the extensive engineering required in the reclamation of a new site from the swamp.

The achievement of new powers of construction and social organization involved some new limitations of freedom and initiative. The growth of specialization also increased the power of social authority, as it made more and more persons dependent on the community. A farmer could feed himself, but a smith had to be fed, so he wanted a strong social authority which would insist that he should not be allowed to starve, or receive an inadequate return for his products.

Specialization makes society far more complex, and this in itself leads to further development of the technique of social organization. It also leads to the concentration of production at a few sites, because specialist production is more efficient. Stone Age farmers usually made their tools as they went along, from stones picked up in the fields. Every member of the community spent some of his time on making tools. But after the invention of copper founding, a few specialists could make enough copper hoes and axes for the whole community. The community therefore began to look to some group of specialists in a particular place for its supplies of tools. These tendencies, and others, were creating in the great river valleys of the Nile, the Euphrates and the Indus the conditions for the growth of a highly complex form of social organization, in which social power was centralized, and numbers of dependent specialists were organized in dense communities at a few places.

This type of social organization is described as urban. The positive qualities of high and permanent fertility in the great river valleys were the fundamental conditions for its birth, and its growth was assisted by the excellent river transport, which facilitated the exchange of materials, or trade, necessary for a specialist system of production.

After this development had become established, the negative qualities of the valleys began to exert a stimulating effect. The lack of metallic ores and wood for fuel inspired pioneering expeditions to distant countries which returned with new knowledge of geography, geology, natural history, and inventions. The discovery of distant sources of raw material stimulated the improvement of transport, and ships and navigation.

In Mesopotamia even stones for implements had to be imported from distant Assyria by the Stone Age farmers, as there was no local supply.

II

Origins of Arithmetic and Geometry

THE establishment of complex communities of specialists on permanent sites, or cities, was accomplished by the relatively sudden increase in population, unparalleled in earlier times except by that which occurred between the Old and the New Stone Ages.

The organization of life in the large and concentrated populations which could now be supported by a more efficient system of production presented numerous new problems. Storehouses of durable construction for keeping large surpluses of food were required. These were made of wood, and then of stone. The Mesopotamians had no stone, so they invented bricks. The city storehouses were essential to its life. For this reason, they were sacred, and were associated with the ancestral gods. It is not improbable that the utilitarian role of storage was more important than the celebration of religious rites in the first stone and brick buildings. The separation of the temple from the storehouse may have come later. The building of domestic houses out of stone and brick came later still.

The management of the central stores of grain, and the agriculture and trade by which they were accumulated, required a banking system, and was impossible without efficient means of keeping accounts and records of transactions. Owing to the superior importance of measuring food and money, arithmetic was invented before writing, so that mathematics is older than literature. The oldest known documents, both from Sumer and Egypt, consist of numerals only.

The development of geometry probably received a strong stimulus in Sumeria through the invention of bricks, as many relations between lengths, areas and volumes are very simply illustrated by walls, cubes, and pyramids constructed of bricks of uniform size.

The growth of cities at different points along the banks of the same rivers, in lands which had already been completely settled, produced new elements of competition. The city populations used their food surpluses and technical skill for creating armies, in order to establish hegemony over their neighbours. Chief priests in city temples and other local leaders became generals, and as a result of their conquests, kings. Menes settled inter-communal disputes in Egypt in 3200 B.C. by conquering the whole country. Sargon conquered Mesopotamia in 2750 B.C. These kings began imperial expeditions for subduing the distant countries which provided raw materials, after they had unified their own countries.

The documents which rank next in age to the earliest numerical records of temple accounts are records of wars between neighbouring cities, and the treaties for ending them.

The expansion of the social unit from cities to countries and empires enormously increased the concentration of wealth, and the technical problems of management. The process of achieving it exerted steady pressure for the abbreviation of calculations and records. By 2000 B.C. the Babylonians had invented a numeral system, in which the value of the symbol depends on its place, like that of the symbols in our own decimal system. They used a place-sign for zero about 500 B.C., but did not use it for calculation. With this mathematical equipment, much of which was subsequently lost, they were able to make calculations with an ease unequalled thereafter until A.D. 1590.

The great development of Babylonian mathematics accompanied the conquest of the Sumerians by the Akkadians, who were a semitic people. The Sumerians had created an elementary system of mathematics. The Akkadians swiftly developed its maximum possibilities, and afterwards Babylonian mathematics suffered a long but slow decline. According to Neugebauer, the phenomenon resembles the assimilation and extension of Greek and Indian mathematics by the Arabs. Knowledge of Babylonian mathematics reached India, and was probably the source of the growth of Indian mathematics. The Akkadian mathematics largely consists of abstract problems concerning lengths and areas. The subjects of problems were chosen only to illustrate methods of calculation, and the attitude shown in much of their work is philological.

It seems that very great advances in mathematics are connected with new contacts between cultures. A short period of rapid progress may then occur, while the possibilities of the new set of fundamental conceptions evolved from the contact are worked out. When the new mathematical tradition has been established, fundamental departures from it do not occur, until it is supplanted in the next great change of civilization. If this theory is correct, fundamental advances in modern mathematics would appear to be impossible, because the population of the whole of the world is now in good contact. Perhaps the fundamental advances in the future will be due not to contact and assimilation between peoples with different cultures, but to assimilation between social classes with different cultures. Modern science, with its balance of theory and practice, would seem to owe much to contact between leisured scholars and manual technicians, and may be an expression of increasing assimilation of the two classes. It is possible that a fundamentally new mathematics will not be created until our own civilization has died, and the rediscovery of its ruins has provided inspiration to new peoples thousands of years hence, who will look at our mathematical knowledge with a new perspective, and see in it possibilities invisible to us, owing to the particular cast given to our minds by the civilization we have inherited.

Writing was gradually evolved from pictures to systems of conventional signs. The Egyptians reduced their hieroglyphics to 500 symbols and the Sumerians their cuneiform script of wedge-shaped marks to 1000. Even after two thousand years of development, writing remained difficult. A long apprenticeship was needed in order to learn it. This had profound social effects. The scribes became separated from the other specialist technicians. They were kept at the communal expense during their long studentship, and at the same time associated with their teachers, who were members of the executive staff of the palace and temple. While they and their profession required respectability through their associations, other technicians, whose skill may be learned more quickly, lost status.

In a document of about 1200 B.C. an Egyptian scribe gives the advice: 'Put writing in your heart that you may protect yourself from hard labour of any kind and be a magistrate of high repute. . . .' 'The metal worker at his task at the mouth of the furnace' has 'fingers like a crocodile', and 'stank worse than fish-spawn'. . . . 'The weaver in a workshop is worse off than a woman' . . . he squats 'with his knees to his belly and does not taste fresh air'.

As the social status of trades and professions crystallized, they and the associated technical knowledge acquired certain degrees of respectability and vulgarity. Medicine was highly respectable because it was of urgent personal interest to the powerful. The causes of disease are obscure, and treatment had been associated with magic from very early times. Surgery was less respectable, because the poor were more liable to accidents than the rich, and the causes of wounds are usually obvious. The scribes accepted medical knowledge as highly respectable, and therefore willingly wrote about it. They wrote less on surgery because they rated it lower.

The ancient Egyptian writings on surgery contain an outstanding work, which is probably a copy of an earlier work of 2500 B.C. This contains a classification of wounds which may occur to parts of the body, starting with the head and passing to the feet. Methods of examining the wounds, the conclusions to be drawn, and the treatments to be given are described objectively, and are evidently based on skilled observation and experience. The most remarkable feature is the plain statement that fourteen of the cases described in detail are incurable. This attitude towards illness is entirely alien to the magical, which would never admit lack of control over life and death.

Early surgical is superior to early medical science because it is a manual technique, which makes its facts so much more reliable. But that which gave it quality as science depressed its professional status, so scribes were loth to record new surgical knowledge, and thus hindered its improvement.

The social stratification that accompanied urban development received a big impetus through the development of organized warfare. This was probably an urban invention, as there is no good evidence that serious warfare existed in the preceding New Stone Age. Successful war provided vast supplies of captives besides land and booty. It was more profitable to exploit than to kill them. They were turned into species of slaves. The harnessing of domesticated animals suggested that they also might be harnessed as sources of power. Though not as strong as oxen, they could compete with them because they were more intelligent. Others were trained in the crafts of metal-working, weaving, pottery, etc.

The technicians of equalitarian farming communities, who had invented agriculture and metallurgy, the wheel and the sailing ship, bricks and the arch, wine and the solar calendar, presently found the status of their occupations depressed to that of slavery.

The techniques of numerical notation and writing were invented while the social traditions which provided the matrix of the superb creativeness of the millennia 6000–3000 B.C. were still alive, though declining with the rise of slavery.

The rate of invention slowed down, in spite of the increasing wealth, after slavery had become established as an essential and ancient part of the social system; say by 2600 B.C. From that date, until 600 B.C., there were perhaps only four great inventions, the Babylonian place numerals in 2000 B.C., iron metallurgy in 1400 B.C., alphabetic writing in 1300 B.C., and aqueducts for city water supplies in 700 B.C. Only two of these were made within the immediate influence of the ancient cities, as iron metallurgy was introduced by the less advanced Hittites, and the alphabet was invented by Phoenician traders on the less-developed frontiers of the Babylonian and Egyptian empires.

The introduction of efficient iron metallurgy provided far cheaper and more durable tools. These brought within human power the possibility of clearing the dense forests, and solving the technical problems of life in temperate regions which are more difficult than those in sub-tropical regions. The centres of civilization were gradually transferred through iron to the temperate regions of the earth, where they still remain.

The notable decline of invention after the stabilization of city life in Babylonia and Egypt occurs in parallel with the increase of slavery, the loss of status of craftsmen, and the concentration of wealth. The decline has been greatly obscured by the invention of writing, which was made about 3500 B.C., shortly before it began. Owing to writing, the details of the slow growth of knowledge during the period of decline are infinitely better known than the circumstances of the major inventions of farming and metallurgy in the previous creative age. The great bulk of the new written knowledge has produced a delusive impression of its qualitative importance.

Writing, including numerical notation and mathematics, was crippled as an instrument for the creation of knowledge soon after its invention, owing to its monopoly by scribes attached to the governing classes and despising manual technique. The scribes came to believe that manual knowledge, which is the basis of mechanics, biology, chemistry, physics and geology was unworthy of the honour of record in the aristocratic technique of writing. This attitude continued beside a great use of mathematics in trade and architecture, and it had the effect, not of reducing the volume of mathematics used in these practical affairs, but of deflecting intellectual interest from the application of mathematics to subjects which were socially respectable. The subjects of highest respectability were religion and magic. They are imaginative, and consist of collocations of ideas which do not have any necessary relation with reality.

Writing is a technique. Its origin was practical, and it has marvellous qualities. But like all other technical inventions it has limitations. It is not particularly suitable for describing the phenomena of the natural world. It is impartial in its description of error and truth. Some day, an inventor will devise a recording technique which will be automatically incapable of describing anything except the truth. Writing will not do this. In fact, in the short run, it spreads error more easily than truth, because it will record a free association of ideas which has little relation to reality. After these collocations of ideas are described in writing, they acquire a delusive reality from the reality of the script. The phenomenon is the basis of the popular belief in the truth of the printed word.

The early writers acquired social prestige. Owing to this, anything in writing was important, and because important was assumed to be true. The scribes presently convinced themselves that writing was not a recording, but a creative process. The mere act of writing established the reality and truth of the meaning. Through this evolution, the scribes divorced writing and calculation, as techniques for assisting creative thought, from the manual techniques that are the most fertile source of new facts about reality, and applied them to the pseudo-facts of prophecy and astrology, from which knowledge could apparently be multiplied with flattering facility. Writing, like radio, was at first disappointing. It propagated and stabilized a great deal of error, besides much truth. It assisted conquerors to manage empires. With the other technical inventions it was seized and exploited by proprietary kings and priests who valued it as an aid to aggrandisement and prestige, rather than the conquest of nature for the benefit of humanity.

During the three thousand years of Mesopotamian and Egyptian supremacy from 3500–500 B.C., mathematics became more and more an aid to the accumulation of riches and the exploitation of astrology in the former country, and to the erection of pathological monuments in the latter. Its progress was disappointing, but through the long period the amount was considerable.

The earliest written documents of Mesopotamian origin, dating from 3500 B.C., contain addition and multiplication, and the area of a field is found by multiplying the length and breadth. Contemporary vases are decorated with chequer patterns which illustrate the rule.

Two systems of numerals were used in the fourth millennium B.C. A decimal scale was used for measures of grain and beer, and a sexagesimal scale for numbering loaves.

During the third millennium the sexagesimal ousted the decimal scale, and place value, multiplication tables, tables of reciprocals and square and cube roots were introduced. In the second millennium B.C. simple quadratic and cubic equations were solved with these aids. Illustrative examples of the solution of particular problems in the calculation of the division of inheritances, rate of interest on loans, the dimensions of wells and storehouses, and the graduation of water clocks, were compiled. This mathematical technique was not applied to astronomical problems until one thousand years after its use in trade, architecture and military science had begun.

Observational astronomy made more progress in Mesopotamia than in Egypt because of the retention of the lunar calendar, while the latter had adopted the solar calendar. The lunar calendar is more complicated, and is useless without incessant

2*

correction based on careful observation of eclipses and occultations. The Babylonians had observed in 2000 B.C. that Venus had returned to the same place on the horizon five times in eight years. Owing to their mastery of observation they were able to operate a time scale based on the division of the earth's rotation into twelve hours, whereas the Egyptians, with less interest in observation owing to their smaller interest in the moon, determined the watches by the length of light and darkness, which varies with the season. The Babylonian time scale, which is still in use, provides a uniform measure for the organization of affairs, and has greatly advanced the quantization of social life and thought, and so assisted the progress of science. The most brilliant astronomical results of Babylonian astronomy were obtained when the supremacy of Babylonia was ending.

A tablet of 650 B.C., that contains information which may be much older, describes an attempt to find a mathematical theory of the progress of the illumination of the moon's disc while it is waxing. The disc is divided into 240 parts, and the spread of the illumination to the parts is recorded from observation. Attempts are then made to subsume the figures in an arithmetical and in a geometrical progression. The solutions are incorrect, but the exhibition of the method of research in mathematical astronomy, and the standard of mathematical technique employed in it, is profoundly important. The Babylonians attempted to discover a mathematical theory of a physical change involving movement, by collecting observations and propounding hypotheses which might subsume them in a formula. There is no difference in principle between this method and that by which Newton discovered the law of gravitation. Naburimanni in 500 B.C. gave the length of the mean lunar month correct to three places of decimals, and Kidinnu in 380 B.C. gave it correct to four places of decimals.

The Babylonians mastered the manipulation of equations, but as they always worked with positive integers and fractions, and as the roots of the majority of equations are not expressible in these numbers, they did not discover the idea of a general solution. Nevertheless, they constructed ideal problems which led to equations having positive and exact solutions. They could not have done this without having the idea that all equations might have a solution, and this was an advance towards the idea of the general solution and formal algebra. The construction of ideal problems is an exercise in abstract thought, and is a large step towards pure theorizing.

The Babylonians also advanced towards formal geometry, but did not discover it. They knew several cases of Pythagoras's Theorem, and could deal with them through their knowledge of squares and square roots. They calculated the height of an arc of a circle in terms of the length of the chord and diameter, which involves similar triangles. But they did not discover generalized geometrical proofs. The limitations of their mathematical knowledge are thrown into sharp relief by their acceptance of π as equal to 3. This shows that their data on the ratio of the circumference to the radius of a circle, derived from the direct measurement of circular objects, were very rough. The standard of accuracy is that of the ignorant slave rather than the instructed mathematician. It suggests that the direct measurement of circular objects, such as axles and cylinders, was delegated by mathematicians to craftsmen-slaves, to avoid the solecism of handling material objects. The slaves would not see the point of recognizing any tiresome difference from the convenient round number three, and the mathematicians would be inclined to believe that all relations created by God are expressible in perfect integers, rather than use their hands to discover the facts of the material world.

12

Origin of Greek Theoretical Speculation

THE urban civilization invented in Mesopotamia and other great river valleys diffused into the stone-age farming communities in the outlying countries. Cities subsisting on trade and industry were established in Crete, on the Greek mainland, at Troy in Asia Minor, and other centres. Their inhabitants had adopted the bronze implements and the techniques invented in the original centres, and through lack of experience and discipline never reached the highest standard of skill achieved by the Babylonian and Egyptian technicians. The populations on the

Mediterranean coast of Asia Minor were in a special position. Owing to their distance from Babylonia and Egypt, their social organization remained far closer to that of the Stone-Age farmers, and therefore retained more of the peasant individualism which was associated with the supreme inventions of the New Stone Age. Their urban civilization was borrowed and, like most borrowed culture, was of the second grade, and for this reason was also less deep. The cultural traditions of Babylonia and Egypt lay on them less heavily, individualism survived, and yet there was a rough knowledge of what the ancient civilizations had accomplished. The Hittites, the Phoenicians and the Greeks, who were members of these populations, were able in these circumstances to make several inventions comparable with the greatest of the previous period. The Hittites invented the iron industry, the Phoenicians the alphabet, and the Greeks generalized thinking. All of these achievements were made by people not over-educated in the urban tradition, independent, and still retaining personal initiative. It is difficult to say which of these three inventions was the most important, but there is no doubt that the Greek contribution is the most fascinating. Generalized thinking, like writing, charms and flatters the intellect, and is also ambivalent towards truth and error.

The individualism of the Greeks has been depicted in the *Iliad*. Individualism is regarded as a Greek invention by many distinguished scholars, but here it will be regarded as a survival from the tradition of the New Stone Age farmers. This internally free Greek society adopted organized warfare and slavery, besides bronze implements from the Babylonians and Egyptians; like them they had two main social divisions: the governing class and slaves. But there was a very important difference. The Greek governing class was equalitarian among its own members by tradition, while that of Babylon and Egypt had grown authoritarian and theocratic. They were unable to share their reverence for the results accumulated during thousands of years of activity in astrology, geometry, and calculation.

Homer's epics describe the struggle of the Greeks for power in Ionia. They are depicted as a young and technically backward people. Some three centuries after their victory, a group of Greek cities had arisen along the Ionian coast. They flourished in their security, and in their trade with Babylonia and Egypt. Their inhabitants heard a great deal of the technical and other marvels of those countries, but as these were the product of a different tradition, they were unable to accept them without examination.

The great Greek contribution to science was started by the Greek gentlemen in the rising Ionian cities, who began to study the hearsay which reached them of the literary and scientific activities of the Babylonian and Egyptian priests.

The first Greek contribution was made by Thales of Miletus. He had acquired great prestige through the prediction of an eclipse, doubtless made with the assistance of the Babylonian knowledge that they occur at intervals of eighteen years and eleven days. He meditated on the Babylonian stories of creation, in which the universe was made out of water by God. This led him to the revolutionary suggestion that the universe consisted of water in a continual state of transformation, and he claimed the theory as his own. The absence of God as the creative agent, and Thales' individualist claim of priority in the idea were original aspects in this theory. The theological scientists of the ancient countries could not conceive of cosmic action without God, and their priestly sense of duty and impersonality made them ascribe any new idea not to the person who discovered it, but to God, or to the corporation of priests to which they belonged.

Thales included the stars besides the earth in his water theory of the universe. His ancient predecessors again would have found this inconceivable, as they believed the stars were gods, while he suggested they were steam from a pot. He proposed the theory that the universe consists of a self-developing process in one simple material. This remains today one of the leading ideas of science. He discovered it by separating theology from the ancient stories of creation, whose data were correctly though crudely drawn from observation of common phenomena.

His idea was refined by his fellow townsman, Anaximander, who proposed that the universe is unfolded in the evolution of a primary substance named the Indeterminate. This was eternal, infinite and endowed with a circular motion. As it persisted in time, the circular motion produced, or determined, features in it. Apparently Anaximander is the parent of the nebular hypothesis. Hot was separated from cold, and fire leapt upwards, forming the fires of the sun, moon and stars. The revolution of the stars was explained by a mechanism of fire and mist. Thales had believed that the earth rested on the primeval water. Anaximander advanced to the abstract idea that it is poised in space because of 'the similar distance from everything'. He deduced that the sea must formerly have covered more of the land because shells and marine fossils were found above sea-level. He suggested that animals evolved from drying mud, and after reaching the land, became adapted to life on it. 'Man, in the beginning, resembled another animal, to wit, a fish.'

He was influenced in making this deduction by the facts of embryology, for he noted that neither adult man nor his helpless offspring could live in mud in their present form, so their ancestors at an earlier epoch must have had intermediate forms.

A contribution towards the explanation of the mechanism of natural change was made by a third Milesian philosopher, Anaximenes. He suggested that the qualitative differences between the products of the stages in universal evolution were due to the rarefaction or condensation of the primary substance, which was mist. Fire was rarefied mist, water condensed mist, and earth condensed water.

The Milesian philosophers did not offer any proof that their theories were correct, or that the facts on which they were based were not delusions. They did not distinguish between the senses and the reason. Heraclitus, another Ionian, was the first to do this. He emphasized the fluxional aspect of nature, and contended that material facts are deceptive because matter is impermanent. He believed that appearances which endure for some time are due to a tension of opposites, or balance of forces in the universal flux, and that they could not be understood by the senses but only through the mind. 'The eyes and ears are bad witnesses for men if the mind cannot interpret what they say.' Heraclitus's criticism deflected attention more to the logical, and away from the observational aspect of theories. He had advanced towards the idea of the separation of mind from matter, though he had not reached the conception that the mind was immaterial. He believed that it was fire.

Heraclitus's theory of evolution through the tension of opposites was adopted by Hegel as the basic idea of his dialectic.

The exaltation of the mental aspects of phenomena by Heraclitus, in opposition to the theories of Thales and Anaximander is related to his social origin. He was a royal aristocrat, while they were merchants, or interested in trade. Anaximander made the first map, which was of the Greek trading posts in the Black Sea.

Thales is credited with the application of geometry to the determination of the distance of ships at sea and the height of pyramids, and to have made a fortune by cornering the presses before a glut in olive oil. It was natural that Heraclitus, as a member of the governing class, was more interested in ideas than in things, as the ruler is more concerned with aims than with the means for achieving them. Nor is it surprising that the aristocratic Hegelian theory of the state should have owed much to Heraclitus's thought.

Thales submitted the fragments of Egyptian and Babylonian mathematics which reached him to the same secular scrutiny that he had applied to the stories of creation. He had heard that a circle is divided into equal parts by any diameter. His predecessors used this fact without further reflection in the solution of problems. But he wondered why it was so, and is credited with conceiving and producing a deductive proof. He is credited with several other discoveries, including the proof that the angle subtended by a diameter of a circle at any point on the circumference is a right angle. These were the first known instances of general proof in mathematics. A general proof of any property of lines or numbers settles it in all cases, as long as the human mind works in its present mode. It eliminates for ever the consideration of new particular cases, and is a prodigiously potent device for saving mental labour. Generalized thinking is apt to appeal to a governing class whose only labour is thought preliminary to command. In addition to its utility, it justly gives the human mind a sense of dignity, and power over nature, though it is liable to produce an intellectual intoxication in which the mind forgets that its knowledge is derived from the material world, and is not spun out of itself.

The rise of generalized thinking among the Greeks is not inexplicable. It was due to various factors. One of them is the necessity for persuasion in an equalitarian community. The members of the Greek governing class were equalitarian for reasons which have been explained, and felt they had the right to reject hypotheses, especially those of foreign origin, unless they were supported by persuasive proof. The acceptance of assertions on authority was contrary to their social habits. Deductive proof is a systematization of the method of verbal argument by which one free man tries to change the opinion of another. It is less necessary in an ancient authoritarian community, where most of the particular problems of living in a certain type of society have been solved, and the solutions have been found through long experience. These solutions of many particular problems are collected, and taught by authoritarian rote, and the pupil is not accustomed to ask for proof, so there is no essential need for the development of a system of proof. It seems that generalized thinking has been invented to satisfy a practical need for a free group in society. The scientific achievements of the Babylonians show that their mental ability was unsurpassed. It is therefore reasonable to suppose that they had as much natural intellectual curiosity as any other people, but this did not help them to discover generalized thinking because that was not premised by their social habits.

13

The Incommensurability of Theology and Surds

THE Ionian Greeks did not know how to establish the truth of their bold naturalistic speculations, because they had not discovered the method of collecting new facts in order to prove or disprove an hypothesis. They did not advance beyond the test, which they had invented, of logical coherence. Their intellectual attitude was modified, and was replaced by a partial recession to that of Babylonian theological science. The chief exponent of this new attitude was Pythagoras, who combined the Ionian discovery of general proof with the old Babylonian number mysticism. He and other Greeks were retreating from Ionia before the advance of the Persians, and fled to Italy, where they founded new centres of study. It is not unreasonable to suggest that they partially returned to Babylonian modes of thought because they were impressed by the superior power associated with Persia, the direct inheritor of Babylonian culture, and had seen how Ionia, together with its thought, had fallen before it.

On the positive side, Pythagoras and his colleagues greatly extended the application of Thales's idea of geometrical proof.

They produced a logical series of geometrical propositions which were incorporated two and a half centuries later by Euclid in the first two books of his celebrated treatise. Pythagoras himself is credited with the famous theorem attached to his name, though his method of proof is unknown. The familiar proof is due to Euclid. The Pythagoreans produced a large volume of arithmetical researches which were partially summarized by Euclid in his seventh, eighth and ninth books. They classified numbers in odd and even, and primary and secondary. They investigated the sums and properties of arithmetical series by studying tables of numbers arranged in various figures, such as squares and triangles. They discovered the theory of proportion, and arithmetic, geometric and harmonic means.

They were the first to teach that the earth is a sphere, and that it is not the centre of the universe. They attempted to explain eclipses by the hypothesis of an invisible counter-earth, which reminds the modern student of the explanation of the variability of some stars due to eclipse by invisible companions. They discovered the arithmetical relation between the length of a stretched elastic string and the pitch of the musical note it emits when struck. This important deduction from the results of physical experiment was uncharacteristic, and all the more impressive, so they attempted to describe the revolutions of the celestial universe in terms of it. The earth and the stars were conceived as revolving around a central fire at distances proportional to intervals on the musical scale, and were supposed in the course of their revolutions to emit notes related to these intervals, which, however, were inaudible to human ears. The spiritual ancestors of these supernatural notes are, perhaps, Babylonian.

On the negative side, the Pythagoreans did not see these brilliant results in a modern perspective. They did not distinguish between reality, and number and form. They identified reality with number and form. They believed that numbers, points and lines were concrete, and not abstractions from reality. In fact, they put the reality of numbers, points and lines first, and denied the existence of any phenomenon that could not be expressed in terms of them. In particular, they believed that number, and hence reality, was restricted to integers and fractions. These views could not easily have arisen except among thinkers belonging to a leisured class. They came into conflict with the generalized thinking adopted from the Ionians.

The Pythagoreans discovered that the square root of 2, which is the length of the diagonal of a square with sides of unit length, could not be expressed as a combination of integers and fractions. One proof is very simple. Suppose $\sqrt{2}$ is expressible as the vulgar fraction $\frac{m}{n}$, (which may be greater than 1). Suppose that it has been reduced to its simplest form, so that m and n cannot both be even. $\left(\frac{m}{n}\right)^2$ must equal 2, so that $\frac{m^2}{n^2} = 2$, and $m^2 = 2n^2$. Hence m^2, and therefore m, must be even. Now if m is even it must be divisible by 2, so it may be expressed as $m = 2p$. Hence $m^2 = 4p^2$. As $m^2 = 2n^2$, $2n^2 = 4p^2$, so that $n^2 = 2p^2$. Hence n also would be an even number. But as $\frac{m}{n}$ is reduced to its simplest form, m and n cannot both be even. Hence the assumption that $\sqrt{2}$ is expressible as a fraction leads to a logical contradiction, which proves that it is wrong. Hence $\sqrt{2}$ cannot be expressed as a fraction.

The Pythagoreans concluded that $\sqrt{2}$ is an irrational number, and all other roots, or surds, were irrational. This discovery strikes moderns as highly ingenious and interesting, but it affected the Pythagoreans quite differently. They believed that the universe was composed of integers and fractions, which were reality. They believed, therefore, that as they had proved that irrational numbers exist, it is possible for reality to be irrational.

They were horrified by this conclusion, which they considered inimical to the reputation of the Creator, and attempted to keep it secret.

The impossibility of expressing $\sqrt{2}$ in terms of integers had further difficult implications. Suppose the diagonal of the unit square were laid along the line O2, which is the continuation of the side O1 to the distance of an additional unit. Its farther end would fall at A, between 1 and 2. Measurement would also show

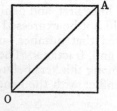
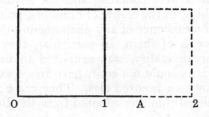

that A would fall between $\frac{4}{10}$ and $\frac{5}{10}$ of the distance between 1 and 2. It followed that $\sqrt{2}$ was slightly greater than $1\frac{4}{10}$ and less than $1\frac{5}{10}$. More careful measurement would show that it lay between $1\frac{41}{100}$ and $1\frac{42}{100}$. This process could be continued beyond the limit of vision and measurement by squaring the numbers. This would show that it lay between $1\frac{414}{1000}$ and $1\frac{415}{1000}$. All of these numbers could be represented as points on the line O2. Now the proof that $\sqrt{2}$ is inexpressible in fraction implies that though the approximation process were continued indefinitely, $\sqrt{2}$ could never be reached, and yet an indefinitely large number of points corresponding to the approximation fractions could be marked on the line. Hence it follows that there are an infinite number of points on the line between those corresponding to $1\frac{4}{10}$ and $1\frac{5}{10}$, and indeed in any other finite interval, however short. Pythagoras had believed that the world was made of points, which had a small but finite size. The discovery that there was no limit to the smallness of points suggested that points were infinitely small, therefore did not exist. The basis of the world was an illusion, so the world itself must be an illusion.

Parmenides and Zeno of Elea in Sicily extended this type of logical argument. The flight of an arrow may be divided into a series of very small movements. During each moment, the movement is very small, and when it is infinitely small, the movement is zero, and the arrow is at rest. But the flight of the arrow is an infinite series of moments, during each of which the arrow is at rest. The arrow is therefore always at rest. They concluded that motion is an illusion, and that reality is uncreated, indestructible and motionless. They identified it with God. The logical difficulties are due to the properties of infinite numbers, and were not solved satisfactorily until recent times.

Their effects on Greek culture and technique were profound. The Pythagoreans had claimed as their chief glory that they had raised arithmetic above the needs of merchants. They boasted that they sought knowledge and not wealth, 'a figure and a step forwards, not a figure to gain three oboli'.

The line of criticism that they had started brought numbers themselves under suspicion as irrational, and their critical descendants banished from mathematics, with unconscious irony, that which the Pythagoreans had regarded as the stuff of the universe. The great mathematician Eudoxus devised a method of handling magnitudes which was independent of their infinite subdivisibility, and therefore of their expressibility in integers. This method, which is a forerunner of the modern calculus of Newton and Leibnitz, was perhaps the greatest Greek achievement in professional mathematics.

14
Solving the Contradictions

NUMBERS, and even diagrams, were subordinated by Eudoxus to a more refined mathematical logic. While they were being relegated to a secondary place in mathematics, they entered the life of society in a new way. Enthusiastic Pythagorean architects, such as Hippodamus, designed new cities on geometrical lines. Their influence was seen in the planning of the Piraeus, and many other cities, including at later dates Alexandria and Pompeii. Farrington remarks that New York, with its geometrical plan and numbered streets, is a typically Pythagorean city.

Sculptors tried to reduce the representation of the human form to an exercise in geometry and arithmetic. Mathematical aesthetics has revived at intervals ever since, not without notable effects. The youthful Clerk Maxwell in the middle of the nineteenth century, wrote his first paper, at the age of fourteen, on improved methods of drawing ovals of the type seen in Greek friezes, and his invention of the colour triangle, by which all colours may be made by a mixture of three primary colours, arose from his attempts to reduce the mixing of colours to mathematical rules. Maxwellian triangular diagrams are now used extensively for depicting the chemical and physical properties of substances containing varying proportions of three components, such as alloys and preparations in chemical manufacture.

Parmenides's proofs that the sensible world is an illusion could not satisfy many men, in spite of their excellent logic. Even the most leisured aristocrat could not feel quite convinced by a conclusion so repugnant to common sense. Philosophers strove to find hypotheses which admitted the existence of change, and were more consonant with common sense, but also would meet his criticisms.

Alcmaeon of Croton sought to prove the reality of sense knowledge by dissections of the body. He discovered the optic nerve, for he observed that the eye is connected to the brain by a nerve, and he correctly concluded that the brain is the seat of sensation. It seemed absurd to suppose that any connection between the eye and brain was necessary, if visible objects were illusions.

Empedocles endeavoured to explain the multiplicity of phenomena by the hypothesis of four primary elements, which he took to be earth, air, fire and water. He suggested that material phenomena were a perpetual reaction between these elements, governed by mutual love and hate. He was groping towards the conception of elements governed by attraction and repulsion, but the idea of force had not yet crystallized.

He developed Anaximander's theory of biological evolution, and his views were paraphrased by Lucretius, who described how animals of strange types were born, but were unable to survive, as they could not gain food, reach adult age or mate owing to their defects.

Empedocles supported his materialism by at least one great experimental discovery. He filled a water-clock, which consists of a tube containing a small hole at the bottom end, and a lid with fine perforations, under water. When the clock was lifted out of the water upside down, so that the small hole was closed with a finger before the clock was lifted out of the water, the water inside the clock did not run through the perforations when the clock was lifted out. Empedocles concluded that air is tangible and exerts pressure. His proof that an invisible thing may have tangible properties strengthened his materialistic hypotheses.

His opposition to Parmenides's hypothesis of the changeless indivisible reality was extended by Leucippus and Democritus. The former came from Miletus and was therefore an Ionian, and the latter was a native of Abdera in Thrace. Leucippus agreed with Parmenides that there was a primary substance, but he disagreed with his assertion that empty space, or void, is unreal. He contended that reality consisted of pieces of the primary substance separated by void. The pieces, or atoms, were each eternal, indivisible, and changeless, but they formed all the continually changing phenomena of the material world by a flux of mutual combinations. This remains the most fundamental conception of the material world yet discovered, and is still the basis of theoretical science. With its aid, and starting from the postulates that 'nothing is created out of nothing or destroyed into nothing', and 'by necessity were foreordained all things that were and are and are to be', which assert the conservation of matter, and the principle of determinism, Democritus gave a hypothetical description of the mechanism of nature whose truth was proved two thousand three hundred years later.

It is possible that Leucippus may have obtained inspiration for his ideas from India. The Indian philosopher Kanada, who may have been prior to him, but was probably not, supposed that matter consists of indestructible and eternal atoms which combine to form the five elements of earth, water, light, air and ether. Aristotle adopted a similar theory of the elements.

15

Medicine Produces the First Balanced Science

THE hypotheses of evolution and the atomic theory were correct, but the Greeks failed to discover how to use them as guides to the collection of new observational and experimental facts which would decide their truth. This was due to the general lack of contact between speculative thinkers and manual workers.

There was one profession in Greece, as in Egypt, which was partially exempt from this rule, for the reasons explained in an earlier chapter. This was medicine, and especially surgery. Greek medicine and surgery, like its predecessors, was descended in the main from the magical and sacerdotal practices of priests. This mixture of phantasy and fact was modified by two new influences; the hypotheses of the philosophers, and the accumulated experience of the directors of gymnasia and military training. The first influence made medical theory more naturalistic, though not much more effective, owing to lack of combination with experiment. The second influence was more important. The directors of gymnasia acquired a traditional knowledge of the treatment of sprains and wounds, which had been accumulated by recording accidents, classifying them into various types, and describing the treatments and operations that had proved most effective for each type. This knowledge involved a combination of the results of long observation with skilled manual operation. It was a basis for conscious attempts to improve the technique of surgical operations, and this cannot be done without an element of true scientific experimentation. Similar results followed from the development of treatment by diet and exercise. The patient was submitted to rational experiments in diet and massage.

A genuine experimental science was founded by these developments in medicine, especially in surgery, diet and gymnastics. It was distinguished by systematic observation, skilled manual operations, and rejection of magic. Its best achievements are exemplified by the writings attributed to Hippocrates of Cos. These contain the clinical observations of several diseases recorded through their duration for several weeks. The treatment is described, and the fatal end in the majority of cases is faithfully recorded. The observations are frequently masterly, and all are entirely free from superstition.

Epilepsy, known as the Sacred Disease, is described as 'no more divine than any other. It has a natural cause, just as other diseases have. Men think it divine merely because they do not understand it'.

The sense of scientific method had developed so far that the Hippocrateans not only rejected superstition, but attacked the speculative philosophers, and 'all those who attempt to speak or write about medicine with an hypothesis or postulate as the basis of their argument'. They recommended philosophers to restrict their speculations to things in the sky, or under the earth, as these are not accessible to inspection and test. They claim that medicine has accumulated a large quantity of reliable data, and has discovered a principle and a method by which many discoveries have been made over a long period. If the researcher starts from these data, and uses this principle and method, he will, if he is competent, make further discoveries, but if he professes to advance knowledge by any other means, he is a swindler.

The Hippocratean writings contain the first description of scientific method which contains all its elements. Their authors had clearly understood that systematic observation, theory, and experimental test all had a part in the complete scientific method. Yet their instruction was soon forgotten and they were not the chief parents of modern science. How did this happen, in spite of the priority and brilliance of their work?

The Hippocrateans had the correct scientific method, but they could not advance science quickly because comprehensive scientific theories could not be derived from the material to which it was applied. The facts of human physiology are extremely complicated, and are among the most intractable subjects of research. The facts of medicine are unsuitable material for the foundation of science because they are not sufficiently simple.

The Hippocrateans' development of science was limited by the nature of the material presented to their study by their profession. The limitation was drawn by professional interest, and was social in nature. They were doctors first and scientists afterwards. Science did not develop quickly until its method was applied to the simpler phenomena of mechanics and physics, where it could soon deliver comprehensive results.

Medicine has given very much inspiration to the development of science, but it is not its chief parent. Many parts of it are still scientifically crude, and those parts which have become scientific owe their character more, on the whole, to advances in biology, chemistry and physics, inspired by other techniques.

Greek evolutionary and atomic theory failed because its proof depended on facts which could be learned only by systematic observation and experiment in regions of technique banned as socially disreputable. Greek medicine failed because comprehensive theories could not be derived from unsuitable material. Not even the correct combination of observation, hypothesis and experiment is sufficient to guarantee the progress of science. The choice of suitable material for study by this method is equally important, and if this is prevented by social prejudice or limitation, science will not advance.

16

The Social Roots of Platonic Philosophy

THE Greek conceptions of evolution, atoms and deductive proof remain one-half of the method of science. These great ideas were discovered by the inhabitants of the coastal cities of

Ionia and Italy, before Athens had become the chief city in the Greek world. The dominance of Athens was due to the increase of her economic and military power, and was confirmed by her defeat of the Persians. Hoover remarks that 'the silver mines of Mt. Laurion formed the economic mainstay of Athens for the three centuries during which the State had the ascendancy in Greece, and there can be no doubt that the dominance of Athens and its position as a sea-power were directly due to the revenues from the mines'. Their prosperity was great before the Persian invasion. 'In the year 484 B.C. the mines returned 100 Talents to the Treasury, and this, on the advice of Themistocles, was devoted to the construction of the fleet which conquered the Persians at Salamis (480 B.C.).' After the triumph of Athens, her leaders began to spend some of the spoils on the extension of culture. Philosophers from the Ionian and Italian towns were attracted by the new possibilities of earning a comfortable living by teaching. Anaxagoras of Acragas in Sicily, who was a philosopher in the Ionian tradition, came to Athens and converted Pericles from a belief in superstition. He asserted that the sun was a red-hot stone, and the moon an earthy body, and he gave the first correct explanation of the origin of the moon's light, and the nature of eclipses.

Athens at this time was the richest and most powerful Greek city, but was culturally undeveloped. Her relation to the rest of the Greek-speaking world resembled that of New York to Western civilization in, say, 1900. Hart has described American civilization as lush. Athenian civilization had the same quality at this date. Athens produced no scientist of the first order in the whole of her history, and only two philosophers: Socrates and Plato. The scientists and other philosophers came from other cities, and settled in the metropolis, as Einstein, Fermi and Landsteiner settled near New York.

Anaxagoras's progressive Ionian hypotheses grafted uneasily on to the less advanced ideas of the prosperous Athenians, who believed that the sun and moon were divine, and that Anaxagoras's naturalistic hypotheses of their constitution were sacrilegious. He was presently accused of atheism, and he had to flee, in spite of Pericles's influence.

Farrington has remarked that the painful adjustment to new ideas which occurred in Athens after the triumph over Persia is reflected in Aeschylus's works.

The Ionian philosophy was never accepted in Athens. Its limitations were becoming clear, and thinkers were beginning to perceive that it had no future. It consisted almost entirely of vast logical constructions based on a few observations, and truth became obscure in a maze of arguments. No one discovered that the Ionian hypotheses could be made fruitful by combining them with systematic experiment.

The internal struggle for power in the Greek world, which succeeded the triumph over Persia, was reflected in the Peloponnesian War. This conflict excited the extremest corruption of politics and morals, and every weapon, including the sceptical Ionian logic, was used to discredit opponents. Sophists denied the existence of truth and goodness, and supplied plausible arguments to justify tyrants.

The Greek hypothetical science so far discovered was not in fact capable of solving current social problems, but the urgency of solution increased with the growth of Athenian imperialism. The disorder which affected Greek society was felt by many men, and of these the most gifted was Socrates. He believed that it could not be resolved without the reformation of the individual will. Society would not be good unless absolute goodness existed, and was recognized and adopted as a guide to conduct by its members.

Socrates did not succeed in deriving any help from Ionian physics and biology towards the solution of the problem of the individual will because these sciences appeared to be irrelevant, and their relativistic character seemed to throw doubt on the existence of any absolute, including that of goodness. He concluded that Ionian science was inimical to the good life, and attacked it.

He believed that mathematics provided the evidence for the existence of absolute and divine truth. He adopted the Pythagorean view that reality consists of abstract ideas, such as mathematical triangles and circles, to which the features of the material world imperfectly approximate. The laws governing the relations between the perfect geometrical figures of reality are absolute truths. They are independent of experience, since, he contended, no one is convinced of geometrical truths by measurement of rough material objects. Mathematical truths are always and everywhere the same, and are therefore eternal. As the apprehension of absolute mathematical truth apparently did not depend on experience, Socrates concluded that it was due to a faculty of the soul inherited from a previous life, and was evidence for the immortality of the soul. As mathematical truths were the same for God as for man, they were divine, and illustrated the nature of God's mind.

Socrates was convinced that mathematics acquainted him with things which were absolute, divine and eternal. Confident that such things existed, he sought for the corresponding ideas of absolute, eternal and divine goodness, as guides to conduct. He applied logic to the traditional conceptions of goodness in order to purge them of accretions from the material world, and reveal their perfect, eternal and divine form.

The governors of Athens at the time were persons who had secured democratic election through flattery of popular prejudices. They resented his criticism of traditional conceptions, and suspected that his views, like those of Anaxagoras, were subversive. They framed a case against him, and sentenced him to self-execution.

Socrates had addressed himself to wealthy and aristocratic young men in the hope that they would influence public affairs under the guidance of his opinions. One of these was Plato, who witnessed the final developments of Socrates's thought, and his end. Plato was profoundly shocked by what had occurred, and decided to devote his life and wealth to the propagation of Socrates's philosophy, and the training of a better type of statesman. He founded the Academy for this purpose, after some years of travel and study, when he was about forty years old. His institution lasted for nine hundred years. Plato used his unsurpassed ability to extend Socrates's conceptions of divine, absolute and eternal, mathematical, ethical and aesthetic truth, which existed independently of experience. He sought to base physics and astronomy on mathematics, and banish observation and experiment from science.

The subtle and beautiful new arguments in support of the Socratic principles fascinated the leisured Greeks, and soon made Plato the most famous philosopher in the Greek world. He was wealthy, and hated political democracy, as the death of Socrates had been decreed by democrats, and was a rigid adherent of the philosophical idealism he had so greatly extended.

When he was about sixty years of age he was called to Syracuse to advise the young tyrant Dionysius II, who had just ascended the throne, on the reform of the Government. He began by insisting on mathematical instruction for all members of the government. This procedure soon collapsed, and Plato returned to Athens in an atmosphere of amiable ridicule.

At about the same time, a change occurred in his philosophical principles. He admitted that experience was a factor in the acquisition of knowledge, and this led him to formulate the distinction between matter and mind, which is now an habitual conception of ordinary thought. But he did not relinquish his old Socratic position. He used his new insight to increase the subtlety of his supporting arguments. In his latest work he made a comprehensive attack on Ionian science. He denied that nature is prior to the mind, and contended that it is formulated by the mind through its interpretation of experience. He advocated worship of the Gods, and the persecution of those who would not obey the principles of what he believed to be absolute goodness. He divided humanity into three classes, consisting of rulers, soldiers and workers, and advocated the inculcation of lies and superstition in the lower classes to preserve their subjection. He said that 'any meddlesome interchange between the three classes would be most mischievous to the State, and could properly be described as the height of villainy'. He sketched the constitution and methods of the totalitarian state.

The philosophy of Socrates and Plato may be divided into major and minor parts. The major part consists of the rejection of naturalistic and experimental science, the assertion of the priority of mind over matter, and the support of religion and authority. The minor part consists of criticism of crude conceptions of the mind, religion and authority. This produced positive results of great importance, which entitle Socrates and Plato to their fame. They also encouraged the study of mathematics by their assertion that it was the basis of mental training and acquaintance with reality. But the major part of their philosophy was retrogressive. The executioners of Socrates destroyed him because they were aware that his friends were aristocratic, and they suspected them of desiring to suppress the democratic development in Athens.

Platonism may be regarded as a retrogression, though on a higher, subtler plane, to the authoritarianism and theocracy of the ancient empires. Ionian science was superseded by Platonism because its hypotheses were inadequately combined with observation and experiment, and it could not provide quickly enough the solution of the practical problems of organization created by the development of Greek society. It was easier to restore order by the imposition of imperialism from above, than by remedying the defects that lay at the foundation of the social structure.

17

A Partial Return to Ionian Realism

THE greatest pupil of the Academy was Aristotle. He was the son of the chief physician to the king of Macedon. It has been explained in earlier sections that medicine was one of the few reputable manual occupations in antiquity. This was one of the conditions which enabled it in the Hippocratean school to acquire a true scientific method. Aristotle may have helped his father in operations, and have learned something of the Hippocratean method while he was still a boy. After this formative experience, he left Macedon at the age of seventeen and went to Athens to study in the Academy. He was overwhelmed by the brilliance of Plato's teaching, which was in the latest and most profound phase, and he remained under its spell until Plato's death about twenty years later.

As a good Platonist, his first studies dealt with mathematical and physical subjects, and he wrote treatises on astronomy and physics. The Platonic philosophy is seen at its worst in these subjects, and Aristotle's treatises reflected its defects. He asserted that the heavens are spherical, because they are perfect and the sphere is the perfect form; and as their motion is eternal, and only circular motion is eternal, they must revolve in a circle.

He began his discussion of the properties of matter by asserting that earth and fire are contrary elements, one naturally moving downwards, and the other upwards. The existence of two more elements are deduced from earth and fire by Pythagorean arithmetical speculation. Earth is a solid and has three dimensions, and is therefore represented by the cube numbers 1 and 8. There are two arithmetic means between 1 and 8, i.e. 2 and 4, so these two Pythagorean realities indicate the existence of two more elements, evidently water and air.

These fantasies arose from his adoption of the Platonic belief in the prior reality of ideas. But he was incapable of entirely uncritical acceptance of speculations, and even in his early work began to modify his conception of the status of ideas. He asserted that geometrical forms inhere in material objects, and he distinguished clearly between form and matter. This distinction led him to formulate his theory of causation in terms of material, formal, efficient and final causes.

Aristotle presently conceived his four elements as materialized out of a primitive potential stuff by form. The elements are each distinguished by two primary qualities. Fire is distinguished by being hot and dry; air, hot and fluid; water, cold and fluid; and earth, cold and dry. He supposed that two elements might be transmuted into each other through their common quality. The alchemists presently justified their search for transmutation on his theory.

He explained the formation of metals and minerals by a theory of two exhalations, the vaporous and the smoky, which always exist together in greater or less proportion. The vaporous exhalation was produced by the sun's rays when they fall on water, and is cold and moist. When it is absorbed by the earth, it is compressed and dried and is the chief constituent of metals. The smoky exhalation is produced by the sun's rays when they fall on earth, and is hot and dry. It is the chief constituent of minerals. As the exhalations are never entirely pure, metals and minerals each contain the four elements, but metals consist chiefly of water and some air, while minerals consist chiefly of earth and some fire.

The phlogiston theory of chemical combination, which immediately preceded the modern theory of chemical combination, was gradually evolved during two thousand years from Aristotle's theory of the constitution of metals.

When Plato died, the direction of the Academy passed to his nephew, who was a mathematician. The Pythagorean tendencies of the teaching increased, and became unpalatable to Aristotle, whose thought was moving in the opposite direction. He left the Academy, and continued his critical revision of Platonic theories. As he had begun to restore the status of the reality of matter relative to form, he began the restoration of the status of sensation relative to reason. He concluded that reason is inseparable from sensation as form is inseparable from matter, and he became doubtful of the immortality of the soul. The inseparability of reason and sensation suggested that mental events might be affected by physiological conditions. If this was so, the truth of any idea could not be certain unless its freedom from physiological interference had first been ascertained. Truth was uncertain without preliminary physiological research into the behaviour of the thinking organism.

After about thirty years of study, Aristotle penetrated the Platonic maze, and concluded that systematic observation was necessary to the acquisition of knowledge. He founded the Lyceum, and devoted himself to biological research. Farrington has commented on the new elation of spirit which animates the style of his writing after he has discovered a better path to knowledge. In his great biological works he describes five hundred species of animals, and dissected fifty types himself. His classification of animals was not superseded until the eighteenth century. He recognized that whales are mammals. This was subsequently forgotten until the sixteenth century. He detected the heart in an embryo chicken in an egg four days after it had been laid. He noted a feature in the copulation of shell-fish which was not rediscovered until the nineteenth century.

His final submission of theory to observation is shown in his discussion of the reproductive process in bees: 'The facts have not yet been sufficiently grasped; if they ever are, then credit must be given to observation rather than to theories, and to theories only in so far as they are confirmed by the observed facts.'

Aristotle, like Hippocrates, discovered the true scientific method through the study of biological material. He was the son of a doctor. Is it not probable that his devotion to scientific research in his later years owed much to the unconscious attitude learned in his childhood, and that a large part of the mental effort of his middle years was spent on escape from flattering Platonic fantasies?

His scientific triumph, like that of Hippocrates, was also incomplete. The Lyceum was soon closed, though the Academy persisted for nearly a thousand years. Platonism was more congenial than the later Aristotelian science to the Athenian society humbled by Alexander the Great. The study of science at

Athens became fitful, and was illuminated only by gleams, like those of Heraclides, who was the first to suggest that Venus and Mercury revolve round the sun, and that the apparent revolution of the heavens is due to the rotation of the earth on its axis. The centre of the cultivation of science was transferred to the new capital at Alexandria.

18

Imperial Science

ALEXANDER THE GREAT was one of Aristotle's pupils. He instructed two thousand officers throughout his empire, which extended from Spain to India, and from Russia to Egypt, to collect scientific and political information of interest to his former tutor.

Aristotle could not have accomplished his remarkable work on the classification of animals without being supplied with data by an imperial service. Conversely, an empire cannot be managed without exact knowledge of its extent, topography and contents. The accumulation of knowledge was of practical value to the new administration.

Alexander had learned respect for culture from Aristotle, and he knew from experience the practical value of knowledge. His best officers acquired the same view. After his death the empire was divided among his generals, and one of these, Ptolemy, became king of the Egyptian part, and established his government at Alexandria, where he energetically cultivated the tradition. He called Strato, the contemporary director of the Lyceum, and other scholars to his capital to establish scientific research. The Lyceum was closed after the loss of its director, and its unique philosophical library was transferred to Alexandria. A system of organized scientific research was created around these nuclei of men and equipment, through the enthusiastic encouragement of the Ptolemies. They established the Museum, which was a development of the personal schools of Plato and Aristotle, into a university, where many specialists could study the numerous new subjects which were branching from the comprehensive studies of the earlier masters.

The Museum had its superb library, lecture halls, dissecting rooms, zoo, botanical garden and astronomical observatory. Its staff consisted of about one hundred professors, and included most of the best scientists in the world, owing to the attraction of the unique equipment and high salaries. It was opened about 300 B.C., and one of its earliest professors was Euclid, who joined the staff when he was about thirty years old. He died after teaching in Alexandria for about twenty-five years. His treatise on the *Elements* of mathematics which remained a standard textbook for two thousand two hundred years, and became the most famous ever written, consists of a systematization of the geometry and arithmetic taught in the Academy, but freed from philosophic fantasies. Though a large part of the results given in the text was discovered by his predecessors, he devised the thoroughly logical order. He invented the familiar form of enunciation, statement, construction, proof, and conclusion. As he wished to develop the proofs in an evolutionary order, in which each new proposition could be deduced without additional assumptions from those already proved, he had to exclude many ancient proofs which would not fit into the order, and discover new ones. Euclid's geometry is derived from the properties of real objects and is based on mensuration. The degree of its dependence on the concrete objects of the world of common experience was not realized until the development of projective geometry in the last century. Euclid's geometry is a very special case of a more general geometry.

Euclid was a profound mathematical investigator besides being a great logical systematist. He discovered the twenty-five different incommensurable magnitudes which may be expressed as the square root of the sum or difference of the square roots of two commensurable magnitudes. No advance on this study of incommensurable magnitudes was made for one thousand five hundred years.

He followed the Platonic rule of using only those constructions which could be made with a ruler and compasses. He wrote several other works, including one on conic sections, and another on physics. This dealt with optics, which was needed in connection with the stage. It is significant that it starts with a mistake, for he asserted that objects must be seen by rays emitted from

3

the eye in straight lines, 'for if light proceeded from the object we should not, as we often do, fail to perceive a needle on the floor'.

Aristarchus of Samos was twenty years younger than Euclid. He came to Alexandria, and was the first to propose that the sun was the centre of the universe, and that the earth revolved around the sun. He calculated the distances of the sun and moon, and the ratios of their radii to that of the earth by correct methods.

Archimedes was forty-three years younger than Euclid, and graduated in Alexandria. His predecessor's textbook had already become a classic, for he quoted it by book and proposition in the course of his own proofs. Archimedes returned to his native Syracuse after his studies, as he was a member of the royal family, but as a mathematician he retained contact with Alexandria.

Archimedes used only two principles in addition to those employed by Euclid. He assumed that of the lines joining two points, the straight line is the shortest, and of two curved lines which join the two points, that which is nearest to the straight line is the shorter. He knew no trigonometry or algebraical geometry, but he derived a process close to the integral calculus from the method of exhaustion. He deduced the area and volume of the sphere, and the area of the parabola, the ellipse, and the spiral curve which bears his name, with this limited equipment. Mathematicians agree that this exhibition of skill has never been surpassed. He also wrote works on mechanics and hydrostatics which contain the only two important general results obtained by mathematical physics in antiquity. He stated the exact theory of the lever, that 'magnitudes whose weights are commensurable will balance if they are hung at distances which are inversely proportional to their weights'. He deduced this formula from the axioms that equal weights placed at equal distances from the point of support balance, and equal weights placed at unequal distances do not balance, but that which hangs at the greater distance descends. No improvement on his proof was made until A.D. 1586, and a fallacy in his argument, by which he assumed that a number of weights spaced out along one arm of a lever will have the same turning effect about the support as if they were all collected at their centre of gravity, has been noticed only recently. As Cox has remarked, Archimedes seemed to have deduced a physical truth from axioms assumed as self-evident apart from experience, though careful scrutiny shows that he did not succeed. But his theory of the lever was of immense practical value, for it enabled engineers to calculate the dimensions of levers for any particular task. This saved time, and prevented accidents due to attempts to move excessive weights by weak levers.

Archimedes deduced the centres of gravity of many figures, including parabolic areas. He probably found them by experiments with parabolic shapes cut from sheets of thin material, and then proved that the point must be the centre of gravity by geometry.

His interest in hydrostatics was aroused by an effort to determine whether the gold in the crown of his relative, the king of Syracuse, was pure. The goldsmith had been provided with a certain weight of gold, and the crown was of the same weight, but it was suspected that some of the gold had been removed, and replaced with an equal weight of silver.

Archimedes observed while in a bath that the pressure on his body increased as its submergence progressed, so its apparent weight in water must be related to its volume. He obtained pieces of gold and silver of equal weight in air, and weighed them in water, and found that the apparent weight of the silver was now less than that of the gold. It was evident that the purity of the crown could be tested at once by comparing its weight in water with that of a piece of pure gold which had the same weight in air. According to tradition, the experiment proved that the goldsmith had defrauded the king. The discovery of Archimedes's Principle was inspired by a commercial transaction.

Archimedes proved that the surface of a fluid at rest is part of a sphere whose centre is at the centre of the earth. He deduced that the pressure on a floating body is equal to the fluid displaced, and he solved problems such as the limit of density of a paraboloid which will float in water in equilibrium.

Archimedes gave great aid to his city when it was attacked by the Romans. His catapults and other contrivances prevented direct assault, and the city was captured only after a long siege. He was killed contrary to orders in the sack of the city after it had been captured. His patriotism was reflected in his prose, for he persistently used the Doric dialect. But his style was elegant and powerful, and gave a perfect expression of his ability. His fame as an inventor was immense, but he left no accounts of his devices, as he believed that researches that aided manual labour were disreputable.

The third great mathematician of the early Alexandrian period was Apollonius. His ability was systematic, like Euclid's, and he succeeded in giving an exhaustive account of the geometry of conic sections, the curves formed by slicing a cone in various directions. Little practical use was made of his researches for two thousand years, until Kepler employed his geometry of the ellipse in the account of planetary motions.

The greatest geographer of antiquity was Eratosthenes, who was twelve years junior to Archimedes, and one of his personal friends. He was librarian to the university at Alexandria, and was also distinguished in astronomy, athletics, and literary composition. He proposed the Julian calendar containing one extra day every four years, and he measured the diameter of the earth, and may have obtained a result correct within fifty miles. He had observed at Syene on Midsummer noon that the sun was directly overhead, as it was visible from the bottom of a deep well. At the same moment, when the sun was observed from Alexandria, its angle from the vertical was one-fiftieth of the circumference of the circle. The radius of the earth is easily calculated from the distance between Syene and Alexandria, and this angle.

Eratosthenes used his skill in astronomy for improving the accuracy of maps. He incorporated existing geographical knowledge in a map of the world as known to him, which consisted of the countries between Gibraltar and the Ganges. He divided the map with reference lines which are forerunners of lines of latitude and longitude.

The work of Eratosthenes was of great practical value to the maritime empire of the Alexandrians. Geography was a reputable form of knowledge, as it was personally necessary for the directors of military and economic operations. Like the measurement of time, it provided a means through which practical affairs and pure astronomy could fertilize each other.

The greatest astronomer of Greek antiquity was Hipparchus, who studied at Alexandria about a century after the time of Eratosthenes, and then settled in the island of Rhodes. He was a very accurate observer, and discovered the procession of the equinoxes (due to the swaying of the earth's axis, like that of a top). It has the effect of altering the apparent position of the fixed stars by fifty seconds of a degree each year. Hipparchus estimated the effect at fifty-nine seconds a year. He gave the lunar parallax, the angle subtended by the earth's radius at the centre of the moon, as fifty-seven seconds, which is virtually correct. He measured the eccentricity of the sun's apparent orbit, which is the degree of its deviation from a perfect circle, and obtained a figure correct within about five per cent. He determined the duration of the year within six minutes. He made several other fundamental astronomical measurements. In addition, he invented or established the epicyclic theory to account for the observed irregularities of planetary motions. This accurately described all astronomical observations then known, and improved the accuracy of the forecasts of eclipses. He was inspired by the appearance of a new star to compile a catalogue of the positions of 1080 fixed stars. This catalogue was lost, but his scheme was repeated by Ptolemy in A.D. 137. Tycho Brahe did not catalogue more than 1005 stars in A.D. 1580, as, like Hipparchus, he was still limited to the naked eye.

Hipparchus virtually invented trigonometry and was the first to denote the position of places on the earth by their latitude and longitude. No fundamental improvement on his theoretical astronomy was made until the time of Copernicus, and little on his observations until the invention of the telescope. His achievement was based on a good knowledge of Babylonian astronomy, combined with the mathematical theory which had been elaborated in Alexandria, and his own ability.

Notable advances in biology were made during the first fifty years' study at Alexandria. Herophilus systematized anatomy, and compared the structures of dissected human and animal bodies. He was the first to distinguish clearly between arteries and veins, and he recognized the brain as the centre of the nervous system and the seat of the intelligence. He gave certain parts of the brain the names they still bear. His contemporary Erasistratus also studied the brain, and distinguished between the main brain, or cerebrum, and the lesser brain or cerebellum. He associated the complexity of the convolutions of the brain with degree of intelligence, and he distinguished between motor and sensory nerves.

19

The Decline of Science at Alexandria

THE advances in sciences described in the last section occurred within one hundred and seventy-five years from the establishment of the Alexandrian science schools in 300 B.C. They were accompanied by comparable advances in other branches of culture, as grammar was evolved by the study of the accumulated materials in the libraries, and the observation of the increasing difference between contemporary language and that of the older manuscripts assisted the development of philology.

The early Alexandrians made great contributions to knowledge, but their greatest achievement was systematization. They created the educational system, and made knowledge easily communicable, so that it could be converted into an instrument available to a much larger part of the population. Archimedes was the most gifted Alexandrian. He was a physicist by nature, one who applies mathematics to the interpretation of the properties of matter, but he was unable to develop his chief gift fully owing to the prejudice against manual experiment which he had acquired from his social environment. Euclid was a more influential figure. His method of teaching geometry still has a fundamental part in mathematical education, and in so far as it remains in use, it is one of the chief means by which geometrical knowledge is communicated, and placed at the service of man. It is therefore of great practical value.

Modern teachers of mathematics are, however, no longer under the spell of Euclid. They recognize that his method is still the best for teaching mathematical logic and proof, but that it does not develop skill in solving practical problems by geometry. Other, and equally important methods of teaching geometry are required for this purpose. Matter is not precise, like the abstractions of geometry, and the elucidation and utilization of its properties in physics and engineering depend only in part on command of mathematical logic. The complexity of its properties is far beyond that of the most subtle mathematics, and therefore of the most rigorous logic. The elucidation of its properties depends more on an educated insight into how a material object or machine may work, and this faculty is developed only by deep acquaintance with experimental facts.

The primary value of Euclid's work was in the limited educational region of mental training. It had also high practical value, but this was secondary and not in the most convenient form. Its particular form was related to the changes of structure in society which followed the imperialism of Alexander the Great. Society in Alexandria became more stratified than in earlier Greek cities. The leisured classes increased in numbers and wealth, and could no longer be educated entirely by personal tuition.

The increasing separation between the classes was reflected in the development of mathematics. The primary emphasis was laid on logic, which is a technique appropriate to the intellectual habits of a governing class.

The technique of calculation, which had seriously declined from Babylonian to Athenian times, declined still further during the period of the greatest Alexandrian triumphs in pure science. The Babylonians had had a sexagesimal notation with place value and a symbol for zero in 1000 B.C. The Athenian Greeks had reverted to the use of letters for numerals. The chief numerals were represented by the first letters of their names. This was clumsy, but the Alexandrians replaced it by a far worse system. The numbers 1 to 10 were represented respectively by the first ten letters of the Greek alphabet. The multiples of 10 from 20 to 90 were represented by the next eight letters of the alphabet. The hundreds, from 100 to 900, were represented by the remaining six letters, and three new ones adopted for the purpose. Calculations with these numerals are still more difficult than with those used in Athens. In addition, the appropriation of all the letters of the alphabet for particular numbers prevented the employment of unused letters as algebraical symbols for general numbers. Mathematicians did not care to invent numerous new symbols for representing several unknown quantities, and Diophantus, who lived about A.D. 300, and developed algebraical methods of solving equations, never used more than one symbol at a time to represent an unknown quantity.

The introduction of Arabian numerals centuries later assisted the development of algebra in several ways, one of which was the release of letters for use as symbols for unknown quantities.

The Alexandrian retrogression of arithmetic, which hindered the development of algebra, was due to at least two influences.

Numbers could be handled by geometrical theory of ratio and proportion, whether commensurable or incommensurable. This method was logically exact though inconvenient in practice. It satisfied the intellectual demands of a leisured class. Simultaneously, the social status of arithmetical calculation, which had been relegated to slaves who worked with the abacus, was depressed further owing to the widening class differences.

The original governing class in Alexandria was Greek, and had imposed itself on an Egyptian population. The different origins of the upper and lower classes increased the width of social separation, and this remained after Jewish and polyglot elements had been assimilated into the educated class. Under these conditions, the study of those parts of mathematics (such as arithmetical calculation), which drew inspiration from menial occupations, languished.

20

Alexandrian Mechanics and Physics

ARISTOTLE'S own studies in physics and mechanics were probably made while his thought was still dominated by Platonic theories. He had little time in his later years, after he had acquired a more submissive attitude to the results of observation, to apply his improved scientific method outside biology. But this work was not ignored, as pupils of his tradition applied the method to physics and mechanics.

Strato improved the physical atomic theory, and an Aristotelian whose name is unknown improved the theory of statics. The studies of the latter are reflected in a work on mechanics attributed to Aristotle, though composed after his time. This writer states that the phenomena of the balance may be referred to the circle, and the lever to the balance, while nearly all mechanical motion is connected with the lever. He remarks, also, that the motion of points on the radius of a rotating circle is the quicker the more distant from the centre, and that many marvellous results follow from the motions of circles.

The complete theory of statical moments and virtual work may be elaborated from those statements. For this reason, the Aristotelian tradition in mechanics has been rated by some philosophers higher than the Archimedean. It is true that this Aristotelian writer had a deeper insight than Archimedes into the philosophical principles of statics, but he did not elaborate his insight into an exact theory by experiment and calculation. In contrast, Archimedes derived an exact formula for the lever, but he appeared to derive it from postulates based on instinctive knowledge, indeed on an aesthetic sense of balance, rather than observation and experiment. His result, and his determination to apply mathematics to physical phenomena were progressive, but his attempt to reduce physics to geometrical deductions from postulates was regressive. No one succeeded in extending mathematical physics very far along Archimedes's line, and his work did not exert its greatest influence until after the beginning of the Renaissance, when a body of new mechanical and physical observations had been collected by investigators under a different inspiration. The possessors of these new facts attempted to summarize them in mathematical form. They then began to feel the power of Archimedes's mathematical skill and adopted his method.

The Archimedean mathematico-physical style was the most esteemed in the post-Renaissance period, and Newton adopted it in his *Principia*, for the exposition of his discoveries. The limitations of the Archimedean style are illustrated by the effects of this choice. Newton discovered his results by new modern methods, but he expressed them in the Archimedean style. The Archimedean style was impressed by his authority on his immediate English successors, and was one of the factors which retarded the growth of mathematics and mathematical physics in England for a hundred years.

The works of Strato are lost, but references to them show that he answered Aristotle's objections to the atomic theory of matter by experiment and argument, and incorporated it into the Aristotelian tradition.

The results of the later Aristotelian studies of mechanics and physics are reflected in the writings of Hero of Alexandria. He lived at some unknown date between the first century B.C. and the second century A.D. He gave a proof of the formula for the equilibrium of a balance which depends on the properties of a pulley,

3*

and implicitly, though not explicitly, utilized the concept of the statical moment. The proof is superior to the Archimedean, as it utilizes the properties of a machine which have been learned from experience. By virtue of its origin, it was closer to the engineer's interests, and gave deeper insight into the mechanical advantage of machines, and how it might be increased.

After this achievement, no major improvement in theoretical mechanics was made for more than one thousand years.

Another equally remarkable advance recorded by Hero concerns the theory of the vacuum. The early Aristotelians believed that a vacuum could not exist. They had observed that the force required to draw a wagon or ship was equal to the product of the speed and the resistance to motion. They concluded that if a force were applied to an object in a vacuum, it would change its place instantaneously owing to absence of resistance. This was absurd, and therefore the vacuum could not exist.

Strato criticized this theory, and concluded that an artificial vacuum could be produced. He probably confirmed his views by experiments with syphons. He extended Democritus's application of the atomic theory to the explanation of the properties of matter, and was the first to advance the doctrine of determinism in physics.

Strato's work on the vacuum assisted the students of mechanics to invent appliances involving the motion of fluids. Ctesibus in the second century B.C. invented a hydraulic clock and organ, and a force pump. His pupil Philo invented other machines which will be discussed presently.

The writings of Strato and Ctesibus are entirely lost, and little of Philo's survives. The essence of the theoretical and practical results of their work on vacua has fortunately been preserved by Hero. He writes that every body consists of small particles, separated by still smaller vacua. In general there is no continuous vacuum, and everything is filled by air or water or some other substance unless it is held empty by an eternal force. If a measure of one of these substances is removed, an equal measure of another immediately flows in. A continuous vacuum is impossible without the exertion of a force external to nature, while a partial vacuum may sometimes be produced by artificial means.

These advances in the theory of mechanics and physics during the Alexandrian period were deduced from the study of machines that were already more than one thousand years old. The

Egyptians were using the balance with unequal arms in 1550 B.C. in their shadufs for raising water. These consist of a pivoted beam with a heavy weight at the short end, and a string and pot at the long end. The long end is depressed until the pot is submerged in a well. When it is released the short end with the big balance weight sinks, and the pot is raised. The difficult motion of upward hauling is converted into an easy exertion of downward pressure by the weight of the body. The syphon, which was utilized by Strato to prove the existence of the vacuum and the truth of the atomic theory, was used in Egypt in 1500 B.C. for drawing oil from storage jars. The Alexandrian science of mechanics, like Ionian philosophy, was based on criticism of the inventions and ideas of Egypt and Babylonia.

Hero discussed five machines which he considered simple, because their modes of action could be explained in terms of the principle of the lever. These were the wheel and axle, the lever, the pulley, the wedge and the endless screw. The first of these was a Babylonian invention. The second, fourth and fifth were used in Egypt, and possibly invented there. The pulley was widely used on ships in the first century B.C. These machines were chiefly valued for lifting weights, and exerting pressures. The lever and the screw were employed in oil and wine presses, and pulleys and windlasses in cranes.

The helical screw generally named after Archimedes but probably not invented by him was used for raising water from the holds of ships. Water was raised by wheels carrying vessels. The wheel was mounted so that its lower circumference passed through a stream. As it revolved the vessels were filled and raised. The water began to run out as the vessels reached the higher circumference, and was caught in a channel or receptacle. Vitruvius in the first century B.C. described a wheel of this type about forty feet in diameter, with swinging vessels automatically emptied at the top of the circle, and driven by the flow of the stream against paddles on the circumference. More primitive wheels were usually driven by tread-mills.

The ancient hand-bow was enlarged into a catapult machine in 400 B.C. It is thought that this was first done at Syracuse, where Archimedes devised many military machines one hundred and fifty years later. The propulsion in the improved catapult was derived from the stretching of elastic leather thongs, instead of the bending of pieces of wood. The catapult would throw stone

balls weighing about five pounds nearly a quarter of a mile. As
the leather thongs absorbed moisture, the catapults were sensitive to wet weather. Philo suggested that the thongs should be
replaced by compressed air, or bronze leaf springs. He designed a
compressed-air catapult, but there is no evidence that it was
constructed, and modern attempts to carry out his design show
that it is impractical, as the air is not compressed sufficiently to
give the necessary expansive force. His proposal to use metal leaf
springs was probably original, and indicates that springs were not
generally used in antiquity. He mentioned the flexibility of
Spanish swords as an illustration of the elasticity of metal.

Philo and Hero described many applications of the syphon for
making entertaining contrivances such as altar figures which
poured libations continuously, singing birds, and cups which
contained water at a constant level. They did not analyse the
general principles which govern pressure in fluids, and underlie
the design of hydraulic machines, so they gave a wide variety of
particular designs, but no general principles of design. They did
not describe a vacuum pump, though this may have been used in
antiquity for removing water from the holds of ships. The invention of the force-pump is ascribed to Ctesibus, and was used in
the form of the syringe, and elaborated into water pumps for fire
extinction. A high-pressure water supply could have been
operated with enlarged force pumps, but the pre-Christian
ancients did not develop any general source of power greater
than that provided by human muscles for driving machinery.
Animals cannot be used for this purpose without heavy gearing,
which had not been satisfactorily developed.

Water was distributed by gravity from a nearly uniform level in
the reservoirs and aqueducts, owing to the lack of big force
pumps. Small force pumps for supplying compressed air to
organs were introduced in the second century B.C. The air was
pumped under a vessel submerged in a tank of water. As the
water was displaced from the vessel, the level in the tank rose.
The volume of the vessel was large compared with the capacity
of the pump, so a stream of air at nearly constant pressure could
be obtained from the vessel, and used for blowing the organ pipes.
Hero describes a water organ played by depressing keys that
operate slide-valves controlling the passage of air into the pipes.
When the key was released, the valve was automatically closed by
a piece of elastic bone.

The organ is a development of the bag-pipe, and was operated by bellows before the introduction of the water-controlled pressure chamber. Bellows were used in Egypt at least as early as 1580 B.C. Hero described an organ driven by the wind. The lever of the pump for supplying air to the pipes was lifted by spokes fixed into an axle rotated by a wind wheel. When a gust of wind rotated the wheel, the pump was operated and the organ played a tune.

Air was not the only gas used in Hero's appliances. He described various machines employing the pressure of steam. These included a reaction turbine. It consisted of a sphere mounted on a hollow axle. Steam was admitted to the sphere through the axle, and escaped through two bent tubes at the opposite ends of a diameter at right angles to the axle. The two tube exits pointed in opposite directions, and were parallel to tangents to the sphere. As the steam left the tubes, the steam and tubes moved in opposite directions with the same momentum. As the exit tubes moved backwards, they turned the sphere round and set it spinning on the axle.

Falling weights were used for operating puppet theatres mounted in boxes on wheels. As the weights fell inside the boxes they rotated the wheels through string attachments. The box moved forward and backward, and puppets performed various motions on the top.

Automatic coin-in-slot machines were invented for supplying portions of holy water to temple visitors. The coin fell onto a lever, depressed it, and slid off. When the lever was being pushed down, it opened a water valve, and then closed it again after the coin had slid away.

The length of route marches was usually determined by professional steppers. Hero described a cyclometer containing several pairs of worm and tooth wheels for performing the task automatically. This was the only train of gearing used in antiquity.

Hero's chief occupation was probably surveying. The instrument used by the Egyptians and his predecessors for measuring small angles consisted of a four pointed star bearing plumb lines at its corners. Its use was difficult owing to the swaying of the lines. Hero designed an instrument which could be rotated in the horizontal and vertical planes by worm and screw gearing, and could be adjusted by water-level. No further fundamental improvement in the theodolite was made until the introduction of lenses.

Daylight time in Egypt and Babylonia was measured by the lengths of shadows cast by objects under sunshine. Night time was measured by water clocks. The Egyptian clocks were inaccurate, as the correct principles of design were not discovered, and the seasonal variation of the length of the night was generally ignored. Amenemhat claimed about 1550 B.C. to have made a water clock which gave correct night time throughout the year, assuming that the length of winter to summer nights was as 14 to 12. Water clocks were improved by the end of the pre-Christian era, but were not generally superseded until the seventeenth century A.D. Vitruvius in the first century B.C. has given a vague description of a water clock in which the flow of water was regulated uniformly by a valve. The water ran into a cylinder and raised a float bearing a style, which passed across gradations on a vertical cylinder mounted above the tank. Twelve lines corresponding to the months of the year were drawn longitudinally on the cylinder. Then twelve curved lines were drawn around the cylinder corresponding to the twelve divisions of daylight or night, and were nearly horizontal but not quite, as the length varies with the season. The correct length of gradation for any day could be placed opposite the style by rotating the vertical cylinder, and fixing it according to the date.

21

Rotary Power Machines

THERE is no record of the origin of the most pregnant technical invention ascribed to the five centuries before Christ. This is the invention of revolving grindstones for making flour. The Volsinians are credited with it, though on doubtful authority. It was probably made in the fourth century B.C. Previously, grain had been pounded in mortars with a stone. The new method consisted of feeding grain between two stones, one of which revolved steadily over the other. Owing to the removal of the need for lifting and grinding, as with the pounder, the weight of the moving stone could be increased. Further, as the movement of rotation was uniform it could be performed by a simple machine without intelligence. The revolving grindstones provided the first good opportunity for the application of power to rotational machinery. The first definite reference to the quern or revolving grindstones is given by Cato the Elder, about 200 B.C. In this reference he also states that they were worked by asses. It is remarkable that the revolving grindstones should be associated with the use of power. The first references to hand querns occur later. A lighter and more efficient form consisting essentially of two grooved discs, one of which rotated on the other, was introduced just before the Christian era, and was worked by hand. It seems that the introduction of heavy rotating machinery driven by animal power was contrary to the tendency of the time, and inventive ability was applied to the improvement of the efficiency of the quern, so that the amount of motive power required to operate it was not more than that supplied by human muscles.

While this regressive movement occurred, it had secondary progressive effects. The improved hand quern was advantageous to the independent peasant who could not afford an animal to grind his flour. But as the number of independent peasants steadily declined with the age of the Graeco-Roman era, the chief effect of the improvement was to arrest the development of power-driven machinery.

The obscurity of the invention of the heavy animal-driven quern suggests that it was made in a relatively free non-Greek agricultural community.

The application of the water wheel to corn grinding may have been invented in the first century B.C., though the first description of such a machine occurs in Irish laws written in the fifth century A.D., in the time of St. Patrick. Rome depended on water mills for flour at the end of the fourth century A.D. Windmills were not used for grinding in Europe until the twelfth century A.D. There are Arabian references to windmills in the tenth century, and it is possible that windmills were used for rotating prayer wheels in Tibet at an earlier date. Hero's account in the first century B.C. of a windmill for driving an organ has already been mentioned.

22

Greek Alchemy

THERE is virtually no evidence that the pre-Christian Greeks made any considerable contributions to experimental chemistry. They adopted in general the process for preparing metals, glass, pottery, dyes and medicines which had been invented in previous millennia. Very few accounts of these processes have survived. As urban civilization grew more complicated the value of a knowledge of metallurgy steadily increased. It provided the metals used as currency in an expanding system of trade, besides those used in improved tools and weapons. The stability of the new financial structure depended on the quantity and quality of gold, silver and copper put into circulation. Authorities guarded the technical knowledge of refining and adulteration of metals very carefully, to prevent counterfeiting and inflation. They also wished to exploit the economic advantages of secret processes. These motives combined with the lack of respect for technique as a part of culture to prevent the publication of accounts of metallurgical processes. Diocletian issued a decree at the end of the third century A.D. that all ancient books on the making of gold and silver should be destroyed.

Two manuscripts of this period, dealing with the methods of making alloy substitutes for precious metals, and paste and glass substitutes for precious stones, have survived. These were written in Greek on papyrus by an Egyptian chemist. Like the fragments of technical literature which have survived from much earlier Egyptian periods, they are notably free from credulity, and their author did not believe that he could fabricate genuine precious metals and stones. His technical processes were probably little more advanced than those used in Egypt two thousand years earlier. The pre-Greek tradition of applied chemistry continued beside the Democritean theory of atoms and the Aristotelian theory of the elements. The development of the idea of transmutation which occurred in the second century A.D. owed much to the Aristotelian theory, but less to the atomic theory, though not in conflict with it. According to the atomic theory, all matter consisted of various combinations of one sort of primitive atoms. It followed that different kinds of matter should be capable of resolution into the primitive atoms, and recombined in any desired manner. For instance, the matter of common metals should be capable of resolution into the primitive atoms, and these should be capable of recombination into gold. Transmutation seemed a reasonable deduction from atomic theory. The chief inspiration for its pursuit was neither the ideas of Democritus or Aristotle, but the occult idea of magical change.

Systematic laboratory research on transmutation gradually developed. The Egyptian metallurgists probably did not distinguish between the foundry and the laboratory. They noted unusual phenomena which happened with materials being prepared for definite orders, and adapted these for use in the future. Innovations were usually discovered during the process of manufacture, and not by special investigation. Laboratory research, in which processes themselves are investigated, and the product is of no immediate importance, was chiefly an Alexandrian invention. The research rooms of the Museum encouraged the development of laboratory research, and its results in mathematics, astronomy, biology and mechanics have been described. It did not noticeably affect chemistry until the second century A.D., when important improvements in chemical apparatus were made. Maria the Jewess described effective forms of laboratory apparatus for heating, melting, filtering, distilling and subliming materials. The late Alexandrians who followed her developed the use of the glass flasks and retorts and other pieces of apparatus which have since remained typical of the chemical laboratory.

The late Alexandrians may be credited with the invention of systematic experimental chemistry, in their attempts to manufacture gold. Though the effective parts of their new science, known at first as alchemy, were chiefly derived from the practical tradition of Egyptian metallurgists, other parts were derived from magical and mystical sources. The transformation of one thing into another by magic is a very ancient idea, and always attractive to the undisciplined mind, as it seems to accomplish something without doing any work.

Why should experimental chemistry have been born with mystical elements, when its forerunner in applied chemistry was notably naturalistic, and the sciences of experimental physics and biology had already, through several centuries, made some progress?

The later appearance of systematic experimental chemistry may be due chiefly to the disagreeable and therefore disreputable nature of its processes. The Egyptian scribe of 1500 B.C. who remarked that the metallurgist 'stinks like fish-spawn' has already been quoted. Research in pneumatics and hydraulics became reputable sooner, because its material is less disagreeable. In addition, elementary chemistry is more complicated than elementary physics, so progress in it is more difficult.

The acceptance of chemistry as reputable in the late Alexandrian period was influenced by many factors. The rise of Christianity improved the repute of the slave and craftsman, and this tended to improve the repute of his disagreeable work.

One of the earliest alchemists whose works have survived was a Gnostic named Zosimos. The Gnostics believed that there was an invisible world behind the sensible, and that it was peopled with living abstract entities. They were convinced that they had access to this invisible world, and could enter it after suffering mysterious changes. These were analogous to the chemical changes of materials. They believed, accordingly, that the study of chemical change was a guide to those changes which placed their own spirits in communication with the sources of ineffable knowledge.

Zosimos's works consist of ecstatic visions which may be symbolic descriptions of chemical changes, interspersed with considerable descriptions of chemical apparatus and operations, and injunctions to secrecy. He describes the preparation of mercury and arsenic, and states that arsenic will convert copper into silver. This was evidently a reference to the silvery appearance of copper arsenide. He knew that sugar of lead was both sweet and salt-like, and could be prepared by heating litharge with vinegar.

He discussed the merits of glass and pottery for apparatus, and reported that the best glass vessels came from Askalon in Syria. He joined apparatus together with clay, fat, wax and gypsum, and he used the sun, sand-baths, water-baths, fermenting manure, and furnaces as sources of heat.

The founder of Neo-Platonism was Plotinus, who lived in the third century A.D. He believed that the material universe was a partial manifestation of a transcendental world of spirits. The stellar motions, in particular, had transcendental significance, and revealed aspects of the future. The spirits existed in harmony and sympathy, and the aim of the disciple was to detach himself as much as possible from matter, which was the principle of evil, in order to join this harmony. Neo-Platonism emphasized the ideas of sympathetic action and action at a distance, and the difference between occult and manifest properties. The Neo-Platonic alchemists investigated the properties of matter in the same manner as astrologers studying the stars. They hoped to learn occult properties from the study of material manifestations.

These ideas permeated alchemy and were not subdued until the seventeenth century. Experimental chemistry developed during the decline of Graeco-Roman civilization. The decay of the old social system assisted the chemical experimenter by reducing the social prejudices against him, but it also destroyed much of the old philosophical criticism, and loosed clouds of delusive ideas. The renewed contempt for the material world again weakened the respect for fact and observation, and hurt more than it helped science. Partington has concluded from his study of the origin of applied chemistry that 'the knowledge of the use of materials in the Classical Period, which usually forms the starting point for the historian of science, is almost wholly derived from much older cultures. It represents, in many cases, not an original and vigorous development of national genius, but a decadent form of craftsmanship which had existed for a period often as long as that which now separates us from the best days of Greece and Rome. Just as the modern industrial period has ruined the traditions of craftsmanship, so the irruption of the people of the Iron Age broke the continuity in a traditional use of materials which had developed almost without a break from the period of the Stone Age. The essential methods nevertheless continued with little alteration, as in some cases, such as the art of the potter, they do to the present day'.

Graeco-Roman civilization contributed relatively little to experimental chemistry, but it invented or developed the atomic theory and the germ of the theory of phlogiston, which more than a millennium later proved of fundamental value in the creation of modern chemistry.

23

Alexandrian Machinery Withers

A REVIEW of the technical inventions known by the end of the second century A.D. shows that the concepts of a large number of machines, including force-pumps, automatic slot machines, trains of gearing, water-wheels, windmills, rotary grinders, and even the reaction steam turbine, had been discovered. These machines embody many of the mechanical principles which have subsequently been adopted in productive machinery, but the Graeco-Romans contributed little towards the process of adapting them to productive use.

Hero describes seventy-eight machines in his treatise on *Pneumatics*. Nearly all of these are temple furniture, and resemble the equipment of the temporary fun-fairs opened in shops on short leases in busy modern cities. He describes ten syphon appliances for producing illusions of the type of the apparent conversion of water into wine. A flow of wine is produced from one vessel by pouring water into another. There is another series of appliances depending on the expansion of air by heat. Fires are lit on hollow altars, and as the air inside expands, it passes through concealed pipes and pushes libations of liquids on to the flames.

The expanding air inside the altar may be made to open the doors of the temple automatically. This was done by arranging that the hot air should force water through a syphon into a bucket attached to a rope. As the bucket filled, its weight increased, and dragged on the rope, which was wound round axles operating the doors. These were gradually swung open as the bucket descended. When the fire on the altar went out, the air inside cooled, and the water was syphoned back from the bucket. The bucket automatically returned to its original position through a counterweight, and at the same time the temple doors were closed.

The method of supporting spheres aloft by jets of steam, analogous to that used in modern shooting booths, is described. There are designs for fountains driven with air expanded by the sun's heat; automata which drink and sing, and hot-air blasts which issue from a dragon's mouth. The supply of mixed air and steam for the blasts may also simultaneously make a blackbird sing and a triton blow his horn.

This series of appliances, including automatic theatres, was designed to amuse, delude and impress the mass of worshippers at the temples. It was a contribution towards the technique of managing the ignorant multitude, especially of Alexandria. The social significance of this machinery is seen in its contribution to government rather than production, and in commerce. The automatic slot machine for selling portions of holy water shows that the commercial exploitation of superstition by machinery had reached an advanced stage.

The numerous temple machines were probably operated by attendants on payment of a small fee from the worshippers, and the invention of a device for replacing the attendant and saving the cost of his upkeep could have been achieved only after the mechanization of temple life had passed through many stages of development.

The temple machinery was designed to produce motion rather than do work. Reuleaux has explained that moderns are unconsciously inclined to assume that machines always combine force with motion. He believed that the production of this combination is less primitive than the production of movement alone, and for this reason has asserted that the fire-drill is the first machine, and was invented before the lever. The child is interested in toy windmills, or anything which moves, long before he becomes interested in the possibilities of these contrivances for doing work. He concluded that this was the reason why the uninstructed are so apt to believe in perpetual motion, and why the first machines, in his opinion, were not concerned with the exertion of great forces. The perception that great forces could be exerted by machines occurs at a late stage in their development. According to this view, Alexandrian windmills and steam-turbines were early developments of rotary motions which had not evolved beyond the stage of appeal to primitive wonder, in which pure motion is admired, as in the myths of Mercury, Icarus and Ariel. They were designed to produce motion, and the power obtained from them was a secondary interest. The division between power and motion is reflected in Hero's division of his works into mechanics and pneumatics. The first is concerned with forces, while the second is concerned with motions.

The first source of power was human muscle. According to

Reuleaux, the method of multiplying human power by the lever was invented after the drill for producing fire by motion, in which muscular power is secondary. The first rotary machines primarily designed for doing work, such as the wheel for lifting water, and the quern for grinding corn, were driven by human muscles. The idea that rotary machines could be used for multiplying human power was applied in the screw press.

The development of machines for deriving motions from human power occurred slowly through many millennia. The conception of animals as a source of power is more abstract, and came later. The concept of inorganic power in the form of water is still more abstract, and was held as yet uncertainly by the end of the Roman era. The classical world never succeeded in formulating the concept of pure power abstracted from its medium of operation, such as human or animal muscles or falling water.

The substitution of animal for human power involved important changes in the conceptions of power, which had to be conceived as something that might exist independent of the human body and will. This considerable psychological difficulty was accompanied by technical difficulties of employing animal power which were never adequately solved in classical times. Lefebvre des Noëttes has made a study of the methods of using animal power which has yielded important results. He has shown that the Greeks and Romans never discovered how to design an efficient harness for horses. They placed the collar high on the neck, and attached the traces to the collar at the back of the neck. If the horse was driven hard, it was choked by the pull on the collar, and owing to the high point of attachment, was reared up on to its hind legs. Consequently, it could not exert more than a third or less of its possible effort. In efficient harness the collar rests on the shoulder blades, and the traces are attached at each side of the body, just above the fore shoulders. This improvement was not used in Europe until the Middle Ages, though the Chinese had achieved it at a much earlier date. The Graeco-Romans also failed to invent iron horseshoes. This limited the use of horses for transport on hard roads.

The horse is about as strong as ten men. Owing to the inefficiency of the classical harness it could not usefully exert more than one-third of its strength, and was effectively not stronger than three men. As it was far less intelligent and manageable, (the proverbial definition of unmanageability is the act of 'kicking

over the traces'), there was on the whole not much advantage in
employing it as a source of motive power. In addition, horses eat
more than men, and the dry lands around the Mediterranean are
not rich in fodder. This difficulty did not arise in the rich grass
lands of north-western Europe, and when civilization developed
there in the Middle Ages the horse had a more important part in
technique than it had in classical times.

The substitution of animal for human muscular power was not
very easy in Mediterranean countries. Nevertheless, the failure
to invent efficient harness in classical times is due far more to
indifference to the problem, rather than intrinsic technical difficulties. A moderate social demand for the reduction of human
labour would have inspired the not very difficult improvements
of harness which would have made animals far more efficient
sources of power, and this would have accelerated their substitution for human beings.

Animal power could not be exploited without the development
of efficient and strong rotary machinery, and as its adaptation was
retarded, the development of efficient forms of heavy gearing was
retarded.

The backwardness of the development of efficient heavy gearing in turn retarded the search for sources of power greater than
those provided by animals.

The technical difficulty of converting pure motion machines
such as Hero's windmill into power-producing machines was too
great to be overcome without the intermediate development of
the use of animal power. As this was not accomplished satisfactorily, the technician did not evolve the moderately heavy
rotary machinery suitable for the utilization of animal power, and
which provides the basis of mechanical development for the
successful utilization of greater forms of power.

Usher has commented on the importance of the psychological
difficulties in technical invention, and ascribes the slowness of the
development of technique in classical times to these, rather than
the prejudice against manual labour in a society based on slavery.
He has explained that primitive inventions occur in the sphere of
perception. The inventor solves his problem by modifying a tool
or process whose parts are all before him. He may scarcely be
aware that he has solved any problem, and the modification may
be slight in itself though technically of great consequence. A very
great invention such as the cultivation of plants may well have

come into existence through a series of almost unconscious actions. Owing to the obviousness of such improvements to all ordinary persons after they have been made, their invention is not rated highly, and the inventor is not highly esteemed.

The notable poverty and unreliability of the early history of invention, and the failure to record the names of early inventors whose work has created the main part of civilization, is partly due to the apparently trivial nature of inventions which occur in the sphere of perception available to all normal men. They did not seem very remarkable at the time, and neither the inventor, nor the process of technical improvement gained much prestige from them.

The situation changed when technical invention passed from the realm of perception into that of conception. James Watt did not invent his improved steam engine by modifying the parts of a Newcomen engine. He invented his engine with a separate condenser in his imagination, on the basis of a knowledge of the abstract theory of latent heat, after engaging in the repair of a model Newcomen engine.

Those without abstract scientific knowledge could not understand the explanation of the superiority of the Watt engine, so they found the invention far more impressive than those made in the sphere of perception, and naturally remembered the inventor's name. But inventions made in the imagination on the basis of abstract scientific ideas are not necessarily more important than those made in perception.

The prestige of the profession of invention has, however, risen with the transfer of the process of invention from perception to conception, and from the sphere of manual to mental work.

The perceptional nature of early invention helps to explain the lack of prestige of technical processes. It did not seem to be clever. But cleverness is one only of the tests of value. Was the invention useful, and of benefit to humanity, and if so, did the inventor receive fair reward and esteem? Classical society was not much interested in these questions because its small class of free men could live comfortably without arduous work, and could seize the benefits of inventions made by slaves without engaging in invention themselves.

24

The Influence of the Social Repute of Manual Work

THE thesis that technical invention advanced slowly in classical society because at that time it involved the exercise of processes in perception rather than conception, and therefore was deemed trivial and beneath the attention of educated men, implies that technical invention advanced slowly because it was easy. While this conclusion probably contains an element of truth, it does not offer a complete explanation, for it is difficult to believe that invention was not cultivated because it was deemed trivial. Humanity does not desist from easy activities unless prevented by external influences. The failure of invention to develop rapidly while almost entirely in the perceptual stage suggests that the influences which were retarding the development were not inherent in, but external to the process of invention. Inherent difficulty also fails to explain some aspects of the slowness of the early development. If consciousness of the inherent difficulty of technical invention were the retarding influence, the fame and historical record of the inventors in classical times would be far greater, as the magnitude of their achievement would have been better appreciated. Neither the ease nor difficulty of invention furnishes an adequate explanation. Inventions are of virtually infinite variety, and their production presents many sorts of problems. The production of successful inventions in different fields needs different qualities, and will not be achieved unless persons with those qualities exist. The slowness of invention might apparently be due rather to the lack of inventors with suitable talents. This would not explain a general failure of invention, as it is improbable that the stock of human inventiveness varies much in different periods. An analysis of the fundamental problems involved in inventions, and the mode of thought of their inventors would provide information of great value, especially for the interpretation of the histories of these inventions and inventors, but the detailed picture of particular cases in any age should not be allowed to obscure the outlines of the general conditions of invention. When inventions and inventors of nearly all varieties are sterile the cause will more probably be found in general features of the age, rather than in peculiarities of current inventive problems.

As the inventors of the classical period were working with real objects in the sphere of perception, they were manual workers, and they exercised their inventive abilities under the conditions which governed manual work. An examination of these conditions will reveal some of the influences which bore on an inventor in that period. Manual workers were slaves. As they included nearly all the inventors, most of the technical inventions of the classical period were made by slaves. This embarrassed some of the philosophers, such as Posidonius, who asserted that technical inventions were made secretly by philosophers and given by them to slaves in order to conceal acquaintance with the disreputable processes of manual labour. This conventional opinion was denied by Seneca, who contended that technical inventions were made by craftsmen, and instanced central heating through hollow walls by hot air, and shorthand, as inventions made by slave craftsmen in his own day. These important inventions made under conditions of slavery demonstrate the vitality of human inventiveness, and show that creative work may be done without personal freedom. The belief that dictatorial social systems must rapidly collapse owing to the decay of technical creativeness in the absence of freedom is misleading.

The condition of gold miners in Egypt in the first century B.C., or rather earlier, has been described by Diodorus Siculus. 'The kings of Egypt collect those condemned for crimes, captives taken in war, persons ruined by false accusations, and therefore sentenced to imprisonment, sometimes alone, sometimes with all their families, and condemn them to the mines, thereby at once inflicting punishment upon the sentenced, and extracting vast profits out of their labours. Now these convicts, in great numbers, all in fetters, are kept at the works, not merely all day, but throughout the night also, getting no intermission of labour, and carefully guarded against escaping. For guards are set over them of foreign soldiers, and speaking a different language, so that it is impossible for the prisoners to corrupt any of their guards by speech, or by motives of humanity. The ground containing the gold they first heat with long-continued fire, and so render full of fissures, before they apply manual labour to it; but the rock that is soft and capable of yielding to moderate labour is cut down with the tools stone-cutters use by myriads of these poor wretches.'

The strongest men broke the marble-like rock with iron pick-axes, and carried lamps on their foreheads in the dark galleries. They 'bring to the floor the fragments of the cut rock, doing this under the lash and cruelty of an overseer'. Boys meanwhile crept beside, and picked up the broken mineral and carried it to the mine's mouth. 'Here those above thirty years old receive from them a fixed measure of the broken ore, and pound it in stone mortars with iron pestles.' The women and older men, working two or three to a machine, ground the granulated ore from the mortars in hand-mills, until it was as fine as flour. One group of skilled workmen washed the gold out of the powder, and another melted it into ingots.

The extent of slavery increased with the growth of the Alex-andrian and Roman empires. The Romans were originally farmers, and preserved a sentimental regard for the land and its processes after they had become urbanized. The soldiers of the early republic, whose victories provided the basis of Roman power, were farmers. They subdued Italy and Greece, and then the whole of the Mediterranean world. These fighting farmers were absent from their farms for periods of months and ulti-mately of years. Their land required cultivation in their absence, and they naturally arranged that this should be done by the numerous captives made in their campaigns. The early free farmers were largely replaced by slave labourers. This movement was accompanied by a concentration in the ownership of land. Many of the original individual owners were killed in the inces-sant wars on the frontiers, and their lands were left under weak protection. The survivors were promoted in military rank, and grew rich with booty. They bought the old small farms from the families of their slain colleagues, and amalgamated them into larger units. The size of these estates led to the accumulation of large quantities of raw materials, and the creation of an appro-priate capitalistic system of trade. The Romans exploited the estates by slave labour working under slave bailiffs. The system did not grow without resistance from the expropriated smaller farmers. The Gracchi led a great campaign against the movement at the end of the second century B.C. but they were struggling against a fundamental social movement, and were defeated. The degree of this development by the first century A.D. is reflected in the social criticisms of Seneca. He complained that estates had grown to the size of provinces through the gradual purchase of neighbours' fields by fraud or gold. Between 150 B.C. and A.D. 250, three-quarters of the population of the Roman Empire were slaves, and at the market in Delos slaves were sold at the rate of ten thousand a day. The later campaigns did not provide a sufficient supply of slaves, and the shortage was remedied by unofficially organized kidnapping and piracy.

25

The Influence of Roman Social Conceptions on Science

THE Roman conquests were substantially complete by the time of Julius Caesar's death. Augustus devoted his energy to the consolidation of the gains. This situation influenced the direction of the development of Roman society, including that of the institution of slavery. The number of captives made in the campaigns decreased, so the replacement of slaves by fresh captives became less easy. Romans were compelled to pay more attention to the production of slaves at home, and as Gibbon has written, they were obliged to use 'the milder but more tedious method of propagation'. This involved the encouragement of family life, and the increase of stability and comfort in the social conditions of slaves. These changes were reflected in new laws. The power of a master over his slaves was not limited by law under the Republic, but an increasing number of legal limitations were introduced under the Empire. Augustus and his successors were also much concerned with the decline in the numbers of the Roman families. They made numerous laws encouraging the increase of families in all strata of the population, and eased the regulations of manumission. A complicated caste system of nobles, free men, freedmen and ranks of slaves was evolved. A slave received payment which was held by his master but protected by the law. This payment, or peculium, included tips, money, land, houses, shops, rights, and the possession of inferior slaves, the analogues of the gentleman's gentleman.

The highest ranks of slaves were sometimes richer than their masters, and included wealthy doctors, captains of vessels, teachers of science, and bankers' agents. They could use their peculium for the purchase of freedom. They then became freedmen, and could enjoy such privileges as were not restricted to the free-born. A few freedmen ultimately rose to be senators, knights and provincial governors, and many qualified for the admired civil service. The son of a freed slave was free-born, so in two generations the family of a slave could theoretically rise to any position in the state.

The slave did not usually differ in appearance from a free man. He wore the same type of clothes. The Senate rejected a proposal for a slave uniform on the ground that it would impress slaves with their own numbers and potential power in the state.

Under a good master slavery could be a school for qualification as a capable citizen. A slave could learn writing, calculation, trades and agriculture, and according to Cicero could save enough to purchase freedom in six years. If he was originally a barbarian captured from a German forest, he became trained in Roman habits, and acquired a more advanced tradition. In this perspective, J. L. Myres has remarked that 'slavery is a compulsory initiation into higher culture'. It was not without value as a training for regular work, and an instrument for unifying society.

The finely graded structure of Roman society under the Empire was held together by punishment and force. The Romans believed that slaves were unable to tell the truth except upon the rack, so torture was the normal method of their legal examination. Owing to this circumstance, slaves were often trusted better than free men with large sums of money and big commercial transactions. The owner felt he could more easily get at the truth by the torture of slaves than the verbal examination of free men, if any chicanery was suspected.

The more fortunate ranks of slaves belonged to colleges which consisted of social clubs, craft guilds and burial societies. They enjoyed feasts, parties, and entertainments. The colleges included freedmen who mixed with the slaves on an equal social footing.

As Martial writes: 'You don't realize the cares of a master, or the advantages of a slave's life. You sleep well on a rug; your master lies awake on a bed of down. You salute no one—not even your master; he salutes in fear and trembling a number of patrons. You have no debts; he is burdened with them. Do you fear the torturer? He is a martyr to gout.'

A similar attitude was expressed by a distinguished German engineer during a visit to London in 1939, when he said to an English friend that the beautiful feature of life in Germany under National Socialism was that it was no longer necessary to think. One had only to obey.

26

The Internal Collapse of a Social Order based on Slavery

ROMAN slavery in the peaceful period of the Empire was not entirely brutal. The close relations between the master's family and his slaves could not have continued, and the complete social structure could not have survived unless there had been some elements of social adjustment and toleration between owner and slave. The slaves' possibilities for acquiring wealth and comfort explain why they made important inventions of the sort mentioned by Seneca, even though such contributions did not remedy their lack of human dignity.

No civilization was possible at the time without slavery because the machines which could replace slaves had not yet been invented. There was a consciousness that slavery was an essential part of the contemporary social system, and this made owners look after slaves carefully, just as a modern owner carefully tends his machinery. Modern negro slavery, unlike classical slavery, is entirely anti-social because it is not essential to the productive system of modern society, which possesses efficient machines. The social atmosphere of later Roman slavery was probably not so offensive, owing to the recognition that the institution contributed an essential element to the existing order.

The defects in social psychology produced by slavery cannot be avoided, even if the system may be economically justified in ancient societies. Dio Chrysostom, who lived in the second century A.D. and was adviser to Trajan, was the first Greek writer to assert that slavery is contrary to the law of nature. He said that the chief characteristic of slaves is that they are quite incapable of helping themselves. This lack of initiative is reflected in the fact, noted by R. H. Barrow, that in spite of the immense remains of Roman history and inscriptions, no Roman slave has left a sketch of his life and working conditions. A class which comprised three-quarters of the subjects of Rome has left no autobiographical account of its mode of life. Many slaves had sufficient means and literary skill, but none believed that his life was worth describing.

A large number of gravestones of slaves bear inscriptions which show their owners' concern with social status. The problem of status produced an inflammation in the consciousness of the members of the minutely-graded classes of Roman society. Ambitious and able slaves were preoccupied with the acquisition of freedom, and the transference of manual tasks to inferior slaves. The preoccupation with status was inimical to the objective study of manual processes, and the phenomena of nature. This influence was one of the causes of the decline of science in Roman society.

Opposition between science and slavery is perhaps reflected in the attitude of Pliny. This indefatigable student of natural history was a liberal, and made special arrangements to secure the manumission of many of his own slaves and those of his friends. But advocacy of a liberal operation of the system did not indicate disapproval of the principle.

The philosophers of classical antiquity offered an explanation for the establishment of their society on a basis of slavery. Aristotle suggested that humanity was divided into two sorts, one which was fit to govern, and the other to produce. The first sort only was entitled to social rights and privileges, and should be restricted to rulers and soldiers. The second sort was necessary to society but was not entitled to have any rights in it, because, in his view, producers were not of value to society through their own will, but only through the directing intelligence of the governing class. The rôle of producers was purely passive, and disappeared if the active principle of government was removed. The passive producers were not a part of society, though necessary to it, just as a field which produces grass is necessary for supporting a cow, though not part of the cow. Aristotle did not hold this theory consistently, as he ordered his slaves to be freed when he was dying.

The lack of contact in feeling between the ruling classes and slaves is illustrated even by the noblest writers. Cicero discusses in his treatise *On Duty* whether one should lighten a ship in a storm by casting slaves or a favourite horse overboard, and concludes that the slaves should go first. He asks whether slaves should be fed in time of scarcity. Cato the Elder recommended that worn-out slaves should be sold or allowed to die.

The lack of regard for slaves, and its degrading effects, are strikingly illustrated by Graeco-Roman sexual conventions. Farrington has remarked that Pindar, Horace and Paulinus of Pella, who were respectively Greek, Roman and Christian, and who flourished at the beginning, middle and end of Graeco-Roman power, recommended the prostitution of slaves. Horace and Paulinus advised young men to satisfy their appetites with slaves rather than free women or men, who might subsequently prove troublesome.

Those men and women, including clerks, foremen and craftsmen, who were engaged in productive and manual work, and were familiar with the problems of technique, were slaves and subject to the discouragement of degradation. The individual cannot invent or discover without optimism, as he will not try new experiments unless he believes they may be successful. If he has no hope in life, he is without any source of constructive energy. The most remarkable feature of the retardation of the rate of technical advance in classical society is not the decline of many parts of technique in Roman times to an almost static condition, but the continuation of small positive improvements. Inventiveness was not entirely repressed in classes of technicians that remained enslaved for millennia. The failure of these ages of slavery to repress invention entirely suggests that men have large resources of delusive optimism, which encourage improvement even when it is of no advantage to them; or that the tendency to invention is very tough and will endure the utmost discouragement, and that men will strive for betterment against all obstacles. If the latter explanation is the truer, it will encourage those who pursue progress.

The concentration of the ownership of land in the Roman Empire produced vast concentrations of wealth. These provided the governing class with the means for fantastic dissipation, and helped to extinguish their inspiration for invention, as they could satisfy their desires without any creative effort. The division between the highest and lowest members of the population became wider, and initiative on the part of the slave craftsman more pointless.

The government of this society based on slavery was chiefly concerned with the regulation of the relations between the members of the minority of free men. It had no primary interest in the processes of production, and accordingly developed law rather than science. It was not primarily interested in the development of productive machinery because it had vast supplies of human machines, described by Varro as 'articulate instruments'.

The administration of a slave empire which grew continually larger, while methods of production remained static, ultimately proved too much even for Romans. The bureaucracy became top-heavy, and absentee landlords lost touch with the problems of cultivation. The fertility of the soil in many areas was exhausted, and the threads of the system fell apart.

The Romans had brought many lands under large-scale administration and cultivation. The descendants of the slaves that they had attached to the new estates acquired a little freedom after the Imperial power had decayed, and became the ancestors of the medieval serfs. These peasants had a very low standard of life, but they did not forget the small technical improvements added during classical times.

The Babylonian and Egyptian inventors achieved less fundamental inventions than their neolithic ancestors. The Greek technicians achieved less than the Babylonians and Egyptians, and the Romans still less than the Greeks. The peak of the creative effort of the Greeks occurred while their neolithic tradition was still fresh. The Romans passed more suddenly from small farming to highly-developed slavery. They adopted this from the Greeks and were unable to criticize its products and ideas with the independence with which the Greeks had examined the products and ideas of their predecessors. Their proximity to the Greeks hindered their assimilation of Greek science because it prevented them from viewing it objectively, so they turned against it. The Romans were far more ignorant than the Greeks, but they had conquered them. They attempted to excuse their ignorance by despising the works of those whom they had conquered, and they asserted that they need not study science when it could be secured from an enslaved Greek. Virgil wrote that war and government were the proper occupations for

4

Romans. The Roman victory increased the resistance to the growth of science. The Romans devoted their ability almost wholly to the development of law and administration; the sole section of culture in which they excelled the Greeks.

This one-sided development encouraged a disastrous opposition between science and administration, between the creative and the organizing forces in civilization, which still persists, and is one of the causes of modern social disorder.

The Franks, Germans, Goths and other barbarians who succeeded the Romans were in a more fortunate position. Like the Greeks who succeeded the Babylonians, they lived in tribes of small farmers which preserved some of the freedom of neolithic societies, and they were able to view Roman society independently, while inheriting many of its technical accomplishments.

27

The Roman Economic System and Science

THE economic disadvantages of slavery were noticed by a few observers in antiquity. Hesiod commented on the economic advantage of free labour for some tasks, and in the first century B.C. Varro wrote that hired labourers were more profitable than slaves for work in malarial swamps. Similar observations were made in the Southern states of North America during the period of railway construction. Hired Irish labourers were less expensive than negro slaves for the construction of railways through swamps, and thousands of them died at this unhealthy work.

The Romans had adopted slavery during their period of military expansion. A system of production based on slavery was particularly appropriate in this period, when military took precedence over civil requirements. When society had settled under the Empire, direct economic interests exerted more influence. Landlords at peace were more interested in deriving the maximum profit from their estates than in the organization of society for effective military action. They tried to increase profits by reducing the costs of production, and presently noted that under peaceful conditions, when slaves must be replaced by propagation, the costs of slave labour might be higher than those of free labour. Without recognizing this fact very clearly, the Roman rulers passed laws for increasing the proportion of free labourers. Julius Caesar decreed that the proportion of free labourers on the land should not be less than one-third. The conditions of an increasing number of slaves were gradually improved until they approximated to those of free labourers. This change was due far more to the influence of economic motives than to Christian propaganda in a society whose aims had changed from conquest to defence and economic development. From the second century A.D., free labour was slowly but steadily encouraged. Many freed slaves tended to enter trades and professions, and the number of free small farmers increased. The conditions of the workers employed in the factories of the prosperous owners of estates did not improve in proportion. Most of these remained slaves. The social conditions of those who used machines continued to be bad, even when those of other working classes improved.

The pattern of Roman productive organization was the self-contained estate. The Roman aristocrat aimed at supplying all his needs from his own estate. He built small factories for supplying local needs, and did not usually aim at manufacturing for export. Very few Roman factories contained more than fifty slaves.

This idea of house economy influenced the aim of the economic development of the new provincial towns. They also were self-supporting, and did not manufacture much for export. The Roman cities were not mainly industrial, like modern cities. They were centres of administration and military headquarters, more like modern county towns with barracks. The offices and town houses of the chief officials in every province were in the provincial capitals, while their villas were in the country. The provincial cities were imitations of Rome, and were the seats of government and social intercourse between the members of the local governing classes. While government was conducted from the cities, production was conducted in the country. Consequently, the ideal of the Romans in administration was municipal, while their ideal in production was the system of house economy. The Roman accorded most prestige to citizenship and civil virtues, though his goods and wealth came chiefly from the country and were not made in the city. Roman society was basically agricultural, but its ideals were municipal. The emperors tried to organize production according to the principles of house economy. Rostovtzeff states that Roman industrial organization never reached the scale of the Greek in the Hellenistic period.

The organization of production according to the principles of house economy was one of the influences which hindered industrial development in Roman society, and prevented the accumulation of the data from which science springs. Roman capitalists had two attractive investments only, in land and usury. They had little incentive to speculate and experiment, and encourage new processes of production, which might have inspired improvements in mechanics and science. Local self-sufficiency, the backwardness of transport and the absence of a big market were interrelated, and inhibited initiative and invention. Rostovtzeff has attributed the failure of the Romans to develop big industry to absence of competition. This was due to the feeble demand, and the small number and buying capacity of customers in the type of society they had created. The more vigorous development of Hellenistic industry was due to the export and carrying trade of the Greeks with the foreigners outside their realms. Trading conditions of this type did not exist in the Roman Empire after Augustus, because all the Mediterranean world was enclosed, and organized in innumerable small local self-sufficing units. Though the scale of unification by law and government was progressive, the scale of industrial development was retrograde. The decline of Roman science in relation to Greek science is connected with these events.

The Platonic method of subjecting the masses by teaching them superstition was extended by the Roman Senate. The Greek historian Polybius observed it when in Rome in the second century B.C., and in admiring sentences ascribed the success of the Roman power to its skill in exploiting this technique.

Farrington has ascribed one of the causes of the decline of Greek and Roman science to this encouragement of belief in lies and superstition for political ends. Plato, who advocated fictions for the people, and the restriction of knowledge to the ruling classes, was compelled to attack Ionian natural philosophy. In Roman times, Cicero followed his lead. The Ionian attitude had been preserved by Lucretius, who had acquired it from Epicurus. Cicero strove to suppress the spread of Lucretius's views, and pretended to be ignorant of his works, though he knew them well, and understood their merits.

The objectivity of the Ionian method made its users indifferent to social myths. Epicurus said that 'the knowledge of natural law does not produce men given to idle boasting or prone to display the culture for which the many strive, but men of a haughty independence of mind who pride themselves on the goods proper to man, not to his circumstances'.

His follower Lucretius wrote his great poem on the Nature of Things as a passionate protest against superstition. Farrington contends that the intensity of Lucretius's feeling, unsurpassed in literature, is a reflection of revolt against the increasing exploitation of superstition by the Roman Senate. He explains that Epicurus and Lucretius were philosophers in the Ionian tradition, and through the application of their objective analysis to the Greek and Roman social structure found themselves the exponents of democratic protest against oligarchic dictatorship, which was maintained by the deliberate manipulation of superstition. The suppression of Epicureanism with its democratic connection, in the interests of the ruling classes, led to the extinction of the Ionian method, of which it was the heir. The contemporary and later blackening of the reputation of the Epicureans, and the assertion that Lucretius was mentally unbalanced, were inspired by the desire of ruling classes to discredit philosophers who had been led towards democracy through their study of science. When the Greek and Roman followers of the Ionian scientists were defeated, science also was defeated, and its growth halted.

28

Medical Research and the Reputation of Manual Work

FARRINGTON has drawn attention to Vesalius's ascription of the decline of Greek science to the Graeco-Roman contempt for manual work. He contended that surgery or manual operation was the most important branch of medicine, and that this depended on anatomy, which consequently is 'the chief branch of natural philosophy, since it comprises the natural history of man'.

The Hippocratic practice of manual operation continued until the time of Galen in the second century A.D. Galen persisted in arduous dissections even in extreme old age. According to Vesalius it died out after the sack of Rome by the Goths, when Greek science was forgotten, and Romans relapsed into the habits of their ancestors. Doctors 'gradually declined the unpleasant duties of their profession, without however abating any of their claim to money or to honour . . . Methods of cooking, and all the preparation of food for the sick, they left to nurses, compounding of drugs they left to the apothecaries; manual operations to barbers'.

When the doctors began to leave the preparation of drugs to slaves, it passed out of the control of educated men, and was conducted without criticism. The use of magical preparations and false remedies returned.

The effect of the divorce of manual operation from theoretical training was disastrous to the science of anatomy. The doctor stood over his patient like an architect over a building, and gave verbal directions to the operating slave. This habit prompted the doctor to take more pride in his verbal knowledge and less in the experimental facts of anatomy.

Verbal knowledge became separated from manual knowledge. While the doctor lost an accurate and lively grasp of anatomy through his avoidance of personal operation, his slave acquired some rudimentary knowledge from manual experience but was unable to benefit much from it. He could not read the learned treatises which recorded existing knowledge, and was unable to relate what he had observed to what was known. He could not understand much of what he had seen, and could do little to preserve or advance the science. This procedure survived until the beginning of the Renaissance. Professors of anatomy seated themselves at a distance from the cadaver and verbally directed ignorant assistants to make the dissections. These were botched before the students' eyes, while the professor 'contemptuously steered the ship out of the manual'. Students could have learned more by watching a 'butcher in his stall'.

The virtually complete separation of theory and practice which occurred in medicine in Roman times reflects the general Roman tendency to learn earlier science by rote. The successors of Galen taught anatomy for twelve hundred years before they discovered that dissections he described were not of human bodies but of monkeys.

The governing classes were accustomed to issue orders on the basis of theoretical knowledge. Statesmen and generals were the ideal examples of this type. Doctors attempted to qualify for the same status by reducing medicine to an issue of orders.

The Romans were developing a tendency exhibited long before by their Greek predecessors. Plato divided science into two sorts: theoretical and practical. He gave the theory of numbers as an example of theoretical science, and carpentry as an example of practical science. He was of the opinion that gentlemen might take an interest in pure but not in practical science; in the theory of numbers but not in carpentry.

The social system of slavery tended to separate theory from practice. The advance of science since the Renaissance has been marked by the return to a balanced combination of theory and practice. Vesalius was aware that his own discoveries were due to his combination of theoretical study with intense practical work on dissection, and he announced that this was the correct method of discovery, and called on the young to advance science by its aid.

29

Reflection of Roman Conditions in Roman Science

THE Roman interest in country life stimulated the observation of plants and animals. This is reflected in the writings of Virgil, and the compilations of nature study by Pliny, who believed that nature was for the service of man, and also in the realistic representation of plants and animals in Roman art. If contrary influences had not existed, this development of observation would have been beneficial for science. The Greeks made less realistic representations of plants. Their idealization in art was related to geometry rather than observation, and its defect as an ally of science is the same as that of geometry. It is too theoretical.

Singer has remarked that the non-scientific attitude of the

Romans was related to their rhetoric and stoicism. This was connected with the prestige of words in a society in which the governing and productive classes were sharply separated. In a democracy, oratory and realistic discussion are essential. Under dictatorship oratory is transformed into rhetoric. Roman rhetoric, unlike Roman nature study, was idealistic. This was due to its association with the city, and the expression of a governing class not personally engaged in production, and therefore not interested in material observation. It was the natural mode for the description of Roman grandeur, which was concerned with administrative rather than productive values.

While the Roman agricultural interest inspired nature study, the municipal interest inspired drainage and sanitation. Rome had subterranean sewers in the sixth century B.C. The citizens gave much attention to the drainage of marshes to prevent the spread of malaria. They adopted the system of water supply by aqueducts, and in the course of centuries constructed fourteen, which ultimately provided a daily water supply of 300 million gallons. The daily water supply for London in 1939 was 313 million gallons.

The greatest Roman contribution to medicine was the hospital system. This, again, was a product of organization rather than invention. The Romans organized hospitals at suitable centres in the Empire, especially for the service of the army. These later provided the pattern for the medieval hospitals. The status of physicians rose steadily. In 450 B.C. they were slaves, but four centuries later Julius Caesar had conferred citizenship on all physicians practising in Rome.

The enormous architectural constructions of the Romans demanded considerable engineering knowledge. Roman architectural technique was expounded by Vitruvius, who wrote in the first century B.C. His descriptions of buildings and machines are notably realistic. He advocates the design of ornaments by 'imitations of reality', and he writes in a style free from literary mannerism, which is intended to present his matter in the most effective way to works managers and skilled artisans. His book has recently been retranslated by Granger, who compares his writing with that of Michelangelo, who wrote in a rough direct style; and of Leonardo da Vinci, who was notably inept in languages. Leonardo did not learn Latin until late in life, and he used the written language of a Florentine shopkeeper of the lower class.

The connection between social status, literary style, and freedom from mysticism in workers such as Vitruvius and Leonardo is significant for the explanation of the development of science. Galen practised in Rome, but was the son of a wealthy Greek architect. He boasted that his competitors wept because they had not been able to obtain such a good education owing to poverty, and had less genius. He scorned those who spent the morning visiting their friends, and the evening in dining out with the rich and powerful. Thorndike remarks that he complained that the rich men could see the use of arithmetic and geometry, which assisted them to keep their accounts straight and build comfortable houses, and of divination and astrology, by which they sought to learn who would die, and whose fortunes they might inherit, but they had no appreciation for pure philosophy though they admired rhetorical sophistry.

Galen did not consider that utility is the proper motive for encouraging science. He asserted that the study of the parts of the body revealed a divine design, and provided the data for 'a truly scientific theology which is much greater and more precious than all medicine'.

He admired astrology, and opposed the atomists because 'they despise augury, dreams, portents, and all astrology', and deny the existence of a divine artificer and an innate moral law. He regarded atheism and disbelief in astrology as comparably disreputable.

The repute of astrology was due to primitive belief in magic, and was strengthened among educated men by the Stoic philosophy. Stoicism had been founded in Athens in the third century B.C. According to its tenets, all things, including the soul, were material, and interconnected by forces. These forces were a refined species of the concepts of action at a distance, evolved by magicians in prehistoric times. The good life consisted of a proper adjustment of the process of living to nature, made by controlling the interconnecting forces through reason. The theory of the macrocosm and the microcosm was consonant with this view. Features of the larger universe, such as the stars, were connected by forces with features in the microcosm or human body. For instance, the constellation of Leo is connected with the heart, and Pisces with the feet. Life could not be adjusted to nature without a knowledge of nature and astrology, so Stoicism encouraged nature study and astrology. The theory of the macrocosm and microcosm is not purely speculative. The dependence

4*

of all life on the sun, and the lunar periodicities in women's lives are suggestive of connections between man and the stars. Given such facts, elaboration of connections by speculation seemed plausible to minds which had not thoroughly assimilated the technique of experimental proof. Even so great a scientist as Ptolemy, whose studies of the refraction of light by air and other media were one of the most outstanding contributions to experimental physics in antiquity, and whose astronomical and geographical works were authoritative for nearly one and a half millennia, was an ardent astrologer. In his treatise on astrology, the *Tetrabiblos*, he describes how the influence of the planets and stars on the body and mind, and on disease, may be calculated. The sun warms and dries, the moon cools and putrefies, Saturn chills and Mars emits a parching heat. Jupiter is lukewarm, Venus moist, and Mercury changeable. The fixed stars exert their influence in conjunction with planets.

The spread of Stoicism had important effects. Its assertion of the interrelatedness of all phenomena contradicted the beliefs of polytheism, and prepared the path to the belief of those who, with Pliny, asserted that 'Deity only means nature'. Virgil was a monotheist and regarded the world as a work of art made by God. Uneducated Romans remained with the belief that the various phenomena of the world were governed by a multitude of gods. Stoicism produced a profound division in religious views between the governing class and the lower classes. The latter retained the orthodox faith taught by the priests, while the former were sceptical of it. This class division in belief damaged the solidarity of Roman society, and contributed to its decay.

The Stoic view that all the phenomena of the world are interconnected implied that the events of human life are determined, and their course may be forecast. Astrology was the technique by which this could be done.

The Christians were opposed to Stoicism because of their belief in free will. Their opposition to determinism led them to attack astrology. But this was not because it was based on unconfirmed speculation. When Galen wished to give an example of this, he referred to the Christians. Someone had been unduly speculative in his presence, and he said he felt 'as if one had come to a school of Moses and Christ and had heard undemonstrated laws'.

Thorndike remarks that the Christian writers of the Roman

period regarded all things as contemptible compared with divine revelation, but apart from that, they had more respect for Greek philosophy and science than any other system of ideas. He comments on the views of Basil, who lived in the fourth century. 'At all events,' said Basil, 'let us prefer the simplicity of faith to the demonstrations of reason.' After this expression, he quotes good Greek science with sympathy for the illustration of his sermons. He often gave the best current theories of natural processes to hold the interest of his audiences. He spoke of God as the supreme artisan and makes flattering allusions to the value of techniques which support life or produce enduring work, such as the construction of waterways and the development of sea trade. These technical references suggest that Basil's audiences included many artisans, and that Christianity was spreading among manual workers who were oppressed by bad conditions and desired a better world.

Augustine was less sympathetic than Basil to science. He was the son of a man of wealth and rank, and inclined to think in the psychological mode of a member of the governing class, interested in ideas rather than things. He condemned 'the vain and curious desire of investigation' through the senses, which is 'palliated under the name of knowledge and science'. He allowed that astronomy was useful for determining Easter, but not for interpreting the Scriptures. Though he did not rebut the fundamental hypothesis of astrology, he was deeply opposed to it, because he could not combine it with his theory of free will and predestination.

The disintegration of Roman society and its culture was accompanied by the almost complete cessation of effective scientific research, but magic, astrology and the occult sciences did not decline. They may have increased, but this is not easily decided. There was a thick undergrowth of occult science through the best period of Greek civilization, and when the fine flowers of science faded, the presence of the undergrowth, always there, became more prominent. The overwhelming proportion of occult science to true science especially in the period from the founding of the Roman Empire until the Renaissance is demonstrated in the pages of Thorndike's treatise on the history of magic and experimental science. The almost universal failure of even the greatest minds to perceive the elementary fallacies in occult science is frightening.

The basis of occult science is intense human emotion. If a person desires or fears something, he unconsciously observes and criticizes it incorrectly. If he desires the death of a powerful enemy, he will try to secure it by striking an image within his reach. He tries to achieve his end by false analogy, and persuades himself that an imitation of the desired action is as effective as the action itself. He may affect an object at a distance not by performing a motion analogous to one which would do harm, but by a special act. He may hope to make an enemy ill by striking pins in a wax image, or by making a pass with his hands. The motions made in hunting, warfare, and in all branches of technology were known to be effective in their particular spheres. The belief developed that these motions of skill had an effectiveness, even when separated from their object. For instance, the blacksmith's particular way of swinging a hammer would seem to acquire a potency in itself. All of the skilful acts of the technicians became magical acts. From this it was deduced that skilled motions might in themselves possess a potency, and that their performance might influence persons and objects at a distance.

Technology and magic were interwoven, and each motion made in early technical processes was accompanied by incantations, and other signs of the magical power of the skilful act.

The effect of many herbs on the body and mind was real. This encouraged exaggeration of the potency of plants, and beliefs in the magical properties of objects. The belief was acquired that certain stones had life-giving power, and could communicate fertility and strength through touch. Precious stones were deemed extremely potent, and superior to herbs because more durable. The search for minerals with magic potency inspired much alchemical research, and incidentally provided some new knowledge of true chemical processes, and some new materials of real value. The belief in the potency of objects could become so intense that some persons died by mental shock through touching them.

The belief that the future could be forecast by astrology inspired keen interest in astronomical observation which incidentally provided data for genuine science.

The widespread practice of magic during the Graeco-Roman and Middle Ages did produce some positive contributions to science, but the result was small compared with the effort. Magic may be an important source of science in barbarous societies, but the example of these ages demonstrates that in civilized societies it is not.

The nature of the source of scientific development in highly differentiated societies is suggested by the change in the conception of education which occurred between the height and the end of Graeco-Roman civilization. Varro, the friend of Julius Caesar, who was born in the second century B.C., defined a liberal education as a training in nine subjects. These were grammar, dialectic, rhetoric, geometry, arithmetic, astronomy, music, medicine and architecture. Cassiodorus, who lived in the sixth century A.D., had reduced the number to seven by omitting medicine and architecture (which at that time included mechanics).

The decline in status of these particular sciences at a time when science as a whole declined suggests that they contain a combination of qualities exceptionally important for the development of science. Singer has commented on the misfortune that Boethius, the author of the *Consolations of Philosophy*, who was a contemporary of Cassiodorus, omitted the observational and practical parts in his translations of the scientific works of Theophrastus and Aristotle. The decline of medicine, architecture and observational science in the time of Cassiodorus and Boethius was due to an increasing disrepute of the manual part of these sciences. Galen made his own dissections, but his successors relegated theirs to slaves and servants. When the manual part of science is not esteemed, experimental science is stunted, and science as a whole develops slowly, or with a theoretical lopsidedness which, like that of so much of Greek science, is mainly sterile in its own day.

30

The Repute of Labour Begins to Rise

THE internal weaknesses of the Roman Empire were due chiefly to the failure to develop technology. There are few traces of scientific aspiration in Roman authors. One of these occurs at the end of Seneca's treatise on physics. He discourses on the possibility of knowledge and writes: 'How many discoveries are reserved for the ages to come when our memory shall be no more, for this world of ours contains matter for investigation for all generations.' This zest for research was rare, and in the circumstances sterile.

The most famous movement against the bad conditions and pessimism of classical civilization was Christianity. This was started by a manual worker who was probably a master carpenter by craft. His social philosophy of respect for the individual and the poor implied an assertion of the rights of manual workers, and the need for an improvement of their condition. The widespread awareness of social disease disposed some conscientious men in all classes to adopt the new creed. When the needs which had inspired the creed presently created a powerful new institution this, as usual in history, was captured by an astute leader and converted into an instrument of the governing classes. Constantine the Great, who reigned at the beginning of the fourth century, was the agent who incorporated the Christian Church into the apparatus of government. He bestowed on it enormous estates, and made its material interests similar to those of wealthy landowners.

The administration of the Church acquired the features of Roman imperial government, and preserved them after the disappearance of the Empire.

As the Empire weakened it became unable to resist barbarian invasions. The first serious one was due to the flight of the Germans in the valley of the Danube before the invading Huns in A.D. 372. The Roman outposts on the Danube were amazed by the spectacle of a whole nation floating on rafts up the river, in terror of the invaders. These barbarians were allowed to settle within the Empire and their status was established by appointing their king a general in the Imperial army. Like other Germanic tribes they were assimilated. They adopted Roman forms of government, and Christianity. When they revolted, their kings respected Christian privileges and property. They were not hostile to Roman law and the Christian religion, though they barbarized them. The Romanized Church could survive under these conditions, and when the civil administration had disintegrated, the Church could continue to rule by its Roman principles. As Pirenne explains, the Church succeeded in acquiring and maintaining its control over society for centuries, not because it was Christian but because it was Roman.

The more extreme mystical forms of Christianity had led to solitary asceticism at an early date. A movement for organizing these solitaries in groups began about A.D. 348. Benedict founded in A.D. 543 the first organization of monks in Europe. The habits of the solitary ascetics were often unattractive, and apparently an excuse for mere laziness. When their numbers were small, these eccentricities could be tolerated, but when they were numerous they became a scandal to religion. The improvement of the respectability of their lives was one of Benedict's motives. He laid down rules of conduct for them, and ordered them to withdraw from secular life, which made training and discipline easier. Benedict required his followers to honour God by labour, either manual or intellectual, besides prayer. This rule was an unconscious expression of the improving social status of manual labour. But it was not yet easily imposed, as slavery still existed. In some degree, it was a sublimation of slavery. The rule of seclusion assisted the establishment of the rule of work, as the monks could labour in the privacy of the monastery without losing prestige. Later, when the monastic movement had grown stronger, the respectability of manual work could be more openly expressed. The Benedictine rule of work helped to prepare the attitude towards manual work which later made the rise of modern experimental science possible.

Benedict's achievements deeply interested Gregory the Great, who became Pope in A.D. 590. Gregory brought the new monasteries under the central control of the Church. Owing to the rules of work and study, the monastic estates were profitable, and their owners were relatively literate. The Pope had a large new source of income, and a system of relatively competent administrative offices throughout the Empire. He used his new resources for the extension of the power of the Church. He carefully organized and achieved the conversion of Britain to Christianity. The new educated monks were sent to Britain to learn the language and customs of the natives, and he could afford to keep them there for a long preliminary period, until they had mastered their task. Consequently, the British were tactfully converted with the minimum of trouble, and remained exceptionally loyal members of the Church for many centuries. While a new civilization was growing out of the European ruins of the Roman Empire, a social explosion occurred in the Imperial ruins of the Near East.

31

The Material and Technical Bases of Islam

ARABIA is not fertile or rich in easily-available resources, and was never thoroughly colonized by the Romans and Byzantines, because it did not promise much profit. Its population in the sixth century A.D. consisted largely of barbarous tribes organized on the clan system, with polytheistic religious beliefs. The economic condition of southern Arabia had been declining for centuries. This may have been connected with increasing desiccation and political disintegration. It was reflected in the decay of the public waterworks upon which the prosperity of the country depended. Owing to these circumstances Arabs were migrating towards the north and east, and for a long time had produced unrest on the frontiers of Syria and Persia. Signs of reaction in the Semitic countries against Hellenistic civilization had appeared in the third century A.D. Intense hatred of Byzantine and Persian rule had accumulated in the frontier populations of Syria, Egypt and Persia in the sixth century A.D. The oppression which created this hatred had been employed to squeeze tribute for the support of inefficient governments poor in military spirit.

The old tribal religions had sanctuaries in various places. One of the most revered was at Mecca, and consisted of a rectangular hut known as the Kaba or Cube, containing the image of a tribal god. This sanctuary had long been the object of pilgrimages from the surrounding country.

Religious changes were occurring. Sects such as the Hanifs had begun to advocate the supersession of the traditional polytheism by monotheism. Mahomet was born at Mecca in this social and religious environment in A.D. 570. He was employed at the age of twenty-four by a rich woman older than himself, who had been twice married, to undertake a commercial expedition to Syria. He performed this successfully, and became the third husband of his employer. He prospered in trade for some years, and had several children. Then he discovered in himself reforming and prophetic inspiration. He became a fervent monotheist, and acquired vague conceptions of Christianity, possibly from Syrian Christians during his travels. He began fasting and solitary vigils, and had hysterical paroxysms like violent fever, and believed that these were signs of divine inspiration.

He identified Allah with the god of the Jews by instructing his followers to turn towards Jerusalem to pray. Later he ordered them to turn towards Mecca. The act of surrender to the new faith was named Islam, and those who surrendered themselves, Muslims. Most of his early converts were of the lower classes, or slaves. They became unpopular in Mecca, but Mahomet survived through the protection of his tribal clan. The majority of the clan were unbelievers, but would not deliver him to his enemies owing to the tribal tie of blood. The other members of the tribe, though they were unbelievers, would have declared a blood feud if he had been assassinated.

The Meccans lived chiefly by commerce, and were poorer than the Judaised Arabs living in the fertile country to the north, around Medina. The Medinians were superior to their neighbours in mechanical arts and metal working. Power in this community was held by the Jews, but gradually passed to two tribes, who contended for supremacy. Mahomet was invited to Medina to preach his monotheistic religion, and to mediate in this tribal struggle. He established himself and his followers in Medina by exploiting the political situation, and after this emigration from Mecca he ordered his followers to turn towards the sanctuary during prayer. His injunctions improved the position of women and slaves and he severely condemned fornication.

The Muslims suffered great economic hardships in Medina, and tried to relieve their position by pillage, even in the four months when tradition did not permit raids. Mahomet gained his first military triumph in A.D. 623. With three hundred men he successfully attacked a rich Meccan caravan, protected by nine hundred soldiers. He out-manœuvred his opponents by occupying the only well on the field of battle, and exposing them to thirst besides military action. He did not take part in the fighting, but prayed continually, with violent trembling. His victory was received as a miracle, and on his return to Medina he assassinated his opponents, and expelled the Jews and confiscated their property.

Mahomet broke from Arabian military tradition in later campaigns, and used fortifications, which were dreaded by other Arabs, and regarded as dishonourable. The vigilance and discipline of his followers gave him advantages over the superior numbers of his Arabian enemies. His Jewish opponents refused to resist him by arms, though they died rather than accept his religion.

Mahomet had become the master of a large part of Arabia. The ancient pagan pilgrimages to Mecca continued, but Islam was imposed on them. They remained the social mechanism which held the Muslims together. The numerous problems of government and social organization began to press heavily on Mahomet. One serious difficulty was presented by the vagaries of the calendar. The Arabs had measured the year by the sun, but the months by the moon. As these do not fit exactly, they occasionally introduced an extra month when the calendar had become uncomfortably out of step with the seasons. Mahomet attempted to abolish the confusion by announcing in the name of Allah that in future the year would contain exactly twelve lunar months. This made the confusion of the calendar in Islam permanent. The later Muslims had to give keen attention to this problem of the calendar to combine sacred with practical needs, as the religion could not be truly conducted by the faithful without an accurate lunar calendar, and their agriculture and trade could not be carried out without an accurate solar calendar.

This confusion in the measurement of time, due to Mahomet's calendrical decree, inspired the construction of astronomical observatories, whose astronomers incidentally made important contributions to science.

Mahomet died in 632, after he had firmly established his reformed estate and religion. The number of his followers was quite small, but they had good generals and fresh inspiration and discipline. They became the leaders of all the Arabian tribes struggling at the frontiers against the Byzantines and Persians. They were invited by the oppressed Semites in Syria to deliver them, and in A.D. 634 they captured Palestine. They occupied Egypt with similar help from the subject population, and swept along the coast of Africa. They crossed the Straits of Gibraltar in A.D. 711. The armies in the East conquered Persia and Mesopotamia. Within eighty years Islam had created a tremendous empire. The chief source of their success was the rottenness of Graeco-Roman society. In the southern and eastern Mediterranean it collapsed under the attack of a small but determined force. Another source of success was an important innovation in military technique. The later Arabian armies had superior cavalry which achieved most of their military victories. The early Muslims did not have many horses and were not very skilful with them, but they learned the technique of military horsemanship from the Persians, who in turn had learned it from the Chinese.

The efficient stiff curved saddle was known to the Chinese in 200 B.C., and the stirrup by about A.D. 600. These technical inventions were the source of the military efficiency of the Mongolian nomads. They could fight securely from their saddles, and after the invention of stirrups could shoot effectively with bow and arrow while riding at full gallop. This skill was supported by the severe training of the nomads' life, which accustomed them to long rides and swift action, with the minimum of food.

The Arabs learned these techniques from the Chinese through the Persians, and used them against bewildered foot-soldiers in the West. They were not anxious to convert conquered peoples to Islam. They wished to put them under tribute, and could not do this if they became Muslims, as members of the faith could not be taxed. This policy had two effects. It created considerable religious toleration, and concentrations of wealth at government centres. Part of this wealth was spent on the construction of palaces, and the encouragement of culture. It provided the financial support for the scientific activity of Islam.

32

The Muslims Conquer Science

THE Islamic empire spread to Spain and India. The Arabs were a minority in its population, and formed a relatively small governing class. Their first headquarters had been at Medina, and were transferred to Damascus in 661. The capital was moved again to a more central position, when the caliph al-Mansur founded Baghdad in 762. Before this date the Muslims had been continuously active in conquest, and had not produced any literature. They now became more administrative, and began to cultivate the techniques of urban and sedentary life. Al-Mansur engaged engineers, astronomers and scholars to plan, build and manage his new city. These included many foreigners such as the Jew Masha'allah, and the Persian astronomer Naubakht. Masha'allah wrote the oldest book on science which has survived in Arabic. Like so many of the primary books in the history of science it deals with a practical subject, the calculation of prices.

As Baghdad was built on the Tigris it was in direct communication by ship with India and China, and rapidly grew into a great trading centre. Aid in the calculation of prices was welcome. Indian knowledge followed Indian trade. The Indian astronomer Manka was presented at Baghdad by al-Fazari as early as 770. He brought with him the *Sindkind*, or Hindu treatise on astronomy, which was translated into Arabic. Al-Fazari constructed the first Muslim astrolabe and he prepared astronomical tables according to the Muslim calendar. Astronomy was immediately employed to determine the correct dates for Muslim observances, such as Ramadan. This fast occurs in the ninth month of the Muslim lunar year and is not correlated with the solar season, so its limits could not be forecast without astronomical knowledge.

When the Arabs relinquished their nomadic life and settled in the cities they were attacked by diseases from which they had been free in the desert. The doctors familiar with urban diseases were Jews and Greeks, and were invited to practise at the Arab courts. The Arabs noted that their works of reference were in Greek, so they began to translate them. Batrik translated Greek medical works into Arabic soon after the founding of Baghdad, and also Ptolemy's treatise on astrology. This introduction to Greek astrology was an incentive to the study of astronomy. The foreign scholars were far more learned than the Arab governors, and the education of the young tended to be entrusted to them. The demands of construction, commerce, health and education stimulated interest in foreign learning.

Haroun al Raschid ordered the translation of Hippocrates, Aristotle and Galen about the year 800, and his successor al-Mamun established a college for the translation of foreign works, and sent embassies to Constantinople and India to obtain copies of the most important. The college had a large staff of Syrian translators, who were named the caliph's doctors to protect them from attacks by religious fanatics. Yusuf translated the first six books of Euclid, and the *Almagest*, and editions of Apollonius and Archimedes were also prepared. This activity was followed by original research. Al-Mamun had a degree of the meridian measured by a new method. Observers starting from a given point were ordered to walk to the north and the south until they had seen the pole star rise or sink one degree. The distances they had traversed were measured, and their mean taken. Simultaneous observations were made at observatories in Baghdad and Jundeshapur, and used for the preparation of the *Tested Tables* of al-Mamun, and al-Farghani made a compendium of astronomy which was used by Regiomontanus at the beginning of the European Renaissance.

The cultural development at Baghdad was very rapid. Within a few decades the greatest Arabian mathematician appeared. This was Mohammed ibn Musa Abu al-Khwarizmi, the librarian of al-Mamun. He accompanied a mission to Afghanistan and may have returned through India. After his journey, about the year 830, he wrote the famous work *Al-Gebr We'l Mukabala*, which gave the name to the science of algebra, and was the medium by which the Indian numerals and decimal system were transmitted into Europe.

Al-Khwarizmi's work was based on that of the Indian mathematician Brahmagupta, who lived in 660. Brahmagupta wrote a treatise in verse on astronomy, arithmetic and algebra. His arithmetic was largely devoted to the calculation of rates of interest. He worked out the fundamental propositions concerning arithmetical progressions, and solved a quadratic equation. He solved several indeterminate equations of the first degree, and one of the second degree; $nx^2 + 1 = y^2$. Fermat sent this problem to Wallis and Brouncker as a challenge one thousand years later, and Brouncker found the same solutions as Brahmagupta.

Al-Khwarizmi may have learned of Brahmagupta's treatise from Hindu scholars in Baghdad, or during his Indian travels. He may have learned the Indian numeral system from the Hindu tables brought by Manka, or from Arab merchants. Hindu merchants began to use these numerals about the year 700. Arab commerce with India was growing rapidly then, and the Arab merchants probably adopted them at once. The Hindus and Arabs did not use the abacus, so a convenient numeral system was of great assistance in trade.

Al-Khwarizmi gave rules for the solution of quadratic equations, which he classified in five types. He described the unknown quantity as the root (like the hidden root of a plant). He surpassed the Greeks in recognizing that a quadratic equation has two roots. He was familiar with the methods of Euclid and gave geometrical besides algebraical solutions.

Al-Khwarizmi writes in his preface that al-Mamun 'has encouraged me to compose a short work on Calculating by Completion and Reduction, confining it to what is easiest and most useful in arithmetic, such as men constantly require in cases of inheritance, legacies, partition, law-suits, and trade, and in all their dealings with one another, or where the measuring of lands, the digging of canals, geometrical computation, and other objects of various sorts are concerned. . . .'

Gebr is the operation of completing the form of an expression; for instance, an expression may be converted into a perfect square by completing it through the addition of a number. Gebr was used to signify the restoration of something broken, especially bones; the Spanish and Portuguese describe a bone-setter as algebrista. Mukabala, or reduction, comprises the subtraction of equal quantities from both sides of an equation, to reduce it to a convenient form. Al-Khwarizmi starts with the statement: 'When I considered what people generally want in calculating, I found that it always is a number.'

The first third of the work consists of solutions of quadratic equations, without reference to applications. For instance, 'a square and twenty-one in numbers are equal to ten roots of the same square', i.e. $x^2 + 21 = 10x$. His solution is: 'Halve the number of the roots; the moiety is five. Subtract from this the twenty-one which are connected with the square; the remainder is four. Extract its root; it is two. Subtract this from the moiety of the roots, which is five; the remainder is three. This is the root of the square which you required, and the square is nine. Or you may add the root to the moiety of the roots; the number is seven; this is the root of the square you sought for, and the square itself is forty-nine.'

More than half of the remaining part deals with the division of legacies, with other short sections on mercantile transactions, mensuration, capital and money lent. Seven species of legacy are discussed. This is an example: 'A man dies, leaving his mother, his wife, and two brothers and two sisters by the same father and mother with himself; and he bequeaths to a stranger one-ninth of his capital.'

As a widow was entitled to one-eighth, and a mother to one-sixth of the residue, thirty-four forty-eighths remained to be distributed between the two brothers and two sisters.

About one-quarter of the book deals with calculations of inheritances in which the law of inheritance, which leads to the estimation of the quantities handled in the calculations, is interpreted to favour heirs and next of kin, and limit the power of testators to bequeath property or emancipate slaves during illness. The effect of the emancipation of a slave during the illness of the testator is calculated in the solution of the problem: 'Suppose that a man on his sick-bed makes to another a present of a slave-girl worth three hundred dirhems, her dowry being one hundred dirhems; the donee cohabits with her, and afterwards, being also on his sick-bed, makes a present of her to the donor, and the latter cohabits with her. How much does he acquire by her, and how much is deducted?' The solution shows that the legacy of the donor to the donee should be one hundred and two dirhems, while the legacy of the donee to the donor is twenty-one.

Al-Khwarizmi ends his treatise with the words: 'God is the Most Wise!'.

Indian and Arabian algebraists give a great deal of information about the social and economic conditions of their times. The Indian Bhaskara, who flourished after al-Khwarizmi in the twelfth century, discusses calculations on the value of slaves, and mentions that the price of a female slave is at a maximum at the age of sixteen years, and decreases in inverse proportion to the age. At sixteen she was worth about eight oxen who had worked for two years. The prices of food and labour are given, and one learns that the rate of interest on money was three and a half to five per cent per month.

Indian and Arabian mathematics were founded in economic need. The Arabs were traders and lawyers with a positive and practical outlook. They expected calculation to serve commerce, and astronomy to guide the caravans across the desert, or to tell the hours of prayer or the moment of the appearance of the moon of Ramadan. Carra de Vaux remarks that the Arabic language is dry and precise, and recalls the style of Voltaire. It is more suitable for scientific exposition than for poetic composition, or the expression of reverie. New technical terms may easily be coined in it. The Arabs did not write in verse. The writers in Arabic were devoted to exposition rather than original thought. Their books were well arranged, lucid, and impersonal, like good textbooks. They did not address their arguments to individuals, in the manner of the ancient Greeks, and this absence of individual feeling is probably connected with the precedence of exposition over originality in their works, and also with the structure of the social system.

All persons living under an absolute government are servants, and expect to receive and give orders. They do not expect to be persuaded by appeals to their individual reason. In such a society, authors and students approach learning with this attitude. The author is the authority, and instructs the mass of impersonalized students who merely learn, and feel no duty to question what they are taught. This attitude inhibits original research.

The geometer Thabit, who was born in 836, wrote commentaries on most of the great Greek works on mathematics. He translated Apollonius, and discussed the postulates of Euclid. He wrote an early treatise on the sundial, which is probably an Arabic invention, and registers the hours by equal measures at all seasons.

Thabit's achievements were succeeded in 877 and the following decades by those of al-Battani. He compiled extensive astronomical tables, popularized the use of the sine, tangent and cotangent, and gave the fundamental formula in spherical trigonometry which expresses the side of a triangle in terms of the other sides and their included angle.

Abul-Wafa used the trigonometrical formula for the expansion of the sine of the sum of two angles before 980, and compiled a table of sines and tangents for every ten seconds of arc. In the same period Farabi wrote a treatise on music. He was aware that the addition of intervals corresponds to the multiplication of the chords which define them, and therefore possessed a clue to the conception of logarithms.

The first Muslim university was founded at Baghdad in 1065. Omar Khayyam was one of its greatest teachers. He classified cubic equations into twenty-seven types, and showed how they could be solved geometrically from the intersection of a cone and a circle. A similar method was rediscovered by Descartes five hundred years later. Khayyam solved one biquadratic equation, and is said to have stated the first example of Fermat's theorem, that the sum of two cubes cannot be expressed as a cube. He was a follower of the liberal theologians, whom al-Mamun himself had supported, and believed with them that the Koran was created in time and had not existed from eternity, and that theology must submit to intellectual criticism.

The universality of the Arabic language in the Islamic Empire assisted the rapid transit of knowledge from one end to the other. The culture of Baghdad diffused swiftly to the Muslims in Spain. Al-Zarkali, who died in Spain in 1087, wrote an important treatise on the astrolabe, and other Moorish astronomers compiled tables based on the meridian of Toledo, which remained for a long period the chief meridian of reference in Europe.

The Arabian achievements in calculation, algebra and astronomical observation have Babylonian characteristics. The remnants of Babylonian civilization lay within the Islamic Empire, and their impress was not entirely lost.

33

The Muslims Extend Alchemy

THE Muslims followed their predecessors in the study of alchemy with particular distinction. They learned the science chiefly from the works of the Alexandrian alchemists, such as Zosimos and Maria the Jewess, which have been mentioned in an earlier chapter. It is said that Prince Khalid summoned the Christian alchemist Marianus from Alexandria to Damascus at the end of the seventh century, to expound the science. They acquired something from the Hellenized scholars at centres such as the Academy of Jundi-Shapur in Persia, and Harran in Mesopotamia, which survived in Islamic times. Harran had been occupied by Alexander the Great, and its inhabitants retained traditions of Greek and Babylonian science.

The greatest Arabian alchemist was Jabir ibn Hayyan, or Geber. He was born in 721 and became eminent at Haroun al-Raschid's court at Baghdad. Jabir inspired the second importation of Greek scientific books from Constantinople. He studied nearly all of the newly-revealed knowledge, but gave particular attention to alchemy. As has been explained in an earlier chapter, the Alexandrians combined much magical and mystical speculation with their experiments, and Jabir naturally began by acquiring the same conceptions. But when he continued with original work, he gave more weight to experiment and less to speculation. Aristotle had conceived metals as a combination of watery and earthy exhalations in which the former predominated, and his theory had been accepted for a thousand years. Jabir had the courage to propose a more definite theory. He asserted that the two exhalations did not immediately form metals when imprisoned in the earth, but passed through an intermediate stage, in which the earthy exhalation was converted into sulphur and the watery into mercury. The metals were then formed from the combination of these two substances. If the constituents were absolutely pure, they formed gold, and if less pure, silver, copper, etc., in descending degree. The common metals might therefore be transmuted into gold, if the impurities could be removed, and alchemy was the technique by which this might be done. Jabir attempted to prepare metals from the combination of sulphur and mercury, and obtained cinnabar. He concluded that the two principles of which metals are supposed to be formed are not ordinary sulphur and mercury, but hypothetical substances which resembled them.

He was acquainted with crystallization, calcination, solution, sublimation, etc., and attempted to explain their nature. He described methods of preparing steel and other metals; dyes for cloth, leather, and hair; varnishes for water-proofing cloth and protecting iron; and substitutes for inks containing gold. He knew the use of manganese dioxide in glass-making. He was familiar with citric acid and knew how to concentrate acetic acid by distillation of vinegar, and he discovered nitric acid.

The magnitude of his intellectual achievement in science is reflected in his consciousness of the place of experimental research in chemistry. He expressed this in one of the most distinguished passages in Arabian science. He says: 'The first essential in chemistry is that thou shouldest perform practical work and conduct experiments, for he who performs not practical work nor makes experiments will never attain to the least degree of mastery. But thou, O my son, do thou experiment so that thou mayest acquire knowledge. Scientists delight not in abundance of material; they rejoice only in the excellence of their experimental methods.'

Jabir was followed by Razi, who was born in 866. He was not quite so original, but he was far more systematic. He was the first chemist whose writings were almost entirely free from mysticism. He gave comprehensive lists of the instruments used in melting metals, and in general manipulations. The first included the blacksmith's hearth, bellows, crucibles, descensories, ladles, tongs, shears, pestles, files and iron moulds. The second included beakers, glass cups, iron pans, sieves, heating lamps, flasks, phials, jars, cauldrons, sand-baths, water-baths, ovens, hair cloths, linen filters, stoves, kilns, mortars, glass funnels and dishes.

He gave the first systematic classification of experimentally defined chemical substances. These were arranged under the four headings of mineral, vegetable, animal, and derivative. The mineral substances were sub-classified under the headings: spirits (such as mercury, sal-ammoniac and sulphur); bodies (such as the metals); stones (such as pyrites, metalliferous ores, mica and glass); vitriols (such as iron and copper sulphates); boraces (such as borax); salts (such as sodium carbonate and slaked lime). The derivative substances included litharge, red lead, cinnabar, caustic soda and various alloys.

This scheme exhibits a remarkable range of chemical knowledge, and much insight into the chemical relationships between the chief sorts of matter. More chemical facts and technical refinements were added to this scheme by the later Arabian alchemists. By the thirteenth century they had mastered cupellation, the separation of gold and silver by nitric acid, and the extraction of silver by amalgamation with mercury, and they could make quantitative chemical analyses of alloys of gold and silver. But no great advance on this achievement was made until the seventeenth century.

The experimental researches were directed by the theory of transmutation. This aimed at the conversion of base metals into gold, and was naturally combined with the search for elixirs which would restore the vitality of the declining body. It was inspired by the love of gold and life, and power over them. The equipment of the alchemist was virtually the same as that of the metallurgist and craftsman.

34

Further Muslim Successes and Failures in Science

RAZI's excellent work on chemistry was less famous than his comprehensive summary of Greek, Syriac and contemporary Arabian medicine. This was perhaps the longest work ever compiled by one man on medicine. It was a lucid account of the best medical knowledge. In addition to this summary, Razi wrote some original works on clinical and therapeutic medicine. He gave the first clear account of smallpox and measles, and a description of suitable treatment for the smallpox pustules. Four centuries later, Ibn al-Khatib of Granada wrote an equally famous treatise on the plague, or Black Death of the fourteenth century. He described the transmission of plague by garments and persons and the arrival of infected ships in healthy ports, and commented on the immunity of isolated individuals, and nomadic Bedouin tribes in Africa.

The Muslim physicians also made important contributions to pharmacology. The names for some of their preparations, such as julep and syrup, have passed into modern languages. Abu Mansur Muwaffak compiled about 975 a work which contains a description of 585 drugs. He was the first to distinguish between sodium and potassium carbonates. He recommended quicklime as a depilatory, and was acquainted with arsenious oxide and silicic acid, or tabashir, obtained from bamboo, and antimony. He was familiar with the poisonous properties of copper and lead. He recommended a mixture of gypsum and white of egg for making plaster for bone-setting.

The Arabians collected information on many plants and drugs unknown to the Greeks. They introduced camphor from the Sunda islands, musk from Tibet and sugar-cane from India. These innovations arose directly from the extent of their empire and trade.

Their contributions to anatomy and physiology were small. This was connected with the Muslim prohibition of dissection of human and animal bodies, which prevented them from making physiological experiments, and discovering the mistakes in Galen. They contributed virtually nothing to zoology, and little to botany. The prohibition of dissection, and also of the pictorial representation of living organisms, hindered the study of these sciences. Hogben has pointed out that the Arabian conquests, unlike those of the Europeans in later centuries, did not bring unknown fauna and flora to their notice, and were not particularly stimulating to students of natural history. The first Islamic tribes were desert peoples. They may have failed, like the inhabitants of modern industrial cities, to become deeply interested in natural history owing to the poor fauna and flora of their home. The early lack of interest became established as a tradition. The taste of the Arabs and modern citizens for geometrical art may be related to this common feature in their environments.

The construction of the new Muslim cities in Mesopotamia and elsewhere required high engineering skill. The Muslims prepared good works on the principles of mechanics, and the methods of constructing irrigation canals and water conduits. They wrote books on water-clocks, water-wheels and balances. The water-clock presented by Haroun al-Raschid to Charlemagne has become famous. But they did not advance mechanics much beyond the stage in which it was left by Hero of Alexandria before A.D. 200.

The contributions to physics were also small, with one notable exception. This was made in optics by Alhazen, who was born in 965. He criticized the theory of Euclid and Ptolemy on optics, and contended that: 'it is not a ray that leaves the eye and meets the object that gives rise to vision. Rather the form of the perceived object passes into the eye and is transmuted by its transparent body' (the lens of the eye). He established the law that incident and reflected rays lie in the same plane, and he investigated the properties of spherical and parabolic mirrors. He was the first to record the phenomenon of the *camera obscura*. He observed the semi-lunar shape of the image of the sun thrown on a wall in a closed room, by rays entering through a small hole in the window shutters. He studied the phenomena of twilight, and calculated that the sensible atmosphere must be about ten miles high. He very nearly discovered the theory of the magnifying glass, and had much insight into the nature of focussing, magnification, and inversion of the image, and the formation of rings and colours by optical experiment. He propounded the famous problem: 'In a spherical or convex, a cylindrical or conical mirror to find the point from which an object of given position will be reflected, to an eye of given position.' It involves an equation of the fourth degree, which he solved with the assistance of a hyperbola.

Alhazen's optical work was the basis of that of Roger Bacon, and influenced Leonardo and Kepler. His profession was medicine, but he was the first to give an account of the human eye from the perspective of a physicist. Alhazen's remarkable achievement was inspired by medicine and astronomy. As further great contributions to physics were not inspired in Islam by these sciences, it is permissible to conclude that they are not sufficient incentives to the cultivation of physics. Other important incentives were lacking. The small development in Islam of engineering is suggestive. This was probably the chief immediate cause of the limited advance in physics.

The Arabian weakness in engineering is reflected in the personal story of Alhazen. He was engaged by the caliph al-Hakim to discover a method of regulating the annual Nile inundation. He failed, and had to feign madness to save his life.

35

Science and Muslim Society

THE society which supported the technique and culture of Islam had several notable features. It existed in an area which stretched from Spain to India, and lay almost entirely between the twentieth and fortieth degrees of latitude, i.e. just north of the tropics. This area contained an immense length of coastline and many navigable rivers. Its arid lands presented the dangers of thirst, starvation and sand-storms to transport, but were more easily traversed than the muddy and forest-covered lands of western Europe. Apart from the short isthmus of Suez, Muslim ships could sail almost directly from one end of the empire to the other without passing out of sight of land.

These conditions were favourable to transport. As the area contained many ancient and semi-independent civilizations, each producing some characteristic products, there were plenty of materials for exchange. In addition, the Arabs had originally been nomadic, and their religion ordered them to make pilgrimages to Mecca. The growth of trade was assisted by this tradition of movement and favourable conditions of transport, and was facilitated by the existence of a universal language.

The Muslims accomplished many wonderful travels. In the middle of the fourteenth century, Ibn Battuta of Morocco visited Asia Minor, Russia, India, the Maldives and China. On his return, he met a man south of the Atlas Mountains whom he had seen in China.

Their merchants imported 'sables, miniver, ermines, the fur of foxes, beavers, spotted hares, and goats; also wax, arrows, birch bark, high fur caps, fish glue, fish teeth, castoreum, amber, prepared horse hides, honey, hazel nuts, falcons, swords, armour, maple wood, slaves, small and big cattle' from the Northmen on the Volga. Tens of thousands of Arabian coins of the seventh century have been found in Sweden, taken home by the Northmen. Slaves were imported especially from the Slavonic peoples, and from Spain. The spread of Islamic culture was assisted by those who returned. Gold was imported from Africa, and musk, aloes, camphor, cinnamon, indigo and other Oriental products, such as oranges, lemons, apricots, spinach and artichokes were exported to Europe.

This trade led to the development of commercial technique, the influence of which on the growth of algebra has already been mentioned. The forms of banking were improved. The cheque, whose name is derived from an Arabic word, was introduced, and one for 42,000 dinars was seen in Morocco before the end of the tenth century. Other commercial words of Muslim origin are tariff, traffic, risk, tare, calibre, magazine and the German *Wechsel* for exchange. Joint stock companies were formed between Muslims and Italian Christians.

There was a considerable industrial besides trading development. The textile industries were outstanding, and have given the names of their products, such as muslin, damask, gauze, cotton, satin, chintz, shawl, fustian, taffeta, tabby, lilac, etc., to the modern world.

Industry was conducted by the rulers of the state, and not by individual capitalists. The workers were organized in guilds, but had the social status of slaves. The magnificent pile carpet from the mosque at Ardabil, now in the Victoria and Albert Museum in London, is signed 'the work of the slave of the threshold, Maqsud of Kashan, in the year 946' (A.D. 1540). Under these conditions, the quality of craftsmanship reached high distinction, but the industry lacked free capital and individual initiative, and presently declined in competition with Europe.

The Muslim development of sea trade and navigation is also reflected in the words contributed to modern vocabularies. Admiral, cable, average, sloop, barque and monsoon are all Arabic words. The Muslim pilots prepared improved sea maps and instruments through their experience, and one of them conducted Vasco da Gama from Africa to India on his famous voyage. They were the forerunners in geographical discovery and world trade.

It was from Chinese workmen whom they found in Samarkand, when they captured the city in 704, that the Muslims learned how to manufacture paper. The first paper mill at Baghdad was founded in 794.

One of the earliest recipes for gunpowder is given in a Latin work of 1300, which is probably a translation of an earlier Muslim work. It consists of '1 lb of live sulphur, 2 lb of charcoal from the lime or willow, 6 lb of saltpetre. Let the three substances be very finely powdered on a marble slab'. Descriptions of incendiary and phosphorescent substances, and 'Greek fires' (mixtures of petroleum, lime and other materials, which will burn under water) are also given. Incendiary powders and substances which colour flames were a valuable part of the equipment of magicians who wished to impress the public. Some of these, which would be mildly explosive, were known to the Chinese at very early dates, but it seems probable that the Muslim alchemists, with their high chemical skill, improved the recipes and made a large contribution to the development of explosives.

The chief Muslim contribution to science was the revival of the knowledge of Greek science, with important additions in mathematics and chemistry, and lesser additions in astronomy and medicine. The contributions to engineering, physics and experimental biology were small. These features of Muslim science reflect the character of Muslim society and its economic system. The controllers of industry were also the rulers of the state. As such, they had virtually unlimited wealth, and therefore had no strong incentive to efficiency. As skilled mechanics did not possess capital, they could not finance experiments in engineering. The study of machinery could not develop in these conditions. The background of mechanical knowledge necessary for the extensive development of experimental physics could not be accumulated, nor could craftsmen accumulate capital which would give them initiative to seek improvement, and means and leisure to conduct experiments.

In addition to these social circumstances, the Islamic Empire, like its classical predecessors, had a warm climate and was poor in wood and coal, so convenient sources of energy for exploitation as power were not easily available. Muslim society and science suffered from many of the defects of Graeco-Roman society and science. The two societies and the two sciences died from the same social diseases, of which slavery and the lack of free capital were among the most important.

36

The Shape of Western Civilization is Forged

THE first great barrier to the Muslim expansion was presented by Constantinople. This city was founded in A.D. 330 as the new capital of the Roman Empire and of Eastern Christianity. Its site as a military and trading centre was incomparable. It was gradually provided with very strong fortifications, and its population was minutely organized for war and civic life. Owing to the strength of the Byzantine organization, leadership was of less than usual importance, and the city could afford frequent changes of emperors without endangering its security. The walls of the city were of immense strength, and great underground reservoirs and cellars within the city provided stores of water and food large enough to outlast any siege. The Byzantines had a relatively small but expensive and highly-trained professional army. They specialized in heavy cavalry. These Caballarii wore steel caps and mail shirts, with steel frontlets. They carried linen and wool cloaks to cover the armour according to the weather, and each man had sword, dagger, bow-quiver and lance. Their introduction of iron horseshoes in the ninth century has already been mentioned.

5

The Muslim armies were very large, but man for man their cavalry was no match for the Caballarii.

The Byzantines supported their expensive army by the profits of trade and industry. Their ships dominated the Black Sea and the Northern Mediterranean, and the goods exchanged between East and West, and North and South passed through their customs, all imports and exports being taxed at a flat rate of ten per cent. In the sixth century they sent two Nestorian monks to China to steal the secrets of the cultivation of the silk-worm, which they brought back hidden in their hollow staves, and established a silk industry whose processes were concealed from Europe for centuries.

This powerful military, commercial and bureaucratic state protected Greek literature and language from 330 until 1453. For 1,123 years it was an almost impregnable museum of Greek culture. Its copyists supplied a large part of the Greek scientific manuscripts which provided the basis for the Muslim science created from the eighth century onwards. The Muslims were interested only in medicine, science and philosophy, and ignored poetry, drama and history. The second cultural fertilization accomplished by the Byzantines occurred after 1453, when they had to flee to Europe, and brought Greek literature with them. This movement with which the Renaissance is traditionally so closely connected, was humanistic, as Greek science had already reached Europe through Islam. The Renaissance, in so far as it is regarded exclusively as a result of the fall of Constantinople, is of restricted interest for science. The cultural effects of the flight from Constantinople were at first narrowly literary, and on the whole may have been unfortunate.

The Muslims began in 653 to organize combined attacks by sea and land on Constantinople. After incessant activity, their fleet appeared before the city in 674, and their armies attacked by land from April to September without success. The Byzantines counter-attacked the Muslim ships with fire-ships provided with 'Greek Fire', the incendiary material, mentioned in an earlier chapter, which will burn under water, and cannot be extinguished when alight. It is said that it was invented by a Syrian architect named Callinicus, and its composition was kept secret for many centuries.

The Muslims found their second great barrier in France. They conquered Spain in 711, and advanced into France, where they were defeated by Charles Martel at the battle of Poitiers or Tours in 732. Charles's foot-soldiers withstood the attacks of the Muslim cavalry which had previously proved almost invincible. The success of the Franks was not due to the superiority in military skill, but rather to the circumstances. The Muslim army contained few Arabs and consisted mainly of converted Berbers and Spaniards. These heterogeneous troops were led into a northerly region colder than those to which they were accustomed, so they would not have been able to make a sustained campaign without adaptation to a different climate. The Byzantines had noted that the Muslim cavalry was dispirited in cold and rain, and used this knowledge in their tactics against them. The Muslims had not contemplated such extensive changes, and their campaign was a raid rather than an invasion. As their empire was now so large, they tended to look inwards and enjoy their gains, and did not prosecute campaigns on their most remote frontiers with maximum ardour.

Their expansion in the West was halted exactly one hundred years after the death of Mahomet. Shortly afterwards, they began to devote more of their energy and wealth to the development of trade, science and culture, and they accomplished as much in this field in their second century as they had by conquest in their first. When this internal development of civilization had gathered momentum, the Muslims became less interested in further conquests.

Constantinople, Poitiers, and natural barriers, combined with the effects of its own vast size, settled the frontiers of Muslim civilization, and encouraged an internal development of its qualities. The determination of permanent frontiers between Islam and Europe had profound effects on Islam, but even profounder effects on Europe. It destroyed the internal communications, and hence the unity of the Roman Empire. With the coasts of Syria, Northern Africa and Spain under Muslim control, and the remaining coasts harried by Muslim galleys, Christian shipping and trade in the Mediterranean were much reduced. The Muslims, unlike the barbarian invaders of the Roman Empire, were not assimilated, owing to their sharp difference in religion, so their frontiers with Christian countries became barriers. The connections between Rome and Constantinople were severed, and the Western and Eastern parts of the old Christianized empire fell away from each other, and henceforth developed independently.

This event, due to the Muslims, marked the end of Graeco-Roman civilization. Western Christianity was now forced to develop its own life, or be extinguished. As it was dominated by Charles Martel and the Franks, owing to their victory, it developed under the forms of Frankish society. This was the beginning of modern Europe. As Pirenne says: 'A new Europe was created with the rise of the Frankish Empire, in which was elaborated the Western civilization which was one day to become that of the whole world.'

The social forces that have created modern science were released by the changes which occurred in Western European society when it became isolated, and was forced to develop its own potentialities.

37

The Embryo of the Modern World

THE suppression of Christian navigation in the Mediterranean by the Muslims destroyed the foreign trade and communications of Western Europe. Ports such as Marseilles, and trading towns on rivers in the interior, decayed through the lack of the materials of commerce. The remnants of the centralized Roman administration disintegrated, and the ancient offices, law courts, schools and post were closed. The framework of the imperial system disappeared. The social classes which survived were the great landowners descended from the owners of the Roman latifundia, and a population descended from Roman coloni, or peasants who were partly free and partly attached to the soil. Industry was starved by lack of supplies. Manufacture and construction ended, except on a small domestic scale, and with them the demand for slaves, the pure engines of labour. No one not connected with agriculture was needed.

The landowners under the Roman Empire were private persons, and their personal wealth did not legally give them any political power. Everyone was theoretically subject to the Roman laws. When the Roman system had dissolved, there was no longer any legal curb on their power. In addition, owing to the destruction of trade, land was the sole form of wealth, so the surviving landlords had no wealthy competitors for power. They began to remould the political forms of society in their own interests. They increased the ties of the peasants to the land, and gradually converted numbers of free men into serfs. Though they lowered the status and restricted the freedom of a large part of the poorer classes, they did not re-establish slavery. The decay of social organization had made the management of slavery more difficult. There was no longer any efficient Roman service for the capture of escaped slaves, and in a scattered agricultural society complete supervision was impossible. The allowance of some freedom to agricultural workers could not be avoided. The net increase in human freedom gained by the transition from classical to feudal society may be regarded, in some degree, as a concession made by government to save society when it was in danger of complete disintegration. This event seems to suggest that when the survival of society is seriously threatened, the most powerful stimulus which can be given to its members is an increase of freedom. Gibbon long ago observed that the poverty of the barons 'extorted from their pride those charters of freedom which unlocked the fetters of the slave, secured the farm of the peasant and the shop of the artificer, and gradually restored a substance and a soul to the most numerous and useful part of the community'.

Under the Roman system the law on the territory of landowners was administered by independent state officials. When the system decayed and the officials disappeared, the landowners appropriated the administration of law on their own estates. As combined owners and magistrates, their power was much increased. While this was happening, the destruction of trade eliminated the possibility of taxation, so that the Merovingian kings, who had become the dim successors of the emperors, could no longer finance an administration. Their power decreased as that of the landowners increased, and finally slipped into the hands of the largest landowner.

The transference was effected by Pippin. He made an alliance with the Church to obtain moral sanction for his usurpation of the throne of the Merovingians. As successors of the emperors, their power had been purely secular, and based on earthly sources. Pippin acquired religious significance for his title. His coronation was the first consecrated by the Church. Unlike his predecessors, he was a sacerdotal figure besides a king, and claimed that he was called not merely to rule the earth, but to rule it according to Christian morality. Religion was combined with the state, and only those who were Christians could be members of the state. Excommunication became equivalent to outlawry, and furnished the instrument which established the political power of the Church in the Middle Ages.

Charles Martel, who withstood the Muslims, was Pippin's illegitimate son. He had been impressed by the Muslim cavalry at Poitiers, and determined to imitate it. As there was little fluid wealth in the new feudal society, his foot-soldiers could not buy and support horses. Land was the only form of wealth, so he granted them pieces of land sufficient to support a horse, on the condition that they would mobilize for war at his order. He did not scruple to expropriate church property for these ends, and strained the new bonds between Church and State. But he had adapted the organization of the army to the economic system of feudalism. His reform established the military and political power of the landed aristocracy, and created chivalry.

Charlemagne, who was Charles Martel's grandson, conquered the whole of central Europe with this chivalry, and the alliance of religious and political power. He had great character and ability, and attempted to establish an ideal feudal society harmoniously regulated in all of its divine and human aspects. He compiled manuals on the proper management of estates. One of these gives a list of the craftsmen needed on an estate in his day: 'Blacksmiths, goldsmiths, carpenters, swordmakers, fishermen, fowlers, soap-makers, men who know how to make beer, cider, perry and all other kinds of beverages, bakers to make pasty for our table, netmakers who know how to make nets for hunting, fishing and fowling, and others too many to be named.'

He reformed writing and created the script which became the model for modern printers. He encouraged education in church schools to prepare men for administration in the state, and he founded the monetary system of pounds, shillings and pence, which survives in British currency.

The result of this inspired activity was disappointing. As cities had disappeared with the decay of the Roman Empire and the growth of feudalism, there were no centres where wealth could accumulate. Charlemagne and his court travelled perpetually from estate to estate, consuming the contents of the barns and then moving on. The administration had regressed from the sedentary Roman type established in cities, and had become nomadic. The feudal empire was invertebrate. The unifying monetary and cultural reforms were not supported by a firm administrative skeleton, or nourished by a sufficient flow of commerce, and they soon disintegrated.

The coasts of Charlemagne's empire were sealed on the south by the Muslims, and on the north by the Northmen. The foreign trade which might have provided the means for the construction of a vertebrate state had ended in the eighth century and did not revive until the eleventh.

38
A New System of Social Classes and its Effects

THE new society, which had been virtually isolated for three centuries, flourished particularly well in Northern France. The grassland was suitable for the support of horses, and its subdivision had been carried further than in other countries. The climate was temperate, and suitable for the wearing of heavy armour and continuous exercise. One-tenth of the population were minor noblemen and hence professional horse soldiers. Many of these were of Scandinavian descent, though their assimilation was so complete that no Scandinavian word survived in the Norman language. The Normans retained nothing of their Scandinavian ancestors, except an extraordinary spirit of adventure.

Their military technique was perfected during three centuries of evolution. The minor noblemen, with just enough land to support their personal arms, engaged in incessant tourneys. Their sons learned to fight as soon as they could mount a horse. All civil and intellectual technique disappeared, except in a few monasteries, where memories of Roman technique and trade survived.

This Norman military society was able to undertake great aggressions in the second half of the eleventh century. It invaded

Sicily in 1061, England in 1066, and Palestine on the first Crusade in 1099. It became the military instrument of the papacy, which was now the greatest political power in Europe, owing to the weakness of central government under feudalism.

The Church's possession of political power enabled it to use the Normans for its own ends. It launched them against the Muslims in Palestine with the purely religious aim of securing the holy places of Christianity. The Norman knights were unlettered, brutal and pious. They had strong sentiments of devotion and honour. They scrupulously respected the right of sanctuary. They regarded their word as sacred, and interpreted all relations between man and man from the personal point of view. They had no sense of discipline and obedience, and immediately rebelled if injured. They expressed their opinions with the utmost boldness and plain speaking. They engaged in no productive labour, and had extreme contempt for profit-seeking. These qualities were based on their economic and political independence.

Norman society was very different from the contemporary Muslim society. It had little science and technique, apart from that of warfare. But it was free from political absolutism and pure slavery. It contained a relatively large number of small landowners who created a tradition of the independent gentleman who thinks for himself and does things for their own sake without thought of profit. The Normans made few scientific discoveries, but their development of a society with these traditions was a contribution towards the creation of the social conditions under which science can grow continuously. The Muslims failed to create the social conditions in which new major science could take root and grow, in spite of their revival of ancient science.

The second great service to future science performed by Norman and feudal society was equally indirect and unconscious, and very different in character. The Crusaders in Palestine required transport and victuals. These were supplied by merchants and seamen of Pisa, Genoa and Venice. Christian trade and navigation were revived, and from that time, eight hundred years ago, it has expanded nearly continuously. The Crusaders brought Europe in clashing contact with Muslim civilization in Palestine, but little of Muslim science and commercial technique was learned through this contact, owing to the mutual religious hostility.

The effective channel through which Europe received Muslim science was Moorish Spain and northern Africa. Toledo was retaken from the Muslims in 1085. A large number of Arabic manuscripts were left in the city, and a mixed population of Moors, Jews and Spaniards, who knew Arabic and Latin. Translation of the Arabic manuscripts into Latin was organized on a considerable scale, and enterprising scholars from all parts of Europe came to learn Muslim science and read Arabic translations of Greek works hitherto unknown in Latin. Many of these scholars had a passion for translation. Gerard of Cremona journeyed to Toledo to read Ptolemy's *Almagest*, which was not available to him in Latin. He was astounded by the wealth of Arabic works and began translating them with incomparable ardour. He completed nearly one hundred translations before he died in 1187, including Euclid's *Elements*, Ptolemy's *Almagest*, the works of Galen and Hippocrates, and Aristotle's *Posterior Analytics*.

What was the motive that sent Gerard of Cremona, and other scholars, to study in Spain? It was the energy generated by the developing society in medieval Europe. The Crusades had created a new trading class in the Italian ports. They had also stimulated pilgrimages and a general movement of soldiers and pilgrims throughout Europe which carried trade with it. The aspirations of the scholars were an expression of the hope created by the increasing prosperity. Many of them were Englishmen. Adelard of Bath made the first Latin translation of fifteen books of Euclid from Arabic about 1126. Contrary to the general belief, he was not a monk. He certainly visited Sicily and Syria, and probably Spain. He also translated Al-Khwarizmi's astronomical tables, revised for the meridian of Cordova by Maslama.

Adelard composed scientific dialogues for the instruction of his nephew. He rejected unquestioning faith and advocated scientific investigation. He attacked excessive reliance on authority, for: 'I learned from my Arabian master under the leading of reason . . . If you want to hear anything more from me, give and take reason. For I'm not the sort of man that can be fed on a picture of a beef-steak.'

He explains that reason is not sufficient to solve the problems of the universe, and that observation and measurement are necessary. 'Who has ever comprehended the space of the sky with the same sense of sight? . . . Who has ever distinguished minute atoms with the eye?' As Thorndike comments, such questions as these express the need for the telescope and show that the conditions for their invention were maturing. He clearly states the principle of the indestructibility of matter. 'And certainly in my judgment nothing in this world of sense ever perishes utterly, or is less today than when it was created. If any part is dissolved from one union, it does not perish but is joined to some other group.' He discusses the behaviour of water imprisoned in an enchantress's inverted jar, and unable to flow out until air bubbles through the lower aperture. His explanation contains some conceptions resembling chemical affinity, and the experiment, which he describes carefully, is an example of the debt of experimental science to magic. Robert of Chester translated Al-Khwarizmi's algebra into Latin in 1145, under the title *Liber Algebre et Almucabala*, and introduced this new branch of mathematics to the Western world. The connection between England and Christian Spain was not purely cultural. It was strengthened by the marriage of Alfonso VIII to Lenora, a daughter of Henry II, at the end of the twelfth century.

The first original European work on algebra was published by Leonardo of Pisa in 1202. The city of Pisa, as the leading port of embarkment for the Crusades, and a growing trading centre, had customs houses in many Christian and Muslim Mediterranean ports. Leonardo's father was the controller of the Pisan customs house at Bugia in Barbary, and his son was educated by a Muslim teacher. He became acquainted with Al-Khwarizmi's algebra, the Arabic numerals and decimal calculation. He travelled in Egypt, Syria, Greece, Sicily and Southern France, and learned the various methods of calculation used by the merchants in those countries. He published a treatise in 1202, named the *Liber Abaci*, containing an exposition of the best methods of calculation, and the elements of algebra. The work was composed in fifteen chapters. The first seven dealt with arithmetic and its operations. The eighth dealt with the Prices of Goods, the ninth with Barter and the tenth with Partnership. Other chapters were devoted to solutions of problems, square and cube roots, and mensuration and algebra.

Leonardo contributed more than any other man to the establishment of the decimal system in Europe. His knowledge was derived from his contact with commerce, and it was not esteemed in the orthodox universities, especially at Paris. He had great mathematical ability and made original contributions, especially in the theory of numbers. The Emperor Frederick II, King of Sicily, visited him in 1225, and conducted the first mathematical tournament in his honour. This was the forerunner of the competitions and challenges which continued down to the time of Newton, and show the influence of feudal social forms even on mathematics. The competitors were asked to find a number of which the square, when increased or diminished by 5 would remain a square. Leonardo gave the fraction $\frac{41}{12}$, which is a correct solution. The second problem was the solution of the cubic equation $x^3 + 2x^2 + 10x = 20$, by Euclidean methods. He showed that solution by these methods was impossible, but gave an arithmetical answer correct to nine places of decimals.

Frederick had an extraordinary part in the encouragement of science in the thirteenth century. He was of Norman descent, and ruled Sicily, which had the most advanced system of agriculture in Europe, and a population of more than one million. It had formerly been a Byzantine and then a Muslim colony, and had inherited from these civilizations a despotic government, with a competent civil service. As a meeting place of so many civilizations, Sicily was an admirable centre for the communication of Greek and Muslim learning to the West. Frederick lived from 1194 to 1250. He was a despot, but combined a love of power with an interest in art, learning, experiment and magic. The conflict of cultures in his country provided suitable soil for scepticism, and he was reputed to be an unbeliever. The opinion that Moses, Jesus and Mohammed were impostors was attributed to him, and Pope Gregory IX accused him of heresy and blasphemy. This opinion had previously been fathered on others to destroy their reputations. He had bizarre habits, and a harem of Muslim women. He denied the accusations of heresy, and collaborated with the papacy in the creation of the Inquisition. There is little doubt that he was privately atheistical, and persecuted heresy in others from political motives. Lying, torture and perjury were his favourite political weapons, and burning at the stake as a punishment of the Inquisition was first officially recognized in ordinances made by him.

Besides encouraging translators, he had a personal interest in experimental research. He studied falconry and natural history, and was accomplished in the mechanics of architecture. Like Alexander the Great, he used his royal administration to collect scientific information, and provided a remarkable example of the pursuit of research by governmental agencies. He collected scientific information by questionnaires addressed to scholars in Egypt, Syria, Iraq, Asia Minor and Yemen.

Frederick freely criticized Aristotle's knowledge of natural history, especially in connection with falconry. He said that he depends too much on hearsay, and must be corrected from personal observation. He 'rarely or never had experience in falconry, which we have loved and practised all our lives'.

He tested the artificial incubation of hens' eggs. He brought experts and ostrich eggs from Apulia to make similar tests with them. He exploded the fable that geese come from barnacles by sending to the North for barnacles and making the experiment. He concluded that the story arose from ignorance of the nesting place of geese. He sealed the eyes of vultures to discover whether they hunted by sight or smell. He shut a man in a wine cask to prove that his soul died with his body. He had two men disembowelled, one after exercise and the other after sleep, to show the different effects of exercise and sleep on digestion. He reared children in silence to see whether 'they would speak Hebrew first, or Greek, or Latin, or Arabic, or at least the language of their parents; but he laboured in vain, for the children all died'.

He assisted education by founding the University of Naples, where Aquinas studied. He ordered the translation of the medical works of Avicenna, which remained the standard authority for five centuries, and he laid down that medical students should study logic for three years before commencing medicine. He ordered that surgeons should study human anatomy for one year before graduation. His laudable instruction failed, owing to the overwhelming weight of medical literature, and the social status of surgeons. They were regarded as handicraftsmen, and the inferiors of physicians, from whom they were supposed to take orders. Their observations were therefore deemed beneath the dignity of record in literature.

Though accused of scepticism in religion, he passionately believed in magic. Michael Scot and Theodore of Antioch were his official astrologers, and he conducted his military campaigns with their advice. When he was defeated by the Pope's allies before Parma, his enemies exulted in their destruction of his troop of magicians and devotees of Beelzebub and the demons. He became identified with Antichrist, though he led the fifth

Crusade and became King of Jerusalem in 1229. The legend arose that he had never died, but slumbered under a hill. The hero's part in this story was transferred in later times to Frederick Barbarossa.

Frederick II has been described as the first modern man to ascend a throne. He resembled the princes of the Italian Renaissance with his rationalism, experimentation, political cruelty and superstition. The history of Frederick II's activities shows that the relation between toleration and the progress of science is not simple.

39

Manual Labour Acquires New Repute and Mechanics Advances

THE scholars who journeyed in search of Arabic science received their impetus from the social energy created by the developing medieval society. This expressed itself in tremendous constructive works. The French built eighty cathedrals and five hundred churches between 1170 and 1270. Henry Adams estimated that the cost was equivalent to the sum of one thousand million dollars at the dollar value of his day. In the outlying countries, from England to Hungary, building was not much less intense. The social atmosphere of this activity has been recorded by Archbishop Hugo of Rouen in his description of the great cathedral at Chartres. This is perhaps the most wonderful religious building raised in Europe. It is made of very hard stone brought in large blocks from quarries five miles away. Hugo states that the inhabitants of Chartres combined to aid in the transport of materials. The associations admitted no one who had not been to confession, renounced enmities, and reconciled himself with his enemies. After that had been done, and the association formed, a chief was elected. Under his direction, the wagons were hauled by the people in silence and humility. The work was done with feverish rapidity. Hugo comments: 'Who has ever seen!—Who has ever heard tell, in times past, that powerful princes of the world, that men brought up in honour

and wealth, that nobles, men and women, have bent their proud
and haughty necks to the harness of carts, and that, like beasts of
burden, they have dragged to the abode of Christ these wagons,
loaded with wines, grains, oil, stone, wood, and all that is necessary for the wants of life, or the construction of the church?'

The multitude of hauliers remained silent, even when a
thousand and more were attached to the chariots. When they
halted on the road nothing was heard except the confession of
sins and suppliant prayers. At the exhortation of the priests they
forgot all hatred and discord, debts were remitted and the unity
of hearts was established. The contribution of anyone who
refused to pardon an offender was instantly thrown from the
wagon and he himself was ignominiously excluded from the
society of the holy. Priests presided over each chariot and recited
prayers during the rests. Their trumpets were sounded for the
resumption of the haul, and the march was made with such ease
that no obstacle could retard it.

The conditions of work at Chartres are in notable contrast to
those of antiquity. There were no slave-drivers standing over the
human hauliers with whips, and members of all social classes
bent their necks to the harness of carts. Manual labour was
being made reputable. 'Who has seen!—Who has ever heard tell'
of such a thing 'in times past?'

A large part of the wealth required for this construction was
supplied by the inhabitants of the towns growing on the trade
routes revived by the Crusades, and around the new churches.
In the cathedral of Chartres, built in its present form between
1195–1210, the seven great windows were donated by the
Drapers, Butchers, Bakers, Bankers, and other guilds, and none
by noblemen. This *bourgeoisie* was exerting its due power, and
even coming closer than the feudal lords to the most sacred
centres of the contemporary society. It was achieving a new
social status and repute. Its sons could not enter the feudal
nobility, whose membership was determined by ancestry, but
they could enter the Church and had a fair chance of attaining
rank according to their ability. Piety satisfied the conscience of
this *bourgeoisie*, and strengthened its ties with the Church, which
could provide political besides religious careers for its sons.

These members of crafts, trades and professions now acquiring
such a solid position in society, were the descendants of the
medieval servants listed by Charlemagne. They were small

masters employing one or two journeymen and apprentices. They owned their raw material, and the profit on the sale of their products was exclusively theirs. Their customers were fellow citizens and local peasants. Individual craftsmen working on a small scale under these conditions were very insecure, owing to the limits of the local market. They early organized themselves into guilds to regulate competition, and guarantee every member a living. Rules governing the conduct of crafts were gradually evolved. The price of products was fixed. Working by artificial light, the use of unusual tools or the modification of traditional technique, the employment of more than the usual number of workmen, and of wives and young children were forbidden. The most severe prohibition of all was applied to advertisement. This was absolutely forbidden.

The guild rules repressed technical innovation, but they strengthened the social status of craftsmen and manual work. The social energy accumulated by the latter development proved ultimately to be stronger than the bonds placed on technical invention by guild rules. The medieval crafts gave encouragement to the development of technique less by direct contribution than by elevation of the social status of craftsmen. Even when a medieval industry achieved unusual dimensions it made little technical progress. The textile industries of Venice and Bruges had a large export trade, but their technique was not substantially better than that of ancient Egypt.

The construction of the new churches presented considerable technical problems. The weights to be moved were large, even if smaller than many handled by Egyptians and Romans. The invention of the pointed arch and stone vaulting presented problems in geometry and statistics which would have been more complicated than those solved by the ancients, if they had been solved exactly. It seems, however, that the medieval architects reached their greatest achievements by experience and not by analysis. Improvement of design was learned empirically in the construction of one church after another, and from defects in construction revealed by time.

The technical knowledge of a medieval architect has been preserved in the precious notebook of Villard de Honnecourt. He was the architect of the cathedral of Cambrai, part of which had been paid for by Elizabeth of Hungary. After the Tartar invasion of Hungary in 1242, her brother King Bela sent for Villard to rebuild churches. He made sketches of remarkable things he had noticed in his travels between 1243 and 1251. The width of a river is determined by pointing two horizontal sticks at an object on the other bank. The two sticks, which will be inclined at a small angle, are then fixed to a board, and laid on a smooth field. An observer looks along the sticks, and an assistant holds a post until the place where both sticks point at it is found. The distance between the post and the sticks is equal to the width of the river and may be directly measured. The height of a tower is obtained by placing a right-angled isosceles triangle, or half-square, in a vertical plane, with one of the short sides in contact with the ground. The triangle is slid about until the hypotenuse, or long side, is in line with the top of the tower. The height is equal to the distance of the triangle from the base of the tower.

Both of these methods are very crude and inaccurate. Villard gives a solution of a problem in which a man has to place an egg under a pear hanging on a tree, so that if the pear falls it will hit the egg. Two posts are stuck in the ground so that they, and the pear, are seen to be in the same vertical plane. The feet of the posts are joined by a string. The operation is repeated with another pair of posts, and the egg should be laid at the point where the two strings intersect.

He gives some geometrical methods of about equal merit for marking stone to be cut for arches, and a number of vigorous sketches of draped human figures from the life for stone carvings, and a sketch of a lion, which he specially notes as drawn from the life. His perspective is wrong, but some of the figures show high artistic power. He gives an elaborate drawing of a well-known type of perpetual-motion machine.

The technical part of these subjects is disappointing. There are, however, two other entries of great interest. One is a sketch of a self-acting saw mill driven by water power. The saw hangs from a long elastic pole. Four pegs stick out of the axle of the water wheel, and each peg depresses the other end of the saw as it goes round. After a downward stroke by a peg, the saw is pulled back by the elastic pole. This is the first power saw recorded in history, apart from a possible obscure reference to one that existed on the Moselle in the fourth century.

The second sketch is of a machine 'to make an angel point with his finger to the sun'. The drawing is rough, and the true nature of the machine is uncertain. One interpretation is that a rope was wound round the spindle carrying the angel. One end passed over a pulley and bore a weight. The other end was passed round the axle of a wheel, and then through its spokes, and finally over a pulley, where it was attached to a weight. If one weight was heavier than the other, it would tend to fall and pull the rope so that the spindle rotated. But the axle of the wheel would also rotate, and this would make one of the spokes drag the rope sideways. This would stop the fall, and also the rotation of the wheel, which would now recoil. The rope was released, and slipped a bit further, and was again held, and so on. On this interpretation, it is an escapement, the fundamental part of clock mechanism. If this is so, it would be the first record in Europe of an escapement. As Needham, Wang and Price have shown, the Chinese I Hsing had invented the escapement by A.D. 725. Knowledge of this prime invention seems to have reached Europe about five hundred years later. The improvement of the clock became the chief inspiration of mechanical invention in Europe for four centuries.

Besides the acquisition of the escapement principle and other inventions, progress was made in theoretical mechanics. An anonymous treatise on statics, in which the principle of virtual work and a correct discussion of the equilibrium of a balance were foreshadowed, was written in the thirteenth century. It has been attributed to Jordanus, who joined the Dominican order in 1220, but it is not by him.

A weightless bent lever with arms of unequal length was freely suspended at the corner. The ends of the two arms were at equal distances from a vertical line through the point of support. The author asks whether the lever will remain in equilibrium if equal weights are attached to the ends of the arms. He considers the effects of small displacements of the lever from its original position, and shows that they are impossible if no external force is applied.

Hitherto, no writer on the lever had clearly understood that the forces on the arms need not act at right angles to them. In practice, ropes were tied to levers and hauled in directions not at right angles to the arms, but theorists had not started from what happened in practice. They had followed Archimedes, and tried to extend the principle of balance, seen intuitively in a straight horizontal symmetrical lever with equal weights, to levers with unequal arms. Owing to their start from the horizontal lever with forces acting at right angles to its arms, they tended to assume that forces always must act at right angles to arms, and were unable to arrive at the generalized principle of statical moments.

The anonymous mechanician of the thirteenth century had used a principle of displacements which eliminated this assumption, and contained a correct theory of statical moments. He had in fact published the first example of the use of the powerful principle of virtual work. His successors, from Leonardo da Vinci to Willard Gibbs, have founded theoretical mechanics on this principle.

40

The Pursuit of Gain Impels Social and Technical Development

THE agricultural society of feudalism was self-supporting and stable. Its landlords, peasants, craftsmen, clergy possessed some security, and felt no powerful incentive to change. If the isolation from the rest of the world could have continued indefinitely, it might have remained unchanged for many centuries. But it was not completely sealed off by the Muslims and its other enemies. The Byzantine navy controlled the Adriatic and invited imports from its coasts. The lagoons off Venetia were a convenient source of salt, and fishermen who lived there, and had no demand for salt from the self-supporting inland society, were able to export their product to Byzantium. Their trade in this commodity grew considerably in the ninth century and they erected buildings on the islands in the lagoons. This was the foundation of the city of Venice. Owing to its peculiar position and activity it was outside the normal Western European feudal society, and from the tenth century its policy was purely commercial.

The development of Pisa and Genoa as ports of supply for the Crusades started a little later.

The Venetian fishermen who received Byzantine silk for their salt, and the Pisan boatmen who sold food at extravagant rates to Crusaders and received gold and jewels in payment could not consume their new property. They had to find a market for it.

They could not do this within the recognized framework of feudal society. There was no transport for moving saleable goods through feudal countries. The recognized classes of landowners, peasants, craftsmen and clergy accepted the principles of feudalism which were opposed to ideas of commercial profit, interest, and the use of money.

The new merchants of the coasts, who were a species of fisherman, adventurer and pirate, could not find agents in these classes to tout their goods through the feudal countryside. Only landless vagabonds would undertake this. These wanderers, who had nothing to lose, and had picked up knowledge of the world in their wanderings, lived by their wits; listening for news of dearth and famine and rushing to sell dear what they had bought cheap. As they had no social status and security they were also without social duties and enjoyed the freedom of vagabondage.

Numbers of them spread through feudal Europe during the tenth century, and made their headquarters near feudal fortresses or bourgs, and in the communities surrounding cathedrals, many of which had been built on rivers and natural lines of communication.

At first there was no place in the feudal communities for this new class of turbulent merchants. They had to make their position. They gradually established it by their wealth, and the stimulus their commerce gave to the places where they settled, and they formed guilds to protect their interests and ensure their social status.

Cities did not exist in feudal agricultural society, because the inhabitants were tied to the soil and were supported by it. The population was permanently scattered and had no motive for aggregation. Centres such as castles and cathedral towns were for protection and administration and had virtually no part in production. They contained small groups of craftsmen who supplied purely local needs and there was no stimulus to multiply their number.

The free, wild and vagabond merchants who began to settle these feudal centres in the tenth century were without roots in the soil and seemed scandalous to the feudal inhabitants. They were followed by unattached craftsmen and labourers, who presently formed guilds in imitation of the merchants to protect their own interests. None of them could be returned to serfdom, because their owners were unknown.

Besides developing commerce, the merchants spread the idea of working for personal profit instead of feudal duty. Their commercial activity created a demand for craftsmen and labourers, and at the same time the peasants in the surrounding country learned the idea of initiative for personal gain. Numbers of them were attracted to the centres by the new demand for labour. The old bourgs or fortresses and the walled ecclesiastical communities were unable to accommodate the increasing population. The new free and vagabond community settled outside the walls of the bourg, which were presently surrounded by their houses. Then an outer wall was built around the houses, and the enclosed ring was named the nouveaubourg or faubourg. The inhabitants of the ring were named *bourgeois* in the eleventh century.

The *bourgeoisie* began to establish its own system of law within its faubourg. This was based on the principle of personal property, and was in conflict with feudal law. If a peasant who had deserted his lord was within their gates, the *bourgeoisie* would not surrender him. Punishments more brutal than those customary under feudal law were introduced to control their wild and grasping members and protect personal property.

As the *bourgeoisie* did not belong either to the noble or peasant classes, it did not share their class feeling, which was uniform throughout Europe. It evolved a new intense civic feeling and solidarity, which was expressed as strongly against the *bourgeoisies* of other cities as against local feudal lords.

The originally wild *bourgeoisie* settled down and developed its organization of guilds, and after its first struggle for status had been satisfied and the principles of its way of life accepted, it began to subscribe to the church, and contributed magnificent gifts such as the altar windows at Chartres.

The growth of the *bourgeoisie* and its activities undermined feudalism. The increase in the circulation of money produced a rise in prices, and this lowered the real value of feudal dues. Many small landlords were ruined, and large landlords sought to bring virgin land under cultivation to restore their incomes. The Dutch lowlands were drained by new orders of monks who were prescribed to manual labour. The big undertakings led to the creation of the first large-scale agriculture since Roman times.

The urban demand for food gave a new stimulus to the peasant. Hitherto he had produced a definite quantity of food for local consumption only. Now he was encouraged to produce as large a surplus as possible and sell it at a profit to the town.

The increase in production due to the *bourgeoisie* stimulated the creation of new monastic orders. The Franciscans, who lived by begging, could not exist without surplus production, a principle incompatible with feudalism. They were the obverse of the new *bourgeoisie*. By pledging themselves to poverty, they atoned for the *bourgeoisie's* lust for gain, and became its conscience. In return, the *bourgeoisie* kept and favoured them.

The *bourgeoisie* wrested a position beside the nobility and clergy in the state. Progressive kings sought alliance with them against the nobility, and by their aid limited the political power of the landlords. This movement gradually destroyed feudalism and created the national state.

The new technique of commerce was evolved by the merchants in Italian ports and cities. They learned much from the Muslims of banking, bills of exchange, and money-lending, and devised improvements from their own experience. They introduced book-keeping by double entry in 1394. They needed clerks to keep accounts. At first these could be supplied only by the Church, and they wrote in Latin. This was inconvenient, for the *bourgeoisie* conducted its business in the local dialect.

They wanted persons who wrote in the local dialect, so they created a new class of educated laymen, who presently began to write secular literature in the vernacular. Through these scholars the *bourgeoisie* began to think and write for itself and it started to replace the feudal conceptions of life and nature by its own.

41

The Intellectual Weapons are Sharpened

THE Church was the sole framework which prevented Western European society from relapsing into savagery in the sixth, seventh and eighth centuries. Education had passed entirely into its hands, and when Charlemagne sought trained servants for his government, he naturally turned to the Church to provide them. Under his stimulus many new cathedral schools were founded. As the Church controlled education, theology became and remained the chief subject of study, and provided medieval civilization with its characteristic unity.

When Western European society began to revive, a profoundly authoritative theology surrounded the new thinkers. It had apparently carried society through a period of extreme danger and was entitled to its prestige. This theology had been created chiefly by Augustine, through a combination of Christian dogma and Platonic philosophy. These two elements determined the content of subsequent medieval thought. As Harris explains, its history consists of the interaction of a permanent mass of church dogma with an increasing knowledge of ancient philosophy.

The written word, like Christian dogma, had also survived the social disintegration. At the beginning of the revival, when illiteracy was still nearly universal, it also enjoyed exceptional authority. Dogma, Platonism and the written word were virtually sacred.

The first and perhaps the most profound medieval philosopher was Erigena, who was born in Ireland in the ninth century. His philosophy was neo-Platonic. He believed that thought is the only ultimate reality, and that corporeal sensations are mere illusions. He had a sublime theory of orders of creation, which was derived from Plotinus's scale of perfection. Erigena's thought was too difficult and original, and made few converts.

As Brehaut says, the supernatural world appeared ordered and real to the thinkers of the early Middle Ages, while the world of the senses was deceptive and unreal. The exaltation and failure of Erigena's effort in thought may be compared with Charlemagne's in government. Both men in their spheres were too far in advance of contemporary development.

The next revival of thought occurred in the eleventh century, during the period of the Norman expansion, and the founding of the *bourgeoisie*. It was less exalted, and concentrated on the problem of general concepts or universals rather than on Erigena's sublime orders of creation.

Is a general concept such as 'humanity' a real substance, which is always the same and pervades all individual human beings, or is it merely a class name for a group of particular men? Those of the former opinion were called 'realists' and the latter 'nominalists'.

Roscellinus, who was a nominalist, pointed out that if the

realists are correct then the three Persons of the Trinity are not three beings but one, while if the nominalists are correct, the three Persons are individual, and are three Gods.

As Harris says: 'At this abominable tritheism the whole of Christendom stood aghast.' This sort of wrangling was characteristic of the new scholasticism. The number of disputants rapidly increased with the increasing social prosperity in the eleventh century.

Anselm, who lived from 1033–1109, attempted to restate church dogma in the terminology of the new disputants, and was the first since Augustine, who wrote at the end of the fourth century, to write a systematic treatise on dogma. He was a man of profound faith who also appreciated the need for rational explanation, so he tried to re-establish theology on the basis of two principles, one of faith and the other of argument. According to the first: 'He who does not believe will not experience, and he who has not experienced will not understand.' This resembles some of the notions of Bergson, and of those social philosophers who deny that it is possible to understand a social movement without taking part in it. His famous 'ontological' argument for the existence of God asserts: 'God is that being than whom none greater can be conceived. Now, if that than which nothing greater can be conceived existed only in the intellect, it would not be absolutely the greatest, for we could add to it existence in reality. It follows then, that the being than whom nothing greater can be conceived, that is God, necessarily has real existence.'

The new logical inquiry was trenchantly described by Berenger of Tours, who lived from 1049–1088. 'It is the part of courage to have recourse to dialectic in all things, for recourse to dialectic is recourse to reason, and he who does not avail himself of reason abandons his chief honour, since by virtue of reason he was made in the image of God.'

This confident spirit was raised still higher by the famous Abélard, who lived from 1079–1142. He came to Paris in 1100, and immediately made a name by disputing with the leading teacher, William of Champeaux, who lectured in the school of the cathedral of Notre-Dame. He was brilliant and aggressive, and attacked his opponents like an intellectual knight-at-arms.

Students were fascinated by his skill and personality, and flocked to his lectures. He received fees from three thousand at the height of his vogue. But his vanity and intellectual confidence aroused numerous enemies. The old-fashioned mystics such as St. Bernard, who felt that the truths of religion were known by intuition and not by reason, hated him. St. Bernard complained that 'he sees nothing as an enigma, nothing as in a mirror, but looks on everything face to face'.

Abélard claimed to explain God's motives. He said: 'All that God does He wills necessarily and does it necessarily; for His Goodness is such that it pushes Him necessarily to do all the good He can, and the best He can, and the quickest He can . . . Therefore it is of necessity that God willed and made the world.'

He compiled in parallel passages, entitled *Sic et Non* (Yes and No), all the contradictory statements he could find in the Scriptures and Fathers, and he suggested principles by which they could be reconciled, but he did not offer any examples. This comparative method was first used by lawyers, who had rediscovered the codes of Justinian after a lapse of five centuries.

St. Bernard loathed this growth of intellectual criticism. He said that if these scholars had 'once tasted true food of religion, "how quick" they would be to leave those Jew makers of books to gnaw their crusts by themselves'.

Abélard was watched relentlessly by Bernard and the orthodox. They secured the condemnation of his book on theology in 1121. He was shut in a monastery and rarely lectured again. Bernard became Pope, and in 1140 organized his final suppression. He had him accused of striving for an exclusive domination in the schools. 'He treats Holy Scripture as though it were dialectics. It is a matter with him of personal invention and annual novelties. He is the censor and not the disciple of the faith: the corrector and not the imitator of the authorized masters.' Like many other mystics, St. Bernard combined religious intuition with political cunning. He packed the court with Abélard's opponents in church politics, and had him condemned to silence. Abélard died two years later, in 1142.

The radicalism of Abélard's confidence in reason and love of novelty, and his egotism, have always disturbed conservatives. Haskins has described his lively but boastful autobiography as the portrait of the eternal radical by himself. And yet Abélard's thought, as distinguished from his attitude of mind, was not radical, unless an advance towards the moderate Aristotelian realism of the thirteenth century, and away from extreme Platonism, is regarded as radical.

He expressed his view on the fundamental problem of universals thus: 'When we say that Plato and Socrates are both men, we do not mean that there is a mysterious essence "humanity" which, one and the same, gives being to both, but we mean that both have similar essences.'

Very few of the works of Plato and Aristotle were available to Abélard. He was familiar only with the *Timaeus*, in which Plato applies his theory of ideas to science, and gives perhaps the least convincing of all his expositions of idealism; and with the Platonic early works of Aristotle.

Shortly after his death, the translations of the metaphysics and natural science of Aristotle, and his Muslim commentators, arrived in Western Europe, accompanied by Galen, Hippocrates and Avicenna in medicine; besides these, Euclid, algebra, perspective and optics in mathematics and physics, and Muslim astronomical tables based on the meridian of Toledo, arrived about the same time.

The contemporaries of Abélard had already become dissatisfied with dialectic. His student, John of Salisbury, had recorded that 'experience taught me a manifest conclusion, that, whereas dialectic furthers other studies, so if it remain by itself it lies bloodless and barren, nor does it quicken the soul to yield fruit of philosophy, except the same conceive from elsewhere'.

Daniel of Morley left Paris in disgust about 1180, and went to Toledo 'to hear the wiser philosophers of the world'. He attended lectures by Gerard of Cremona, and returned to England with the translations of various Muslim works.

Daniel's initiative in educative travel resembled Abélard's in philosophy. Both courageously advanced into new regions.

42

The Church Tries to Assimilate Science

ALBERTUS MAGNUS, who lived from 1206 until 1280, undertook the systematization of all the new knowledge in philosophy and science. He saw that the Greek and Muslim philosophy could not be merged with Christian theology, and began the separation of philosophy and theology. He noted that 'natural science is not simply receiving what one is told, but the investigation of causes in natural philosophy'.

Besides summarizing virtually the whole knowledge of his day, he made original observations and experiments, especially in biology and mineralogy. He and his colleagues proved by experiment that a cicada goes on singing in its breast after its head has been cut off. He considered that he had proved by experiments in a vessel that a turtle, though a marine animal, would not drink sea water. He disproved the assertion that ostriches eat and digest iron by offering them bits of iron. They rejected these, though they swallowed stones, and bones cut into small bits.

Albert reflected the contemporary interest in observation of nature, exhibited in cathedral sculpture. As Mâle has noted, the depiction of foliage and fruit in Gothic sculpture is so exact that modern naturalists have been able to identify the plantain, arum, buttercup, fern, clover, celandine, hepatica, columbine, cress, parsley, strawberry, ivy, snapdragon, oak leaf and the flower of the broom, as among the original flora of modern France.

Villard de Honnecourt depicted a lobster, paraqueets, the spirals of a snail's shell, a fly, a dragon fly, a grasshopper, a lion, bear, swan and cat in his sketch book.

Albert was the most learned scholar of his day and the pride of the Dominican order.

The Dominicans presently discovered a youth with an extraordinary talent for learning, who was the son of the Count of Aguino in Sicily. This was Thomas Aquinas. He was born in 1225, joined the Dominicans when he was sixteen, and was sent to study under Albert.

The first draft of the adaptation of the rediscovered Greek and Muslim knowledge to Christian dogma had been laboriously completed by Albert. Thomas assimilated this quickly, and while his mind was still young and fresh, began a more systematic, profound, and polished treatment of the same problem; and especially the combination of Christian dogma with Aristotelian philosophy. The chief statement of his thought is in his *Summa Theologica*, the English version of which is published in twenty-two volumes. This was unfinished when he died in 1274, at the age of forty-nine.

Earlier Christian thought, both of the severely rational and the mystically speculative types, was almost exclusively Platonic. Thomas therefore had to find foundations other than the Platonic and the mystical for his theology, if he was to reconcile Christian dogma with Aristotelianism. He had the courage, which was rare in his time, to deny that the existence of God is self-evident, and had such confidence in his reason that he believed he had proved His existence by five conclusive arguments. He said that the existence of God is not self-evident because 'no one can mentally admit the opposite of what is self-evident . . . but . . . the fool said in his heart there is no God. Therefore, that God exists is not self-evident'. He continues: 'A thing can be self-evident in either of two ways; on the one hand, self-evident in itself, though not to us; on the other, self-evident in itself and to us . . . If . . . there are some to whom the essence of the predicate and subject is unknown, the proposition will be self-evident in itself, but not to those who do not know the meaning of the predicate and subject of the proposition. . . . I say that this proposition, "God exists" of itself is self-evident, for the predicate is the same as the subject . . . Now because we do not know the essence of God, the proposition is not self-evident to us; but needs to be demonstrated by things that are more known to us, though less known in their nature—namely, by effects.'

It is interesting to see what sort of arguments Thomas chooses. He says: 'I answer that, the existence of God can be proved in five ways.

'The first and more manifest way is the argument from motion. It is certain, and evident to our senses, that in the world some things are in motion. Now whatever is in motion, is put in motion by another, for nothing can be in motion except it is in potentiality to that towards which it is in motion; whereas a thing moves inasmuch as it is in act. For motion is nothing else than the reduction of something from potentiality to actuality. But nothing can be reduced from potentiality to actuality, except by something in a state of actuality. Thus that which is actually hot, as fire, makes wood, which is potentially hot, to be actually hot, and thereby moves and changes it. Now it is not possible that the same thing should be at once in actuality and potentiality in the same respect, but only in different respects. For what is actually hot cannot simultaneously be potentially hot; but it is simultaneously potentially cold. It is therefore impossible that in the same respect and in the same way a thing should be both mover and moved, is, that it should move itself. Therefore, whatever is in motion must be put in motion by another. If that by which it is put in motion be itself put in motion, then this also must needs be put in motion by another and that by another again. But this cannot go on to infinity, because then there would be no first mover, and consequently, no other mover; seeing that subsequent movers move only inasmuch as they are put in motion by the first mover; as the staff moves only because it is put in motion by the hand. Therefore it is necessary to arrive at a first mover, put in motion by no other; and this everyone understands to be God.'

Thomas does not appeal to religious feeling, but to the phenomena of mechanics.

He derives his second proof from the observation that there is an order of efficient causes in the world of sense. This order cannot regress to infinity, so there must be a first efficient cause, which is God.

The third is derived from possibility and necessity. 'That which does not exist only begins to exist by something already existing . . . Therefore we cannot but postulate the existence of some being having of itself its own necessity, and not receiving it from another, but rather causing in others their necessity.' This being is God.

In the fourth, God is deduced as 'The maximum in any genus' which is 'the cause of all in that genus; as fire, which is the maximum of heat, is the cause of all hot things.'

In the fifth, the existence of God is deduced from the evidence of design in the government of the world.

While he proves the existence of God by reason, he denies that it is possible to attain to knowledge of the Trinity by reason.

He opposes Richard of St. Victor's assertion: 'I believe without doubt that probable and even necessary arguments can be found for any explanation of the truth.'

In his reply, he says: 'Reason may be employed in two ways to establish a point: firstly, for the purpose of furnishing sufficient proof of some principle, as in natural science, where sufficient proof can be brought to show that the movement of the heavens is always of uniform velocity. Reason is employed in another way, not as furnishing a sufficient proof of a principle, by showing the congruity of its results, as in astrology the theory of eccentrics and epicycles is considered as established, because thereby the sensible appearances of the heavenly movements can be explained; not, however, as if this proof were sufficient, forasmuch as some other theory might explain them. In the first way we can prove that God is one; and the like. In the second way, reasons avail to prove the Trinity; as, when assumed to be true, such reasons confirm it. We must not, however, think that the Trinity of persons is adequately proved by such reasons. . . .'

This passage exhibits again Thomas's predilection for scientific ideas, and shows that he had an intellectually correct understanding of the nature of a scientific theory. It follows that the slow development of experimental science in his time was not due to lack of intellectual comprehension of the nature of scientific method, but to the failure of contemporary society to provide a strong motive to use the method.

Thomas devotes a part of the *Summa* to a *Treatise on Man*. He discusses the nature of ideas and of matter, and how the mind acquires knowledge of matter. When this has been done, it is possible to determine whether science gives real or illusory knowledge.

He asks 'Whether the soul knows bodies through the intellect', and replies: 'Science is in the intellect. If, therefore, the intellect does not know bodies, it follows that there is no science of bodies; and thus perishes natural science, which treats of mobile bodies.'

He would have had no patience with modern writers who doubt the existence of the external world, and the ability of science to give real knowledge of it.

He then criticizes Plato's theory of ideas, and Democritus's theory of the discharge of images, as respectively extreme idealists and materialist conceptions of the mode of knowing.

Plato maintained that ideas are immaterial and separate, and that the soul does not understand corporeal things, but separate ideas therefrom.

Thomas contended that this was false because ideas are immaterial and immovable, and 'knowledge of movement and matter would be excluded from science (which knowledge is proper to natural science), and likewise all demonstration through moving and material causes. Secondly, because it seems ridiculous, when we seek for knowledge of things which are to us manifest, to introduce other beings, which cannot be the substance of those others, since they differ from them essentially. . . .
Now it seems that Plato strayed from the truth because, having

observed that all knowledge takes place through some kind of similitude, he thought that the form of the thing known must of necessity be in the knower in the same manner as in the thing known. Then he observed that the form of the thing understood is in the intellect under conditions of universality, immateriality, and immobility: which is apparent from the very operation of the intellect. . . . Wherefrom he concluded that the things which we understand must have in themselves an existence under the same conditions of immateriality and immobility. . . . But there is no necessity in this. For even in sensible things it is to be observed that the form is otherwise in one sensible than in another: for instance, whiteness may be of great intensity in one, and of a less intensity in another. . . .'

'The intellect which abstracts the species not only from matter, but also from the individuating conditions of matter, has more perfect knowledge than the senses, which receive the form of the thing known, without matter indeed, but subject to material conditions.'

He then discusses Democritus's theory, that knowledge is caused by a discharge of images from the object into the human sense organs, and mentions that when Democritus proposed this theory, philosophers had not yet begun to distinguish between intellect and sense.

Plato held that intellectual knowledge did not proceed from sensible knowledge, and that sensible knowledge did not proceed to sensible things, but 'these rouse the sensible soul to the sentient act; while the senses rouse the intellect to the act of understanding'.

But, says Thomas: 'Aristotle chose a middle course. For with Plato he agreed that intellect and sense are different. But he held that the sense has not its proper operation without the co-operation of the body; so that to feel is not an act of the soul alone, but of the *composite*. And he held the same in regard to all the operations of the sensible part. Since, therefore, it is not unreasonable that the sensible objects are outside, the soul should produce some effect in the *composite*. Aristotle agreed with Democritus in this, that the operations of the sensitive part are caused by the impression of the sensible on the sense; not by a discharge, as Democritus said, but by some kind of operation.'

According to Aristotle, the impression caused by the sensible does not suffice, but something more noble is required, and this is the active intellect.

In the intellectual part, there is something active and something passive.

Thomas's philosophy is deeply influenced by the later and scientific works of Aristotle. The tone of his argument does not seem religious to many readers. He was trying to base Christian philosophy on Aristotle, "the least religious of the great philosophers". He rejected Anselm's proof of the existence of God, and proofs of the eternity of the world. He adopted the idea of "potential" from Aristotle, which seems important in the theory of growth and embryological development. A. E. Taylor believes that Aristotle may have obtained the theory of potential from Plato, who writes in the *Theaetetus*: 'In a sense we have none of these pieces of knowledge when we are not using them; what we have is the power.'

Taylor considers that any theory of perception that will meet the needs of science must resemble Thomas's.

It will have to combine, he thinks, as Thomas meant to combine, 'the two complementary positions that our knowledge of the world around our bodies is mediated in fact by highly complicated processes of a very special kind, and that *as knowledge* it is *direct*, *unmediated* apprehension not of "ideas" or "images" but of actual physical reality.'

But in spite of Thomas's critical realism and distrust of speculation without solid root in empirical fact, Taylor considers his philosophy more Platonic than Aristotelian.

Thomas's attempts to reconcile Aristotle's doctrine of the eternity of the universe and the mortality of the soul with Christian dogma do not seem to be very successful. He could not see any flaw in Aristotle's theory of the universe, so he accepted the Christian dogma of the creation of the universe in time by an act of faith.

Aristotle taught that soul and body are one substance, and that the soul is the form of the substance of the body. When form and matter are dissolved at death, the individual is destroyed forever. Thomas tried to evade this conclusion by the supposition that the soul is a 'separable form'. This appears to conflict with Aristotle's theory, and with his own teaching that the universal can only be 'individualized' in matter. Aristotle's doctrines of the eternity of matter and the unity of the intellect, which denied individual immortality, were developed by the Spanish Muslim commentator Averroes, who lived from 1126 until 1198. Thomas made a severe attack on Averroes, but the latter, with his tradition of Muslim science and medicine, approached nearer to the naturalistic core of Aristotle's later philosophy.

According to Averroes matter is eternal, and the theory of a creation is impossible. The universe consists of a hierarchy of principles connected in a transcendental unity. One of these is the Active Intellect. This manifests itself continuously in the form of collective human consciousness and is immortal. The human soul is a fragment of the Active Intellect temporarily detached to animate the body, and after death it rejoins its source.

The soul has no independent existence in immortality and cannot have experiences analogous to those which occur during life. It cannot remember or feel, and is not susceptible to reward or punishment.

This theory was denounced by Muslim fanatics and was incompatible with the Christian belief in heaven and hell. Its holders were indifferent to religious formulae, but Averroes had to protect himself by affirming that the received religions are excellent instruments of morality, and that those who incite scepticism in the people, or demean God before the vulgar, are heretics. But 'the special religion of philosophers is to study what exists, for the most sublime worship of God is the contemplation of his works, which leads us to a knowledge of him in all his reality'.

Averroism was encouraged by Frederick II, the patron of Michael Scot, who came to Sicily from Toledo with translations of Averroes and the later works of Aristotle.

The Moorish culture which had reared Averroes in Spain at the end of the twelfth century was soon repressed by Muslim conservatism. But Averroes troubled the Christian theologians for centuries after his influence in Islam had declined.

Some enthusiastic Thomists believe that Thomas's onslaught on Averroes saved Christianity from intellectual conquest by Islam, and that his victory was even more crucial than that of Charles Martel at Poitiers. This view seems incompatible with the transience of Averroes's influence in Islam.

Only a small fraction of Thomas's writings were concerned with nature and natural science. There are long discussions as to whether men are assailed by the demons, whether there are orders among the demons, whether among the demons there is precedence, whether the mother of God was a virgin, and whether the fire of the final conflagration is of the same sort as our fire, etc.

Thomas says that 'good can exist without evil, whereas evil cannot exist without good; so there is order in the demons, as possessing a good nature.' (They are wicked by their own free will.)

'The demons are not equal in nature; and so among them there exists a natural precedence; which is not the case with men, who are naturally equal.'

The Christian doctrine of human equality has had profound influence on the restitution of the dignity of human labour, and thus indirectly on experimental science. Thomas's order, the Dominicans, were more democratic than the Benedictines, for their abbots were elected for three years only, while the Benedictine abbots were elected for life. The Franciscans and the Dominicans were supported with special favour by the new *bourgeoisie*.

'Joseph is called the father of the Saviour, not that he really was His father, as the Photinians pretended, but that he was considered by men to be so, for the safeguarding of Mary's good name.'

Thomas's system was submitted to detailed criticism by many successors, among whom Duns Scotus was the most outstanding. He was born in 1285 and died at the early age of forty-three. He transferred one doctrine after another in Thomas's system from the province of reason to the province of faith, and as Harris says, the psychological effect was enormous. 'The pre-established harmony between reason and revelation, which was the fundamental postulate of medieval thought,' collapsed with alarming rapidity.

Some believe that Thomas provided the durable basis for all subsequent theology and science. Others believe that his patient, comprehensive and lucid exposition of the natures of Christian dogma and scientific thought left their incompatibility obvious and undeniable.

Some of the modern followers of St. Thomas would like to see a revival of his ordered system of the universe. They dwell on his distinction between persons and individuals and attack liberal society as a collocation of individuals in contrast with St. Thomas's society of persons, and are prepared to go far in attempts to form such a society.

6

Etienne Gilson wrote that 'the so-called Liberalism of the previous generation was but a flattering name for that monster: a human society, not of persons, but of individuals. Against such a Liberalism the brutal reaction of the so-called "Totalitarian State" was, if not justified, at least almost necessarily required.' When the followers of St. Thomas express opinions of this sort, it is as well to recollect their master's long disquisitions on demons and his frequent inability to recognize the intimations of common sense, besides his bold and subtle attempts to find material foundations for religious belief.

43
Roger Bacon and Medieval Experimental Science

THOMAS AQUINAS understood the logic of scientific method, but he did not appreciate the weight of the experimental part of it. He believed that the truth of a theory should be tested by an appeal to experience, but he did not feel that experience should be systematically explored by manual means in order to supply data for new theories. His attitude towards experience was passive and negative.

The importance of the positive experimental part of science was emphasized by his rival Roger Bacon, who lived from 1214 until 1292. Roger Bacon has been celebrated recently as the first modern scientist, and an isolated genius centuries in advance of his time. His works contain many startling passages, and when these are separated from their context, and from the general scientific knowledge of his time, they seem uniquely modern in a medieval scientist. He said: 'The most useful, the greatest, and most beautiful lessons of knowledge, as well as the secrets of all science and art, are unknown.' He quoted with approval Seneca's forecast of the future achievements of science, and his view that he contributed most to discovery who hoped that it could be made. He believed that: 'Machines for navigation can be made without rowers so that the largest ships on rivers or seas will be moved by a single man in charge with greater velocity than if they were full of men. Also cars can be made so that without animals they will move with unbelievable rapidity; such as we opine were the scythe-bearing chariots with which the men of old fought. Also flying machines can be constructed so that a man sits in the midst of the machine revolving some engine by which artificial wings are made to beat the air like a flying bird.' He visualized the invention of small machines for raising and pulling great weights, and machines 'for walking in the sea and rivers, even to the bottom without danger'.

Bacon made considerable contributions to optics, but none of them was perfected. He followed the works of Alhazen, and made experimental and theoretical investigations to improve the knowledge of the laws of refraction and reflection. He attempted to apply this knowledge to the improvement of aids to human vision. He made experiments with plano-convex lenses, and noted that if letters are viewed through a lens 'shaped like the lesser segment of a sphere, with the convex side towards the eye, and the eye being in the air, he will see the letters far better, and they will seem larger to him. For this reason such an instrument is useful to old persons and to those with weak eyes, for they can see any letter, however small, if magnified enough'. He understood that the rays from the object were refracted at the curved surface of the lens, but he did not know that they were also refracted at the plane surface. He explains that magnification is due to the angle subtended at the eye by the image being larger than that subtended by the object. 'It is on the size of angle on which this kind of vision depends, and it is independent of distance . . . so a boy can appear a giant . . . a small army might seem very large, and though far away appear near, and conversely: so, too, we could make sun, moon, and stars apparently descend here below . . .' He suggests that 'glasses can be constructed so that objects at a very great distance appear to be quite close at hand and conversely . . . The heavens might be portrayed in all their length and breadth on a corporeal figure moving with their diurnal motion, and this would be worth a whole kingdom to a wise man.'

Bacon belonged to a rich family and probably earned considerable fees while lecturing in Paris between 1236 and 1251. He spent two thousand livres (or ten thousand pounds in modern money) on the purchase of books, experiments and instruments, journeys to meet scholars, and secretaries. He worked for three years on the construction of a concave burning mirror and spent five hundred pounds on the research. He recorded how the crafts-men who made the mirrors became quicker and more economical with increasing experience. He considered that the ideal student 'makes no account of speeches and wordy conflicts but follows up the works of wisdom and remains there. He knows natural science by experiment, and medicaments and alchemy and all things in the heavens or beneath them, and he would be ashamed if any layman, or old woman or rustic, or soldier should know anything about the soil that he was ignorant of. Whence he is conversant with the casting of metals and the working of gold, silver, and other metals and all minerals; he knows all about soldiering and arms and hunting; he has examined agriculture and land surveying and farming; he has further considered old wives' magic and fortune-telling and the charms of them and of all magicians, and the tricks and illusions of jugglers. But as honour and rewards would hinder him from the greatness of his experimental work he scorns them.' He remarks that he has 'learned more useful and excellent things without comparison from very plain people unknown to fame in letters, than from all [his] famous teachers'. He investigated séances and said that 'when inanimate objects are quickly moved about in the darkness of morning or evening twilight, there is no truth therein but downright cheating and cozenage'.

He was the first European to give a description of the com-position and preparation of gunpowder. His account of the geography of Europe, Asia and Africa, and the size and sphericity of the earth, was quoted by Pierre d'Ailly in his *Imago Mundi*, which was published in 1487, and probably encouraged Colum-bus to attempt to reach the Indies by sailing westwards.

Bacon was commanded by the Pope in 1266 to send him copies of all his works. He compiled his *Opus Majus* to satisfy this order. It is arranged in seven parts. He discusses the causes of human error in the first part; and ascribes it to undue regard for authority; habit, popular prejudice and false conceit of know-ledge. In the second part he explains the value of philosophy to theology. In the third he discusses the study of foreign languages, and shows that each should have its own grammar, and that the meaning of literature cannot be correctly apprehended without scientific methods of textual criticism. In the fourth he describes mathematics as the key to all other sciences, especially astro-nomy, optics, theology, chronology, astrology and the correction of the calendar, and outlines contemporary geography. The fifth deals with optics, and the sixth with experimental science. The final section is devoted to morals, and the relation and duty of man to God. It contains the first comparative study of religions and a proof of the superiority of Christianity.

A summary of Bacon's achievements makes a profound impression, and is the source of the tendency to exaggerate them. Thorndike has made a salutary criticism of excessive claims for him.

When Bacon's works are carefully examined it is seen that his theological motives are just as strong as those of Thomas Aquinas and the other scholastics. He firmly believes in astrology and asserts that 'it is manifest to everyone that the celestial bodies are the causes of generation and corruption in all inferior things'.

None of his lines of experimental work is entirely original. The inspirations may be found in Alhazen, Albertus Magnus, Grosseteste, Abélard and others. He did not make any of the chief medieval innovations such as chimney flues and window panes, the rudder and the mariner's compass, Arabic numerals, paper, lenses and spectacles, and gunpowder. Thorndike doubts the tradition that he was persecuted and imprisoned for many years by ecclesiastical superiors who disapproved of his scientific researches. The Franciscans, to whom he belonged, included many eminent members who had contributed to experimental science, such as Grosseteste.

A reading of Bacon's works suggests that his questioning of authority had two motives, a personal motive due to rivalry and jealousy of scholars such as Albertus Magnus, whose ecclesiastical careers had been far more successful, and an impersonal motive due to a better appreciation of the importance of experiment, as compared with logic, in the advancement of science. Bacon mixes penetrating comment on scientific method with criticisms of the personalities of rivals. This tactlessness would have damaged his career in any organization in any age.

Bacon did not turn any of his researches to practical use, so he was not convincing to the purely practical man. He had not provided his order with any new process for making money.

Nevertheless, the personal failure of his career was significant. His conception of scientific method, if not perfect, was advanced. His statements show that he was conscious that the study of the processes of handicraft was essential to the development of experimental science. His plan of an encyclopedia and his *Opus Majus* show that even if he had not escaped from the integument of theology, he aimed at the creation of an expanding body of science within it. He may not have realized that ultimately this would break out and pursue an independent life.

In Bacon's scientific work there is a combination of logic cultivated by the Church and the governing classes with the technique of the craftsman, and the independence of the *bourgeois*. His failure may be interpreted as due not only to temperamental tactlessness, but to a combination of class cultures in advance of its time. Indeed, his tactlessness may not have been temperamental, but acquired through struggles with cultural conservatism. Bacon, like Boyle, was a pious man who consorted with mechanics, and made experiments. He died in obloquy, while Boyle was universally respected. Does not this suggest that the combination of technique with logic had not the social repute which it had acquired by the time of Boyle?

44

The Growth of Universities

THE chief feature of a university is the granting of degrees to students who obey its rules of residence and pass its examinations. The Greek schools, such as the Academy and the Museum and their Roman imitations, and the monastic schools which alone preserved learning from the sixth until the tenth centuries, did not grant degrees and require precise periods of residence. The formalization of higher education in the shape of university teaching was a medieval invention and occurred in the twelfth century.

The growth of Norman feudalism and the first efforts of the new *bourgeoisie* increased social prosperity in the eleventh century, and created a demand for clerks who could assist in administration. When this occurred, education was entirely controlled by monasteries, and the first effect was to increase the number of students at monastic schools. But the new demand was for clerks who could assist in secular affairs, rather than for monks learned in the nature of the soul. The conduct of education tended to pass from monks to secular clergy less exclusively concerned with pure religion. The teaching in the cathedral schools was more secular than in the monasteries because the cathedral was the centre of a growing town and in closer contact with secular interests. Rashdall sees in the transfer of educational activity from the monks to the secular clergy in the eleventh century the great educational revolution which contains the germ of the university movement.

The new teachers in the cathedral schools supplied a need and attracted increasing numbers of students. At first, the students followed the teacher, as he moved from school to school, but presently the numbers became too large for continuous migration. The teachers tended to settle in cathedral towns which were the only centres that could supply board and lodging for large numbers of visiting students. At this stage, the cathedral schools of Bec, Tours, Chartres and Rheims became famous. Shortly afterwards they were challenged by the cathedral school in Paris. The French monarchy was losing its nomadic character and beginning to settle in Paris as its capital. This stimulated trade and attracted personalities, and the growing city could support a large number of students better than its competitors. The superiority of the Paris school was confirmed by the brilliant teaching of Abélard.

The students who lodged in the neighbourhood of famous teachers were not at first organized. They were individuals in a much larger local population and their activities did not impinge on local life. But when the numbers grew into thousands, new social problems arose. The teachers could not know all their students intimately, and personal recommendation from a teacher was no longer a sufficient qualification. The increasing number of students stimulated intellectual competition and a demand for an objective system of measuring knowledge, and it created a new social class. Nearly all of the students and teachers in Paris were strangers, and they did not take part in the productive work of the city. Their interests differed from, and often came in conflict with, those of the townsmen, or *bourgeoisie*. The students formed associations like those of craftsmen to protect their educational and social interests. The craftsmen named their associations 'universities' or 'guilds', and the students appropriated the name 'university' from them. The application of 'university' was gradually narrowed to denote societies of masters and scholars, and there might be several 'universities' of medical or law students in the same town. The 'universities' were governed by guild regulations of the usual type. The student could not earn a living by teaching until his guild had awarded him a master's degree. This was a teacher's certificate. It was awarded by examination, to prevent favouritism and monopoly. The possession of the master's degree was a proof of competence to teach. In Paris the additional licence to teach was granted by the chancellor of the cathedral.

The educational needs of the students prompted them to organize their new system of teaching and examination. The clash of their interests with the townsmen prompted them to seek social privileges for their guilds or universities. The chief legal enactments which established their privileges occurred after town-and-gown rows, which were class-conflicts between the *bourgeoisie* and the students. After serious fighting between these parties, Philip Augustus laid down in 1200 that Paris students shall be exempted from the justice of lay courts. Oxford's first privileges were granted in 1209, after a riot between *bourgeoisie* and students, when hundreds of students had to leave the city, and went to Cambridge, where they founded a new centre of learning.

The number of students in the new universities was relatively very large. Paris may have contained seven thousand students when her total population was between twenty-five and fifty thousand. This was a fraction of about one in five. Today the fraction is about one in five hundred. The medieval student population was a formidable social class, and the ability of medieval society to support such a vast proportion of students is a proof of its vigour. The proportion at Oxford is at present about one in twenty.

Educational institutions with organized teaching and examinations, and a privileged social position had appeared in the twelfth century at Salerno, Bologna, Paris, Montpellier and Oxford. The word 'university' was first applied to the Paris institution in 1208. The first college for the accommodation of students was founded there about 1180.

The nature of some of the conflicts between *bourgeoisie* and students is seen in the disputes in Bologna over the prices of books, board and lodging. The students' guild forced the prices down by threatening to leave the city, and professors were made to lecture agreeably by threats to withhold their fee.

Universities tended to specialize in training for particular professions. Salerno specialized in medicine, probably owing to its proximity to Islam. Bologna specialized in law. It was at the crossroads of northern Italy, and important railway junctions are now there. Paris specialized in theology and dialectic. This was connected with the growth of the strength of the French monarchy, which attracted alliance with the popes. The French capital became the cultural centre of the Church, which produced the bias in theology, and as the centre of government it stimulated interest in dialectic, which was of professional value to prospective ministers who wished to defeat their competitors in discussions on policy and secure the king's approval. Aristotle's books on natural science were prohibited in Paris in 1215. This shows the bias of the authorities. The prohibition was virtually ignored. The organization of teaching created textbooks and orderly argument. This was accompanied by the perfection of a lucid and precise medieval Latin modelled on French. This contributed much to the clarity of thought which subsequently assisted scientists to define the principles of modern science.

The lectures consisted largely of comments on texts. Students made elaborate notes, and the subjects were debated. The memory of these wrangling debates is preserved in the title given to the most successful candidates in the Cambridge mathematical examinations. The lectures were delivered in the teacher's dwelling or in a hired hall. Alexander Neckam, whose mother was the foster-mother of Richard Coeur de Lion and who was suckled at the same time as Richard, has recorded that in 1200 the textbooks in use included the new logic, science and metaphysics of Aristotle, Boethius on arithmetic and music, Euclid and the Latin translation of the Arabic commentaries on Ptolemy, Galen and Hippocrates. Avicenna had not yet been introduced. Complaints that students neglected classics for professional studies had already begun. The medieval student, especially at Paris, was trained for executive work in Church and state. He looked to the rulers for employment and adopted their social perspective. He was a stranger in the city of his university, and he received his allowance from elsewhere. He determined his own hours of study, and appeared to the local *bourgeoisie* as a member of the leisured

6*

class, as well as an ally and dependant of the rulers. The universities owed their legal existence to resistance against the *bourgeoisie*, and yet the *bourgeoisie* provided the conditions under which they came into existence.

Rashdall is unable to find any explanation for the establishment of a university at Oxford, other than ease of access and commercial prosperity. He writes: 'To its position, too, must be ascribed the rapid increase in the commercial importance of Oxford after the final cessation of Danish devastations and especially after the beginning of the twelfth century. Its early selection by Jews as a business centre marks this development. In short: Oxford must be content to accept its academic position as an accident of its convenient situation . . . only one of the largest towns in the kingdom would be equal to the housing and feeding of many hundreds or thousands of strangers.'

While the *bourgeoisie* simultaneously supported and opposed the universities, it frequently sent its sons there, to pass from its own class into those of leisure and government. Sons of peasants achieved the same social transference. They earned a living by tutoring until they had graduated. The influence of social transference is shown in the development of the mode of conferment of degrees in some universities. It grew more like the bestowal of knighthood than admission to a craftsmen's guild.

The university, which was invented eight centuries ago, still retains its effectiveness as an instrument of social transference, and education for the retention of power. But it is not even yet a perfect instrument for the advancement of science. The universities were progressive in science during the twelfth century. They spread the new knowledge of Greek and Muslim science. When this had been accomplished, they were unable to make many more contributions, owing to their social perspective. They aimed at transference of manual workers into the literary class, so their atmosphere was antagonistic to manual work, and therefore to experiment. The success of Aquinas and the failure of Roger Bacon is partially explained by these circumstances.

After the assimilation of Greek and Muslim science, which was transmitted to Western Europe in books, the universities obstructed rather than assisted the direct development of science. The study of astronomy, alchemy and experimental science was restricted to small groups in Pisa, Marseilles, London, and the other centres of navigation and foreign trade.

The culture of the universities was aristocratic, and most of their leaders were rich men. Abélard was the son of a feudal lord. Bacon was well-to-do, and Aquinas was of royal descent. But Abélard's vulgar inquisitiveness, Bacon's interest in crafts, and Aquinas's pedestrian arguments with their homely material illustrations rose as much from the social energy created by the *bourgeoisie*, as from the vigour of the Norman knights.

The rapid intellectual development slowed down in the fourteenth century. After the scholars at the universities had assimilated earlier science, they could not advance rapidly, as they did not include experimental work in their system.

The lack of new material for study due to the poverty of experimental research sterilized the intellect. In addition, the resources of Western Europe were wasted in the struggle for mastery between France and England, which started at the end of the thirteenth century and lasted for a hundred years. If this disastrous war had not occurred, the Turks would probably not have captured Constantinople in the fifteenth century, and Russian social development might have advanced far more quickly. Thinkers such as William of Ockham, who died in 1349, had clearly recognized some of the theoretical principles of modern science. Ockham announced the principle of simplicity as a director of research when he asserted that 'entities must not be unnecessarily multiplied'. Dirac considers this principle the chief intellectual motive which guided Newton in his search for universal laws. Ockham appreciated the idea of evolution in social organizations, for he said that 'no human institution is absolute or final, and neither Pope nor Emperor can claim exemption from the general law of progress and adaptation'. This opinion was inspired by his part in the class conflict between Church and state. He was engaged by Louis of Bavaria to provide arguments in his struggle against the papacy. Pirenne notes that the handicrafts reached their highest status in the first half of the fourteenth century. A sort of industrial Malthusianism then appeared, and the local market was surrendered to a small number of masters. He believes that this was a cause of the sudden check in urban population and the demand in the next century for the abolition of corporations and the liberty of the handicrafts. In the middle of the same century about half the population of Western Europe was killed by the Black Death.

Intellectual work declined under these conditions. Petrarch

noted in the second half of the fourteenth century how the universities of Montpellier and Bologna had declined since his youth, and how the prosperity, trade, tranquillity and order of those cities had disappeared. Thorndike has commented on the decline of handwriting and prose style in the fourteenth and fifteenth centuries.

The perfected methods of criticism were applied with success in the fourteenth century to the theory of mechanics. Duhem's exposition of the medieval discovery of the principle of virtual work has been mentioned. Buridan and Albert of Saxony gave a correct theory of impetus in the second half of the fourteenth century.

Buridan held that the celestial bodies must obey the same laws as terrestrial bodies. The conditions were prepared for Newton's flight of imagination, by which he saw that the moon should obey the same laws as terrestrial projectiles. Buridan defined mass in terms which foreshadowed Newton's. Albert of Saxony suggested that the motion of a heavy falling body was uniformly accelerated. He discussed the movement of the sun, and the influence of erosion in shaping the geological features of the earth.

Nicolas of Oresmi suggested in the fourteenth century the use of co-ordinates, and was apparently the first to use fractional exponents in algebra. The Black Death inspired Henry of Hesse, who lived from 1325 to 1397, to suggest the possibility of new species of organisms. He forecast that new diseases would appear, and new species of herbs for their cure. He conceived the possibility of gases other than air before von Helmont, for he said that water exhalations are aqueous, while those from earth are earth vapour, and those from flesh, flesh vapour. The alchemists had conceived the nature of gases, and the problems of their density and rarefication were discussed scholastically. Petrus Bonus contended that 'in spirits there are bodies potentially, and in bodies spirits exist'. In mercury the volatile state was foremost while in gold it was concealed.

Various theories of attraction and gravitation were proposed in the fourteenth and fifteenth centuries to explain the relation between the moon and tides, and the suspension of the earth in space. The measurement of small fractions of time was conceived on paper, and records of comets, earthquakes and weather were kept.

Nicholas of Cusa, who lived from 1401 to 1464, suggested

timing the fall of bodies with corrections for the effect of resistance by the air. He advocated the use of the balance in chemical investigations, and suggested two centuries before Hales that the relations between the weights of a seed and the grown plant, and the weights of earth before and after growth, and the weight of ash obtainable from the plant, might be worth investigation. But he did not make the experiment. He believed that qualities could be distinguishable by weighing, and measured the humidity of the air by weighing balls of absorbent material.

Henry of Hesse in the previous century experimented with surface tension.

Thorndike mentions that much attention was devoted at this period to reform of the calendar and the compilation of astronomical tables. He complains that printing is the only medieval invention that has been adequately studied. The mariner's compass and gunpowder were introduced in the twelfth century. Nearly all of the British coalfields were being worked in 1300, and the rudder was introduced at about that date. Thorndike considers that 'the mechanical clock of the early fourteenth century was in a way the parent of all subsequent machinery'.

Ptolemy's *Geography* was translated in 1409. Like the translations of Archimedes, its effects were not entirely fortunate. The early navigators were misled by it, and medieval geographical discoveries were neglected. Medicine may have learned something from the Black Death. It may have gained a better understanding of the nature of infection. Leprosy largely disappeared in and after the fourteenth century. Henry of Mondeville practised antiseptic surgery at the beginning of the fourteenth century. The mercury treatment for syphilis was introduced in the fifteenth century, and remarkable operations in plastic surgery were performed. Thorndike quotes Fagio's description of the Brancas' operations on the nose, which was published in 1456. The elder Branca 'thought out a way to reform and complete dissected and mutilated noses'. He cut skin from the face of the mutilated person and repaired the nose with it. His son improved the operation, and took the skin 'from the arm, so that no facial deformity resulted therefrom. And he inserted the remains of the mutilated nose, and bound them up so tightly that the mutilated person could not even move his head. After fifteen or sometimes twenty days, he would little by little cut open the bit of flesh which adhered to the nose and reform it into nostrils with such skill that the eye could scarcely detect where it had been joined on, and all facial deformity was completely removed'.

These contributions were not sufficient to sustain the pace of inquiry that had been set in the twelfth century. In the thirteenth century the authorities had become generally alarmed. As inquiry spread, heresy multiplied. Many heretics were lynched by the populace between 1020 and 1150. After that time, an increasing number were condemned by prelates. The Church completed in 1233 the formal organization of the Inquisition, as an instrument for the extermination of heresy. Twenty years later, Aquinas showed how a logically impeccable justification of execution for heresy could be deduced from the church dogma. If Aquinas had proposed one hundred years later arguments as impressive as some he had suggested in 1250, he would have found himself in danger of the stake. But this original thinker had died young, and his works had been sanctified before their novelties had been disapproved. The Inquisition, like modern fascism, surprised some of its early supporters in their later years, by striking at the innovations of conservatives as well as radicals.

45
The Inquisition

THE survival of the Church through the dark centuries following the disintegration of the Roman Empire gave it unique power. It became the framework of Western European society, and its power grew during the centuries of primitive feudalism. In those times few had the leisure or training to think about its dogmas, as nearly all were absorbed in the anxious labour of obtaining a bare living. Coulton remarks that in the seventy-three years from 987 to 1059, there were forty-eight years of famine in Northern France, and at least two of these were marked by cannibalism.

The improvement of conditions, which began in the tenth century, and was associated with the growth of the towns and the *bourgeoisie*, provided new quantities of social energy, which throbbed through all the arteries of the social organism. A large part of the new urban wealth was poured into the Church, and a new vigour from the same source permeated religious thought. Dogmas which had acquired immense prestige through centuries of negative acceptance now became the object of positive faith. The new energy at first sought for expression through accepted ideas. It seized the old dogmas and believed in them with a new force. At the same time society was becoming more complicated through its new developments. The travelling traders and the *bourgeoisie* were beginning to fill the orthodox modes of their thought with a new content inspired by their interests. Crusaders acquired some knowledge in the East of other religions. Through influences such as these, men began unconsciously to derive their own interpretations of the ancient dogmas.

The increasing vigour of thought made men more conscious of the evils of contemporary society. This created the illusion that society was growing worse, though in fact it was improving. The new energy of the leaders of the Church at first expressed itself in an increase of passionate faith. They accepted the old dogmas more enthusiastically than ever, with a new determination to make them work.

But the same social development which had provided their own energy also produced a proliferation of divergent religious ideas. The world seemed to the new leaders to be racing towards damnation, and they felt called at the last moment to save it. If they did not do their best, they would be eternally damned themselves.

Pope Innocent III issued a decree in 1199, ordering clergy, magistrates and people to destroy heresy. He wrote: 'The decay of a century tottering to old age may be scented in the corruption not only of the elements, but even in that most worthy of all creatures, fashioned in the image and likeness of God, and set above the fowls of the air and all the beasts of the field in privilege of dignity; nor does he merely fail in these days with the failing century, but he also infects and is infected with the foul canker of old age. For man, most wretched, sinneth at the last; and he who, at his own creation and that of the world, could not remain in Paradise, is now degenerating in these days of dissolution for himself and the whole earth; and, at the end of time, (forgetting the price of his redemption, by trusting himself into the manifold vain meshes of questioning) entangles himself in the snares of his

own fraud, and falls into the pit which he hath digged . . .
Heresies swarm, and the heretic, robbing his brother of his
heavenly inheritance, makes him heir to his own heresy and to
damnation. . . .'

Innocent III gave expression to the current intense belief in
the reality of heaven and hell, and the necessity for eternal salvation by faith. In the view of those who held this belief, a heretic
committed treason against God. He damned himself to eternal
torment and endangered the eternal happiness of all whom he
met or influenced. Aquinas argued that if a man may be justly
executed for treason against kings, how much more justly may
he be slain for treason against God.

Any method of suppressing heresy could be justified by this
belief, because no punishment that could be inflicted in finite
earthly life was commensurable with that suffered eternally in
hell. In the heretic's own interest, the most extreme earthly torture was infinitely justified if it brought him to repentance and
eternal salvation. If it did not, then he should be despatched to
hell by execution as quickly as possible, to prevent him from
corrupting the faithful.

Lucius III had created an episcopal inquisition in 1184 when
he ordered bishops to make the most thorough inquiries into
heresy in their dioceses. The civil authorities were ordered to
punish heretics discovered by these inquiries, under the pain of
deposition, confiscation and excommunication. This decree was
found insufficient, and Gregory IX began to send inquisitors
from Rome to supervise the local investigations. The inquisitors
were chosen from the new and enthusiastic Franciscan and
Dominican friars, whose orders were founded in 1209 and 1216
respectively. They were directed from a central office at Rome,
under the Pope's control, and rapidly evolved a system for conducting their inquiries. The old Roman Imperial law had
recently been rediscovered and its procedure, and permission of
torture, were adopted. The Inquisition assumed that any man
accused of heresy was guilty until his innocence was proved. This
was contrary to the Old Germanic law which has survived in
England and some other countries, and which assumes the
accused is innocent until his guilt is proved. Its judges were
ecclesiastical. Their procedure was secret and withheld from the
civil authorities. Witnesses were concealed, and could not be
cross-examined by the accused, so prosecutions became based

mainly on the stories of informers, spies and provocative agents. The testimony of criminals, which was not accepted in other courts, was acceptable to the Inquisition. Infants could be heard, even against their parents. But neither criminals nor infants were allowed to give evidence for the defence. The accused could nominally be defended by advocates, but as the defence of a heretic was a crime, advocates could not be found. Witnesses could be tortured, so few volunteered evidence for the defence. Torture could not be legally repeated, but this law was evaded by applying portions of one torture at intervals.

The inquisitor with these devices at his disposal very rarely failed to secure a conviction.

When the machinery of the Inquisition had become thoroughly established, confessions could frequently be obtained by the threat of prosecution without any trial or torture, as the rareness of acquittal was notorious. A man needed fanatical resolution to withstand its pressure. And yet many died rather than recant. These were drawn from unorthodox religious sects. The Catharians, who flourished in the south of France, had a horror of making oaths, eating flesh, and cohabiting with their wives. They believed in the Manichaean religion, which is based on the duality of good and evil, and is incompatible with Roman Christianity. It contained ideas drawn from Persia, and other parts of the Orient, and its dissemination in West Europe was assisted by the revival of communications.

Another important heresy arose through followers of St. Francis taking their vows earnestly. These Fraticelli insisted on observing their vows of poverty, and when the Pope claimed the right to overrule St. Francis's instructions, they accused him of heresy. Four of them were burned at Marseilles in 1318 as obstinate heretics.

Still more important heresies arose in the new *bourgeoisie* and handicraftsmen. A rich merchant of Lyons named Waldo experienced a conversion late in life. He became curious to know the true meaning of the Bible and theological works, and paid a priest to translate parts to him. When he had acquired this knowledge he began lay preaching. The Waldensians struck at the Church's claim to control the interpretation of the Bible to the people, and were the forerunners of Protestants.

Nearly all heretics were exceptionally moral, and good citizens. As St. Bernard had observed: 'If you inquire into [such a man's] faith, nothing is more Christian; if into his conversation, nothing is more blameless; and he proves by his deeds what he speaks with his mouth . . . he cozens no man, over-reaches none, does violence to none. Moreover, he is pale with fasting; he eats no bread of idleness; he works with his hands for his livelihood. Where, then, is the fox?' St. Bernard had no difficulty in finding it. 'They do indeed abstain, but they abstain heretically.'

It is possible to grant that the Inquisition was created by pure religious fanatics who believed they were doing their duty. But soon after the machine was created it was utilized by ambitious popes to achieve their ends in the politics of Church and state, and then ambitious princes forced popes to operate it to their advantage and even against the interests of the Church.

The order of the Poor Soldiers of the Temple was organized in 1128 with the aim of protecting pilgrims. These soldiers, dedicated to obedience, poverty, and chastity, achieved great fame. Their rules were extremely strict, and very secret. The Templars became a formidable order of fighting monks, under the command of the Pope, and vast possessions were given to them by their medieval admirers. By 1244, they possessed nine thousand manors, and their houses, or fortresses, arose in all the centres of Christendom. The grand and secret affairs of these houses filled the populace with awe. At the beginning of the fourteenth century, the King of France, Philip the Fair, being short of money, borrowed large sums from them and they protected him from the mob when he tried to evade his financial difficulties by debasing the coinage. He arrested all the Jews in his kingdom, confiscated their property, and banished them. Then he decided to seize the wealth of his friends the Templars. He tried to persuade the Pope to operate the Inquisition against them but did not at first succeed, so he made the Inquisitor of France act against Templars in French dominions on his own authority. All the Templars in France were arrested at dawn on a predetermined date, and their property seized. Extreme tortures were applied with haste, and a large number of confessions were collected. The Pope had to acquiesce in the imposing list; and give his approval to the operation.

The chiefs of the order were made to confess first, and recommend their subordinates to imitate them. They confessed in more or less degree to initiatory rituals which included renouncing Christ, and spitting on the Cross; being kissed by the preceptor on the posteriors, navel and mouth; accepting unnatural lust as lawful; worshipping idols, and ignoring consecration of the host in the declaration of Mass.

It is very probable that some abnormal practices occurred occasionally in a large corps of military monks, but there is no doubt that most of the confessions were false. In England where there was no Inquisition, and torture was against the law, no confessions could be obtained. The Pope therefore threatened Edward II with excommunication if he did not admit the Inquisition. It was introduced for a few months, and the desired confessions were speedily obtained. The Inquisition did not reappear in England until the sixteenth century.

H. C. Lea, the great historian of the Inquisition, writing in 1887, has commented on the fate of the Templars: 'Thus disappeared, virtually without a struggle, an organization which was regarded as one of the proudest, wealthiest, and most formidable in Europe. It is not too much to say that the very idea of its destruction could not have suggested itself, but for the facilities which the inquisitorial process placed in able and unscrupulous hands to accomplish any purpose of violence under the form of law . . . It affords so perfect an illustration of the helplessness of the victim, no matter how high-placed, when once the fatal charge of heresy was preferred against him, and was pressed through the agency of the Inquisition.'

One might have thought that when the government of society could destroy heretics so easily, no one would have the courage to introduce novelties, for fear that they might prove heretical. As scientists pursue novelties by profession, they would presumably have been scrutinized particularly carefully by the Inquisition. It is therefore notable that scientists suffered relatively little under the Inquisition. Lea observes that there are few instances where the Inquisition was invoked to settle contests between free thought and authority. He suggests that this is due to the coolness of the intellect, which does not nerve the thinker 'to maintain his thesis with the unfaltering resolution which enabled the peasant to approach the stake singing hymns and joyfully welcoming the flames which were to bear him to salvation'. He notes that few thinkers from Abélard and Eckhart to Galileo, were prepared to go to the stake for their intellectual beliefs. In his opinion, the only heresies which really troubled the

Church were those which appealed to the emotions of the people, and appealed to the heart rather than the brain.

Lea instances Roger Bacon as a scientist who suffered under authority. Thorndike has discussed this question in some detail, and concludes that the story of Bacon's suppression is unreliable. Lea himself remarks that 'its truth has been not unreasonably denied'. The evidence of Bacon's style suggests that he was cantankerous besides intellectually critical. This may have been due to persecution, but it may also have been temperamental.

The monastic orders encouraged learning as enthusiastically as they supplied staff to the Inquisition. The Dominicans produced Albertus Magnus and Aquinas, and the Franciscans, Bacon and Duns Scotus. Thorndike contends that in relation to science 'the Inquisition bug-a-boo is negligible. Has anyone ever shown that the Inquisition punished a practical invention? It was not for having invented the telescope that Galileo was persecuted. Moreover, Galileo's was an exceptional case, and it cannot be shown that in the thirteenth century the Church persecuted men of science. Rather, popes and prelates were their patrons'. William of Ockham and Buridan, whose contributions to scientific thought have been mentioned, were condemned by the University of Paris for heresy, but this did not do them much harm. Jean de Brescain was forbidden in 1247 to teach, owing to the condemnation of his views on matter and light as heretical. Peter of Abano and Cecco d'Acoli were condemned for heretical astrology. The former died before his conviction was complete and the latter was burned. This cannot be accepted as an unmitigated blow to science. In the fifteenth century humanistic tolerance had spread widely. Alfonso I of Naples put the following puzzle to a preacher: 'A man enclosed a consecrated host in a vase of gold; a month later, on opening it, he found only a worm; the worm could not have been formed from the pure gold, nor from the accidents which were there, without the subject; it was therefore produced from the body of Christ; but from the substance of God nothing but God can proceed, therefore the worm was God.' At the same period Lorenzo Valla made corrections in the Vulgate, and had them accepted.

Lea is of the opinion that if the Reformation had not occurred, the culture of Europe would inevitably have been atheistic, or a sublimated deism. 'The Reformation served a double purpose in checking this tendency to dangerous speculation. It destroyed the hard-and-fast lines of the rigid Scholastic theology, and gave to active intellects a wide field for discussion within the limits of the Christian faith.' Later in the fifteenth century Pico della Mirandola, at the age of twenty-four, 'published a series of nine hundred propositions which he offered to defend in Rome against all comers, paying the expenses of those who might travel for the purpose from distant lands'. These included nearly everything in theology, philosophy and science. His brilliance aroused envy, and he was accused of heresy. Pope Innocent VIII balefully remarked that 'This youth wishes to end badly, and be burned some of these days, and then be infamous for ever like many another.' Mirandola retired into theological studies and died at the age of thirty-two.

At the end of the sixteenth century, during the Catholic reaction against the Reformation, Giordano Bruno attacked orthodox Catholicism, and adopted the Copernican system. He was burned for heresy. But Nicholas of Cusa had argued in 1440 that the earth could not be the centre of the universe and was made a cardinal. Both Bruno and Galileo did not manage their affairs with tact. Bruno returned to Italy after he had been condemned, and Galileo refused to live in Padua, where he would have been safe.

It is possible that the records of the damage to science done by the Inquisition are relatively meagre because science was unable to grow freely in its intimidating atmosphere. It smothered science, and therefore there were few notable scientific developments which it could strike down. But the violent disputes in the medieval schools do not reflect entirely smothered intellects. The relation between the progress of science, free thought and orthodoxy is less simple than is commonly believed. Science and the Inquisition have not always been in opposition. The discovery of America, inspired by the desire to evade the Muslim control over trade with the Indies and attack Islam in the rear, was assisted by the growth of several sciences. Columbus had been led to a more optimistic view of the ratio of land to water on the surface of the earth, and hence the possibility of reaching land quickly by sailing to the west, from Roger Bacon's revision of Ptolemy's geography. He probably read a quotation of Bacon's views in Pierre d'Ailly's *Imago Mundi* which was published in 1487. Columbus was dependent also on the great medieval innovations of the rudder and mariner's compass, and improved methods of calculating longitude based on Muslim astronomy and trigonometry.

One other factor was equally important. This was finance. Columbus approached Henry VII of England for support, but that careful monarch would not invest money acquired by patient honest trade in a speculative voyage. He turned to Ferdinand and Isabella, who had collected great wealth by the Inquisition. They revived the institution in northern Spain in 1480, which at the time was relatively liberal, to coerce the grandees, unify the state, and fill the treasury by confiscations. As part of this plan, in 1492 they expropriated and banished the Jews.

The discovery of America was financed by the spoils of the Inquisition. Complete freedom of thought and expression gives joy, but does not appear to be absolutely necessary for the progress of science. The authoritarianism of Babylonia and the Middle Ages did not paralyse science. One may conclude that the authoritarianism rising in contemporary Europe also will not paralyse science, though it may interfere with the personal happiness and comfort of scientists.

In an ideal society, freedom and order should be in perfect equilibrium. If either is in excess, the progress of science is hindered, but it is not stopped. Complete freedom of thought is not the chief condition for the progress of science. There are other social conditions which may assist science more.

46

Clocks and Mills

THE oldest European mechanical clock whose mechanism is definitely known was built in 1348. Clocks surviving from that date show refinements in the design of their escapements, balances and striking mechanisms which must be the product of considerable evolution. Some particulars of clocks made between 1232 and 1340 are known, while the construction of some of the twenty clocks built between 1344 and 1370 is known in detail. These clocks were built in many countries, including Italy,

England, France, Germany and Switzerland. Their works were made by smiths who had acquired their skill in the construction of mill gears and mechanisms.

In 1364 Charles V engaged a German clockmaker named de Vick to construct an elaborate clock in the royal palace in Paris. It was completed in 1370, and its design has been recorded in detailed drawings.

The weight which drove the clock weighed a quarter of a ton, and that which drove the striking mechanism weighed three-quarters of a ton. The great weights were needed because the parts were so rough, having been made by a blacksmith on an anvil. The main wheels were about three feet in diameter.

This clock had an important influence in history. When it was finished, Charles V ordered the hours and the quarters to be struck in all the churches of Paris, according to the time given by the palace clock. This helped to establish the measurement of time by equal hours.

In antiquity time was measured by the length of daylight, which was divided into twelve hours whose length depended on the season of the year. At an early date, astronomers began to use equal hours, and the early Christians also made use of them. In the early medieval period the variable hour was generally used, because the church liturgy was based on the variable hour.

As urban life developed, the civil population made increasing use of the equal hour. When men were bound to the soil and paid in kind, time and efficiency were unimportant, but when craftsmen became independent and could be hired for short periods, the equal hour was the convenient unit for measuring labour and wages. It assisted the organization of production. Charles V's order was an expression of the increasing influence of the new mode of urban production on the organization of social life.

Clocks indicating minutes and seconds were made in the fifteenth century, and one was used in astronomical observations, for measuring the interval between the transits of the sun from noon to noon.

Tycho Brahe used mechanical clocks at the end of the sixteenth century. He noted their variation with atmospheric temperature and pressure, and kept them in a room heated to a constant temperature. He found they were not as accurate as a fluid clock in which mercury was used instead of water.

The mechanical skill needed to construct these clocks was developed through the construction of mills. The first power mills for purposes other than grinding grain were used in the textile industry for pounding or fulling cloth. Descriptions of them occur in the second half of the twelfth century. These machines were trip-hammers, in which a hammer is raised by a cam on a rotating axle. Machines of the same type were used for crushing oak bark, wood and ore. A drawing of a trip-hammer mill was made by a Hussite engineer in the first half of the fifteenth century. This machine was used for crushing ore. Power-driven grindstones for sharpening metal tools were used in the fourteenth century.

Power was utilized in a variety of machines in the fifteenth century, and the problems of its transmission were gradually formulated to craftsmen.

47

The Origin of Modern Science

SOCIAL life within the medieval castle or bourg was under the complete personal control of the lord. The various servants and craftsmen who supplied food and armour were organized in a hierarchy of authority under his supervision. Every man had his quarters within the bourg and performed his work under his lord's eye. The feudal knight was accustomed to interpret all relationships in personal terms, and the inhabitants of the bourg commanded by him viewed relationships in the same way. They were in immediate contact with the person of supreme authority. They made articles for those above them, and for themselves. Action to make and do things was due to orders from above. When the needs of superiors were satisfied production stopped, apart from the satisfaction of small personal needs. In such a society, as Veblen has pointed out, the notion of cause and effect is conceived in personal terms, and is subjective. Things happen because some superior has willed them, or because objects are possessed by spirits and demons. The religious view of life, in which God has supreme power and all that happens is due to His Will as performed by His regents, ministers and servants, has the same structure. In fact, medieval theology may be interpreted as the product and parallel in ideas of the social relations between the members of feudal society.

The most important topic of discussion is authority, in the guise of God and the lord, and what is due to it. The members of feudal society are in the habit of looking upwards to the lord, and to heaven. They do not regard their daily activities as of first importance, and worth serious discussion.

The persons who began to aggregate around the walls of the feudal bourgs in the tenth century were not members of the society inside. They had no quarters within the bourg, and no fixed place in its social hierarchy. They did not work directly under the eye and personal supervision of the lord within. The principle of personal authority counted much less with them than with the internal inhabitants. The composition of their society was quite different. They consisted mainly of merchants and vagabond peasants who had become independent craftsmen.

Owing to the stimulation of commerce by the merchants their numbers rapidly increased, so that presently the population of the faubourg, or surroundings of the bourg, was much larger than the strictly feudal population inside.

The total number and also the percentage of craftsmen in its population was much higher.

In many instances the original bourg was smothered by the new population, and the lord transferred his establishment to a neighbouring bourg off the new trade routes, and as yet free from the embarrassing new population. He could resume without interference the control of life within his establishment, over the countryside.

The population of the faubourg around his former headquarters now occupied the deserted fortress, and converted the whole city into a stronghold of the new *bourgeoisie* of merchants, adventurers, and independent craftsmen.

This *bourgeois* society carried over many conceptions from the feudal society in which it had been born, and at first aspired to conduct its life according to the same principles. It became as pious as the nobility and vied with it in gifts to the Church. But its fundamental interests were different and presently came in conflict with those of religious feudal society. Henry Adams has commented on the decline of religious ardour visible in the French ecclesiastical architecture of the fourteenth century. He attributes this to the disappointment of the *bourgeoisie* at the return on their enormous investments in the Church in the previous century. They had found that expensive housing of relics did not bring them much benefit in this life, and they began to suspect that it might not in the next.

They had built the cathedrals as a short route to heaven. The expenditure on religion in the thirteenth century turned out to be a sort of South Sea Scheme, and Adams suggests that the Reformation might be interpreted as a reaction of medieval business men against investment in shrines and relics.

Unlike the feudal nobility, the *bourgeoisie* did not receive its living in exchange for the conduct of government, but made it by trade and handicraft. The processes of trade and handicraft were more vital to it than problems of authority and precedence, and presently began to compete with them for its attention. As Veblen writes, matter-of-fact knowledge and work-day information were not fit topics of dignified inquiry in feudal society, but the new *bourgeoisie* began to establish the repute of these topics, along with their own social status.

Successful commerce demands a knowledge of materials. The merchant buying and selling textiles must be able to judge their quality before he can make a good bargain. He studies their feel and appearance, and learns from experience tricks by which they may be tested.

The craftsman handling metals must study their properties in order to make good products. He will note their hardness, elasticity, and rough measures of the temperatures at which they soften and melt. The medieval merchants and craftsmen, like those of antiquity, had a deep interest in, and knowledge of, the properties of materials. But the influence of the *bourgeoisie's* technical knowledge on medieval society was profoundly different from that of ancient craftsmen on slave civilizations. The *bourgeoisie* became the ruling class within their own cities, and their technical interests, as those of the ruling class, tended to become dominant.

The medieval *bourgeoisie* thus accomplished something that had never been done before. They made the properties of materials the chief interest of the ruling class. This subject, owing to its new repute, was studied for its own sake by rich *bourgeois* who had some leisure. A systematic knowledge of the properties of matter, or physics, naturally grew out of it. By the sixteenth and seventeenth centuries, when the interests and ideas of the *bourgeoisie* had begun to dominate the whole of society, noblemen such as Robert Boyle, unconscious of their acquisition of a *bourgeois* outlook, were investigating the properties of matter with outstanding success.

The explanation of how such a man as Boyle could, in the seventeenth century, earnestly investigate queries, mechanical tools and processes, which to a nobleman of the twelfth century would have seemed blasphemous and socially degrading, also explains the rise of modern science.

This is the most potent contribution to human development since the invention of agriculture. It may ultimately surpass in effect the invention of tools, which converted animals into men, as biological science may show how new and better species of men may be produced.

The *bourgeoisie* created the conditions in which modern science, which consists of a balanced combination of experiment and theory, could come into existence. But it did not set out to create modern science. In fact, it has treated science meanly, and the majority of its descendants, the modern business men, still require persuasion to spend money on scientific research. The *bourgeoisie* has pushed through the greatest contribution to culture since neolithic times, largely in spite of itself.

The study of technical processes reveals sequences of relations between material events. Forces may be applied through the medium of chisels and other instruments, salts may be dissolved by water, and metals melted by fire. These relations are described by the conception of cause and effect between material bodies, and are summarized as laws of nature. This material chain of causation, and the laws of nature, appear as independent of the personal authority of God and man.

The investigation of the properties of matter seemed to put God outside nature. The servant of the feudal lord tended to put the world within and under God, as he was himself within and under his lord's authority. The feudal conception was vertical in terms of authority, while the *bourgeois* was horizontal, in terms of sequences of cause and effect, in the multiplication of uniform material products spreading over the surface of the earth. Owing to the conflicting directions of their gaze, the feudality and the *bourgeoisie* were incapable of conceiving the world within the same scheme. The early intellectual *bourgeoisie* did not know this. They assumed that the theory of the world engendered by the preconceptions of their class could be harmonized with the feudal theology. In their attempts to achieve this harmony, they created scholasticism, which demonstrated after four centuries of intense disputation that it was impossible.

48

The Development of Money

CHARLEMAGNE'S establishment of a unified system of currency, weights and measures in the eighth century had already decayed in the ninth century, because feudal society based on agriculture, and virtually without trade, did not need the standardized units which facilitate exchange.

The population in each district was attached to the soil, and was paid in kind. Such small trading transactions as it made were more conveniently conducted in local units. Agriculture and industry in the early feudal period were conducted without capital.

The rise of trade in the tenth century revived the use of money. As trade increased, towns were founded, and hoards of money were accumulated by the new class of merchants. The rate of increase was on the whole slow. Cunningham states that the volume of trade in Europe did not greatly increase between 1300 and 1600, though the methods of conducting it greatly changed.

Feudal society regarded production as a fixed quantity, based on the unchanging output of agriculture. It did not envisage a cumulative increase of production and improvement of technique, though this occurred. As it had no use for capital, it denied the legitimacy of usury, and enforced its opinion through the Church, by the precept: 'Take ye not interest from loans.'

The new class of merchants who owned the growing hoards of money struggled to obey, but with indifferent success. During the twelfth and thirteenth centuries they often directed in their wills that gains from usury should be repaid. This custom disappeared by the end of the Middle Ages.

The merchants devised subtle evasions of the ecclesiastical law. They asserted that the practice of usury with borrowed money was not a sin, and they used fine phrases such as reward, gratuity and consideration, to disguise it. But the feudalists, and their scholastic exponents, remained suspicious, and as Pirenne says, they 'could hardly imagine the merchants' strong-box without picturing the devil squatting on the lid'.

In the twelfth and thirteenth centuries money was lent almost entirely on the security of crown jewels and land, for financing wars and courts. It was not lent for enterprise, but for unproductive consumption, and ultimately medieval bankers were ruined by this system.

As the Church's ban on usury made money-lending difficult for Christian merchants, non-Christians tended to meet the demand.

Ehrenberg mentions that the first general persecution of the Jews occurred in 1096, and the first known record of their money-lending occurs in the same year. They were gradually displaced from money-lending by the North Italians, and then by the Florentines. They were displaced from the larger money business in England, France and the Netherlands before the end of the thirteenth century. The first professional Christian money-lenders were the collectors of Papal dues.

As early medieval production did not need capital, and usury was risky, there were few opportunities for the profitable employment of money. Import and export trade provided the best, and accordingly, the development of financial technique started in the ports. As the first of these in Europe were Italian, the principles of modern finance were invented by Italians.

Banking, which grew out of money-changing; bills of exchange, the lending of money at interest, and commercial companies, were introduced to Europe or invented by Italians. As cargoes were large and expensive their purchase often required the co-operation of several lenders. When this technique had become familiar, it could be used for other purposes, such as the financing of public buildings. The first known voluntary loan to the Venetian Republic was lent by seven persons in 1164.

The possibility of making large profits on the investment of money in trade gave a new type of stimulus to production. The merchants in ports wanted more things to trade with. They urged the production of a surplus of goods above the needs of the local population. This was contrary to the general medieval conception, which regarded the town and its surrounding country as a self-supporting unit. Venice specialized in the manufacture of glass and silk, Genoa in arms, and Florence in the working and dressing of cloth.

As Florence was an inland town, her merchants could not invest their profits in the general trade of a port, so they presently specialized in money-lending.

In the Middle Ages, the craftsmen owned the raw material which they turned into goods. The engagement of craftsmen to work on raw materials owned by capitalists and sold by them after finishing occurred at Florence at the beginning of the fourteenth century. The Florentines specialized in dyeing and finishing raw cloth imported from Flanders. The trans-European trade in this cloth required considerable quantities of capital, and the merchants who profited by it could lend their gains for usury, which often produced larger and quicker profits. A monetary and credit system gradually evolved out of the early Middle Ages' system of dealing in kind.

Accumulation of money, and skill in handling it, made Florence the first banking centre in Europe. Feudal kings who could not find money within their own society found that they could borrow from the Florentine bankers. This gave a powerful stimulation both to warfare and to banking. Feudal military chiefs had hitherto projected campaigns on the basis of their immediate resources of soldiers and equipment. They now found that they could project much larger campaigns with the increased number of soldiers and arms available through borrowed money.

One effect of this was to increase the size of social organization. Successful feudal chiefs became monarchs of unified nations. This occurred first in England and France. The English were particularly fortunate because the whole country had been conquered by William, who was a feudal duke and not a king. The country belonged to him and to his descendants as a feudal estate. The head of the country was determined by inheritance and not by election. The Emperors of Germany, and the kings of France were elected from co-equal feudal lords, and the bonds of allegiance were weak. In Italy, the kingship belonged to the Holy Roman Emperor, but it was a nominal title.

The stability of the English hereditary monarchy had great importance. The English barons and *bourgeoisie* recognized the legitimacy of their title, even through disaster. Instead of dismissing a disastrous king, they inclined to make him submit to some degree of control. The early English kings tried to achieve their ambitions without consulting the barons and *bourgeoisie*, by borrowing money from Florence. This method was curtailed in 1339, when Edward III went bankrupt, and in turn bankrupted the Florentines from whom he had borrowed.

Edward III was forced to borrow from his own citizens, and surrender financial independence. But this had the effect of turning the king's wars into national wars, and increasing the size of military operations. England and France settled on a hundred years of international war.

The financial resources of England and France were insufficient to meet their kings' needs, and the Florentine bankers recovered. The leaders of the second period of Florentine banking were the Medici. Their family became established in Florence in the thirteenth century, but they lent money for three generations before they became the chief bankers in the city. They became leading international money-lenders only in the fifth generation. Giovanni Medici made a fortune by ransoming a Pope, and the family remained bankers to the Papacy until 1476. The family spent 36,000 florins on taxes, public buildings and charity between 1391 and 1434.

Ardigo de' Medici became leader of the guilds, and the popular party triumphed under him about 1314, and Dante, who belonged to the aristocratic party, was exiled. Silvestro de'Medici became leader of the wool carders in the fourteenth century. Cosimo the Elder ruled Florence for thirty years merely by financial power. He was very keen, intelligent and implacable. As a *bourgeois*, he did not care for titles, and he strengthened both his financial and political power by leading the lower classes against the nobles. He ruined the nobles by financial operations, and when they resisted by force, he incited the populace against them. All financial rivals were destroyed and he was enthusiastically supported by the people. He claimed that his acts were always 'for the good of the lower classes, for the good of the people'.

He paralyzed hostile foreign powers by threatening to close his credit business, defeating in this way an alliance of Venice and Naples against him.

He and his descendants had their enemies hung by the heels, and engaged artists such as Leonardo da Vinci to make sketches of them in this position.

Cosimo the Elder once said that he would like to have 'God the Father, God the Son, and God the Holy Ghost all on my books as debtors'.

He and his grandson Lorenzo were interested in Platonism, and engaged Brunelleschi, Ghiberti, Lucca della Robbia, Ghirlandaio, Botticelli, Michelangelo and others to build and decorate their palaces, and became rulers of Florence in this year. Between 1434 and 1471 the family spent 663,000 florins on public services in the city. Lorenzo the Magnificent, who lived from 1449-92, did not distinguish between his own and the city's finances.

The Medici and other banks owed their acquisition of political power entirely to wealth and skill in finance. Banking was revealed as a new method of obtaining power.

Financiers gained political importance in the fourteenth century, and the *bourgeoisie* in the fifteenth century, when it became the third estate. The condition of the fourth estate, or the majority of the people, became after the fourteenth century far less tolerable than in the previous two hundred years, owing to the decay of its medieval rights. Pirenne remarks that the nobles of the fourteenth and the beginning of the fifteenth century, though numerous, were remarkably sterile in achievement, and showed marks of class degeneration.

The Florentines abolished serfdom by decree in 1415. This was followed by technical improvements in agriculture. Rice cultivation was introduced into Lombardy in the fifteenth century, the cultivation of the silk-worm was started in the Midi, in Flanders the triennial rotation of crops was abandoned, and fallow was sown with clover. Spain and England sacrificed the cultivation of cereals to sheep-farming.

A proletariat appeared about 1450, which had lost the protection lent by organization in guilds, and was completely at the mercy of the employer.

The development of commerce re-established the ancient saying that 'money is the sinews of war'.

The procuration of money for financing war became the chief economic topic in the Renaissance. When Louis XII of France decided in 1499 to conquer Milan, the Condottiere captain whom he consulted on means replied: 'Most Gracious King, three things must be ready: money, money and once again money!' Machiavelli believed that if one had soldiers one could find money. He was opposed in this opinion by his friend the historian Guicciardini, who was not so far-sighted in theory but had a better judgment of contemporary politics. Their disputes foreshadowed the main problems of modern social science, concerning the conflict between labour and capital.

The Italian cities were the first powers who accumulated sufficient money to be able to prosecute war by its means. They could afford to pay soldiers, whereas feudal princes could not.

The feudal military system had been an advance on that of the German tribes, in which there was no division of labour and all free men were liable to bear arms. The feudal vassal could not be asked to perform more than his feudal due, and was therefore not under strict military control. The cities, with their still greater division of labour, were able to create a class of paid soldiers under permanent discipline.

Under the feudal system arms had been a profession. Through these mercenaries, who arose in the fourteenth and fifteenth centuries, it developed into a form of manual labour.

The introduction of cannon in the fourteenth century, and of muskets in Germany about 1459, made military equipment far more expensive, and converted the supply of arms into a heavy industry requiring large capital.

Spears, swords, bows and arrows could be made by soldiers and blacksmiths, but iron founding was a highly-skilled specialist's industry.

The supply of armaments was the department of production in which the transformation of dealing in kind into a money and credit system proceeded most swiftly.

In Italy the conduct of war became the province of private companies of Condottieri or mercenaries. Whereas the feudal duty to serve was based on a public code, the engagement of mercenaries obeyed the laws of private property, and in effect made blood purchasable by money.

Warfare became a more democratic pursuit, in which the skill of engineers, gun-founders and artillerists was of the first importance, and the men who had this knowledge belonged to a class other than the nobility. The nobility in the Italian cities abandoned the profession of arms in the fourteenth century and

7

the population did not undertake their own military defence. The discovery that money could give more power than feudal rights undermined feudalism. The population of the Italian cities treated feudal lords and serfs with scorn when they found they had the power, and the release from feudal subjection gave them a great new confidence. They had found that money and commercial enterprise were stronger than the feudal system, so they cultivated wealth and individualism. This was contrary to the doctrine of the Church, and the scholastic philosophers.

As Ehrenberg explains, they searched eagerly for an alternative to the medieval authorities and found it in the classics. They did not turn to the classics merely because they were fond of philosophy and archaeology, but because they needed a rival to the wisdom, sanctified by age and faith, of the schoolmen.

The Renaissance, or re-birth of classical learning, was in effect a manœuvre by the triumphant bankers and merchants to fortify their new ruling position with cultural defences. As Pirenne remarks, the urban spirit must be regarded as the prime and remote cause of the Renaissance. If that movement had been due merely to the recovery of classical literature, it would have occurred in Charlemagne's time.

The success of the new moneyed classes and their methods of making a living, gave prestige to social novelty and experience. When feudal men saw that money-lenders, the class held in deepest contempt by feudal society, could become lords of the world, their principles were shaken, and they felt impelled to give more attention to the facts of experience, and the possibility of novelty.

The confidence that entirely new things were possible encouraged the search for them. Man studied nature and human nature, and became interested in himself. So, while one set of intellectual leaders disinterred the classics, another set explored the possibilities of men and things. Both sets presently became fascinated by the discoveries revealed through the new direction of their interest. The influence of the first set was in many ways reactionary. Dante showed the new comprehension of the variety of personality, and confessed his desire for fame, which was a classical and not a medieval conception; he was perhaps the first modern man who ascended a mountain to admire the view. Petrarch also admired mountain scenery, which was regarded with horror by medieval men. They revived the social ideas of the old slave civilization. They disdained manual labour, and created the prejudice in favour of the liberal professions, which still survives. Pirenne considers that this prejudice is 'largely responsible for the indifference to the lot of the lower classes which characterizes the modern era'.

Cosimo de' Medici encouraged Platonic philosophy as 'the fairest flower of the ancient world of thought', and Lorenzo the Magnificent patronized scholars such as Argyropoulos, Ficino, Valori, Acciajuoli Pandolfini and Pico della Mirandola, rather than Leonardo da Vinci, Pacioli, Toscanella, Amerigo Vespucci, and other Florentines who were advancing towards the discovery of America and modern science, and he destroyed the independence of Florence. The first set, known as Humanists, encouraged the search for antique statues and the architectural study of the ruins of ancient buildings.

The study of ancient sculpture and architecture provided an art that could be set against the Gothic, which was a symbol of feudal culture. The self-indulgence of the new rulers emancipated from medieval doctrine was justified by citation of the habits of Roman emperors, and political assassins and conspirators appealed to the memory of Brutus and Catiline.

The new social system based on commerce and credit could not be operated by men without intellectual ability.

The Italian bankers who became rulers were abler than their feudal contemporaries, and knew how to base policy on economic statistics. As they were a new ruling class, they were free from the caste-feeling of feudalism, and their business made them use men of every social class. This fostered the esteem of ability, and led on to the cult of personality, and the admiration of any sort of behaviour, as long as it was interesting.

Numerous independent cities, and individualists of many sorts, grew in the new soil of a commercial society. They became superior in credit and industrial technique, and in personality to the men of the North, where feudalism lingered. But while Italian society was becoming more varied, it was also disintegrating. Less advanced countries, such as England and France, were developing national unity, though dependent for cultural progress on the Italians. For five hundred years after the Norman Conquest, there was virtually no important contribution to culture that was specifically English. But when the centre of the world was transferred from the Mediterranean to the Atlantic by the discovery of America, England was able to take advantage of the new opportunity created for her by circumstances, because her population was unified in a relatively stable social system.

The Italian statesmen were acutely conscious of the anarchic weakness of their country, but their policy was governed, in spite of their judgement, by the tradition of individualism created by the new commercial societies. The most determined attempt to unify Italy was made by Caesar Borgia.

He was a Spaniard and did not possess the individualist feeling of the commercial Italian. It is thought that he aimed at the destruction of the Papacy, which attracted so much foreign intervention in Italy. This policy secured Machiavelli's secret admiration, and he believed that the existence of the Papacy was the cause of Italian disunity. The city republics and principalities could not be forced to co-operate while foreign powers were setting them against each other, in plots aiming at the control of the Church's political policy.

Caesar Borgia annihilated the Orsini and Colonna factions, which had prevented any social stability in Rome. He forced his father Alexander, who was the Pope, to assist in systematic murders of the higher officials of the Church, to secure their influence and incomes. The Venetian ambassador reported in 1500 that 'every night four or five murdered men are discovered —bishops, prelates and others'.

When Caesar had destroyed a large part of the higher officials of the Church, and had terrorized his father into acquiescence in the murder of his best-beloved son, and was ready to destroy his father too, and seize the Papacy, he accidentally poisoned himself and his father with a sweetmeat intended for another.

This accident defeated his plan. The horrors of his reign had stirred the conscience of the Papacy, and when he was gone, this led to internal reforms. His attempt to destroy the Papacy promoted its revival and his failure left Italy disunited. Pirenne remarks that 'the absence of any political unity in Italy, which Machiavelli regretted so bitterly, was doubtless the condition of her breaking with the past. Never having been squeezed into a single State, Italy was then able to become, in respect of the rest of Europe, something of what ancient Greece was for Rome.'

Caesar Borgia had demonstrated the difficulty of imposing unity if the social system operates according to individualistic principles, and has trained its members in individualistic forms of behaviour. Under these circumstances the extremest use of force fails, even when applied by the ablest men, for he had recruited the best soldiers and officers in Italy, and had engaged Leonardo da Vinci as his chief engineer.

49

Borgia's Engineer

LEONARDO DA VINCI was born near Florence in 1452. He was the illegitimate son of an able lawyer, who became one of the chief legal advisers to the Medici. He showed remarkable artistic talent in his youth, and was apprenticed in the shop of Andrea Verrocchio, a distinguished painter, goldsmith and craftsman who, like many of his colleagues, had some knowledge of sculpture, architecture and engineering.

Verrocchio had adopted the naturalistic style of painting developed by Masaccio, which emphasized fidelity to observation and analysis of the structure of a subject. This required a thorough knowledge of the optics of perspective, and human anatomy.

An apprentice in Verrocchio's shop would also learn the techniques of gold-working and sculpture. These involved metallurgical knowledge concerning the casting of gold and bronze, and the preparation of alloys. As the craftsmen had to prepare their own paints and materials, and could not buy them ready-made, they needed a considerable knowledge of chemistry.

F. I. G. Rawlins has remarked that 'the studio of the medieval artist or craftsman was very much more than a place where pictures were painted or pots were fashioned. It combined the functions of workshop and laboratory for the master's own activities, and for the instruction of his pupils. A long apprenticeship was demanded of those whose ambition it was to become master-craftsmen, and much of this period seems to have been devoted to an intense and intimate study of materials, which included the preparation of pigments, and the application of sundry metallurgical principles, such as those of metal refining and extraction. In a word, this was a hard school of training in the properties of matter'.

Artists were also expected to organize the festivals that were an important feature of contemporary social life. They had to paint masks and construct entertaining mechanical puppets. As architects, they had to learn the elements of statics and the mechanics of lifting machinery.

A person with an aptitude for one or more of these techniques could learn in an eminent shop, such as Verrocchio's, much of what was known about them.

Leonardo quickly mastered the existing knowledge in all of these techniques. He was interested in everything and fond of discussions with other experts. After he had completed his apprenticeship and joined the guild of painters, he became a notable figure, very strong and beautiful as he 'stood in rose-coloured cloak and rich gold hair', talking to his friends.

He received a few commissions from the Medici, but they were interested in the application of painting to literary topics, rather than in the significance of painting, and the information its processes reveal about the nature of the world and man.

Leonardo apparently did not feel that his interests in the crafts and mechanics were congenial to the Medici, and looked elsewhere for an opportunity. He became painter and engineer to Ludovico Sforza in Milan, and remained there until 1499, when the city was captured by the French. He returned to Florence, but was unable to secure a satisfactory appointment. He was engaged by Borgia as chief engineer in 1502, and travelled through Italy advising on military constructions during 1503.

When Borgia's policy failed, he had to seek another position and returned to Milan under French patronage. He lived in Rome from 1513 to 1517, and advised the Papal Mint on technical processes, and amused the ecclesiastical authorities with mechanical toys. His experiences were unsatisfactory, so he accepted a position as painter and engineer at the French court. He settled in the south of France and died there three years later, in 1519.

Leonardo first left Florence about 1483. Colvin has suggested that 'his exclusive belief in experimental methods, and slight regard for mere authority whether in science or art made the intellectual atmosphere of the Medicean circle, with its passionate mixed cult of the classic past and of a Christianity mystically blended and reconciled with Platonism, uncongenial to him'. He applied to Ludovico Sforza, who had usurped the control of the principality of Milan, for an appointment. Ludovico was engaging writers, artists and engineers to celebrate, embellish and strengthen his state and so justify his usurpation. A draft of Leonardo's letter of application exists and reads: 'Most illustrious Lord. Having now sufficiently considered the specimens of all those who proclaim themselves skilled contrivers of instruments of war, and that the invention and operation of the said instruments are nothing different to those in common use, I shall endeavour, without prejudice to anyone else, to explain myself to your Excellency showing your Lordship my secrets, and then offering them to your best pleasure and approbation to work with effect at opportune moments as well as all those things which, in part, shall be briefly noted below.

1. I have a sort of extremely light and strong bridges, adapted to be most easily carried, and with them you may pursue, and at any time flee from the enemy; and others, secure and indestructible by fire and battle, easy and convenient to lift and place. Also methods of burning and destroying those of the enemy.

2. I know how, when a place is besieged, to take the water out of the trenches, and make endless variety of bridges, and covered ways and ladders, and other machines pertaining to such expeditions.

3. Item. If, by reason of the height of the banks, or the strength of the place and its position, it is impossible, when besieging a place, to avail oneself of the plan of bombardment, I have methods for destroying every rock or other fortress, even if it were founded on a rock.

4. Again I have kinds of mortars; most convenient and easy to carry; and with these can fling small stones almost resembling a storm; and with the smoke of these causing great terror to the enemy, to his great detriment and confusion.

9. And when the fight should be at sea I have kinds of many machines most efficient for offence and defence; and vessels which will resist the attack of the largest guns and powder and fumes.

5. Item. I have means by secret and tortuous mines and ways, made without noise to reach a designated (spot) even if it were needed to pass under a trench or a river.

6. Item. I will make covered chariots, safe and unattackable

which, entering among the enemy with their artillery, there is no body of men so great but they would break them. And behind these, infantry could follow quite unhurt and without any hindrance.

7. Item. In case of need I will make big guns, mortars and light ordnance of fine and useful forms, out of the common type.

8. Where the operation of bombardment should fail, I would contrive catapults, mangonels, *trabocchi* and other machines of marvellous efficacy and not in common use. And in short, according to the variety of cases, I can contrive various and endless means of offence and defence.

10. In time of peace I believe I can give perfect satisfaction and to the equal of any other in architecture and the composition of buildings public and private; and in guiding water from one place to another.

Item: I can carry out sculpture in marble, bronze or clay, and also in painting whatever may be done, and as well as any other, be he whom he may.

(32) Again, the bronze horse may be taken in hand, which is to be the immortal glory and eternal honour of the prince your father of happy memory, and of the illustrious house of Sforza.

And if any of the above-named things seem to anyone to be impossible or not feasible, I am most ready to make the experiment in your park, or in whatever place may please Your Excellency—to whom I commend myself with the utmost humility, etc.'

Leonardo gave the first place in this application to military engineering, and the second to civil engineering. He mentions his qualification as a painter incidentally. The draft exhibits worldly sense, and was skilfully composed to appeal to Ludovico. It has often been said that it did not express his own opinion of the relative worth of his work in painting and in other subjects, but it does agree with the distribution of energy in the works that survived. He was the first painter who utilized the contrast of light and shade. His predecessors had been restricted to line and colour. He was the first to eliminate stiffness in the depiction of human figures and make them appear fully alive. The contributions form a considerable fraction of the whole technique of painting. But he finished very few pictures. Not more than twelve have survived.

In contrast, he left five thousand pages of manuscript notes on scientific and technical researches. These included several treatises in which a general problem, such as flight, was investigated systematically, and hundreds of notes on isolated problems.

When Leonardo studied, sciences were not well-defined. His researches would now be classified under engineering, mechanics, hydraulics, aerodynamics, and anatomy; with striking comments and isolated experiments in physics, geology, physiology, botany and meteorology.

He began to make these notes before he left Florence in 1483, and added to them until he died in 1519. They are the product of forty years of continuous effort, and form one of the largest and most sustained intellectual efforts that has been made by man. One wonders, then, how Leonardo has acquired the reputation of a finicking genius who made a disappointingly small use of his great gifts. This has arisen through the contrast in intelligibility between his work in painting and in science.

His paintings present their meaning directly. As he defined a good painting by the degree of perfection with which it imitated nature, he meant his paintings to have the maximum degree of intelligibility. Everyone, according to the measure of his intelligence, could directly apprehend their merit.

But access to the meaning of his scientific researches was not so direct. Though they are illustrated by thousands of his sketches, they are written in mirror-writing. He was left-handed and could write more easily backwards, from right to left. This prevented his manuscripts from being read without special training. In addition, his notes were discursive, and had not been prepared for publication. Thoughts on quite different aspects of nature were often jotted down on the same page at different times, presenting the reader with a fascinating but perplexing jumble.

He apologized for this in a note written in 1508. He says: 'This will be a collection without order, made up of many sheets which I have copied here, hoping afterwards to arrange them in order in their proper places according to subjects of which they treat; and I believe before I am at the end of this, I shall have to repeat the same thing several times; and therefore, O reader, blame me not, because the subjects are many, and the memory cannot retain them and say, "This I will not write because I have already written it." '

This passage shows that Leonardo intended his notes to be read, and did not wish to make them difficult and mysterious.

7*

His verbal explanations were often obscure, because the terminology of science was still crude, and his results frequently contained new knowledge, for which there was necessarily no name.

These are the primary reasons why Leonardo's achievements have been so much misunderstood. The main volume of his work was done in science, and owing to the form of expression and the newness of the ideas it was as unintelligible to his contemporaries as a treatise in German on the theory of relativity is unintelligible today to an Englishman who knows no mathematics or German.

The difficulty of completing a scientific investigation was far greater then than now, as the evolution of the scientific method was not yet complete. The miscellaneousness of Leonardo's researches corresponds to the stage reached in the evolution of scientific method in his day. But the old complaint that he failed to complete his works through finicking is not entirely unjust. He worked excessively slowly at his paintings, and he doubtless might have put his scientific notes into publishable form. He could have employed a secretary to transcribe them into normal handwriting.

The descriptions, sketches and proposals of military inventions in his notebooks include tanks, breech-loading cannon, rifled fire-arms, wheel-locked pistols, steam cannon, and submarines. Of the latter he writes that he must explain 'How and why I do not describe my method of remaining under the water for as long a time as I can remain without food; and this I do not publish or divulge on account of the evil nature of men who would practise assassinations at the bottom of the seas by breaking the ships in their lowest parts and sinking them together with the crews who are in them'.

He invented or depicted the life-belt and diving suit. He gave numerous sketches of attachments for divers' face-masks, nose-clips, and tubes for supplying fresh air to the diver. He depicted a lively figure of a youth skiing over the water on bladders attached to his feet, pushing and supporting himself by sticks with floats on their ends. He sketched various designs of paddle boats driven by hand or foot cranks.

He depicted the polygonal fortress with outworks, later ascribed to Dürer and Lorini.

His work on canalization had military and civil applications.

He proposed a canal two hundred miles long through Lombardy, which would pass over mountains, and he was consulted by the officers of the Florentine army besieging Pisa on the project of diverting the River Arno, so that the city would be starved of supplies. He made improvements in canal locks and gates, and invented dredges of two types later ascribed to Besson.

His contributions to architecture included designs for elevated streets. The visitors, and wood and wine and such things were to enter the houses by the elevated streets, while sewage and other evil-smelling things were to be removed by the lower street. He designed horse-stalls which could be kept clean, and a chimney which rotated with the wind, to prevent smoke from being blown back into rooms.

He gave detailed attention to the design of textile machinery. The textile trade and industry had been the foundation of Florence's power, and the improvements he proposed would have increased its ability to meet competition. His proposals and sketches include a rope-making machine which foreshadowed that of March; silk doubling and winding-machines of types ascribed later to Zonca; and woollen-spinning machines of a design later ascribed to Jurgens.

He gave an incomplete sketch of a power loom, and sketches of a gig mill for raising the nap on felt, and a shearing engine for cutting cloth and felt hats.

Usher remarks that apart from silk reeling and twisting and the fulling mill, increasing the homogeneity of cloth by clamping, all textile inventions used in western Europe had been acquired from the Near East. Leonardo's notebooks reveal an attempt to apply power to the chief textile machines. The power was to be obtained from water mills or horse-driven winches. Water power had probably been applied to silk reeling and twisting prior to Leonardo.

He was aware of the significance of his design for the power loom. He wrote under it: 'This is second only to the printing press in importance; no less useful in its practical application; a lucrative, beautiful and subtle invention.'

His spinning machine had a flyer, which guided the thread evenly, wound the bobbin, and would mount four spindles simultaneously.

He was consulted by the Papal Mint on the improvement of coining during his residence in Rome from 1513 to 1516.

He sketched elaborate designs for rolling, drawing and hammering gold bars. Rolling and drawing had been used for light work at least since the twelfth century, but Leonardo proposed to apply them to heavy work. He also proposed improved methods of stamping out the blanks for coins. Improved coining machinery inspired by Leonardo's designs was subsequently constructed at Augsburg and Nürnberg, the centres of the financial activities of the Fugger.

He sketched designs for scores of new and improved machine tools. He invented the anti-friction roller bearing. He made beautiful sketches of link chains, exactly similar to those now used on bicycles. These were later ascribed to Vaucanson and Galle. He sketched a universal joint before Cardan or Hooke. He sketched bevel, spiral and stepped gears, and varieties of cranks and gears for converting longitudinal into rotary motion. He sketched a machine for cutting files automatically, and a screw-cutting machine, in which the pitch of the cut screw could be varied by gears from standard leading screws.

He sketched paraboloid compasses, later ascribed to Galileo, and proportional compasses, later ascribed to Burgi; the turret windmill, later ascribed to Pascal and Agricola; and varieties of cranes and presses, including a prevision of the hydraulic press of Bramah. His treatise on flight contained sketches for the parachute. He says: 'If a man have a tent roof of calked linen 12 bracci broad and 12 bracci high, he will be able to let himself fall from any great height without danger to himself'. He invented the helicopter and made small models that would soar. He made thin wax figures which floated in the atmosphere when filled with air.

The appearance of a drawing in Leonardo's notebooks does not necessarily imply that he was the original inventor of the device, or even the improvement of it. He may have independently invented an old device, such as the Chinese invention of the wheelbarrow, which was for long ascribed to Agricola and Pascal; or he may have learned of it by hearsay or wide reading. His extraordinary skill in drawing enabled him to formulate and record any mechanical idea pictorially. It provided him with a facility available to very few men before the invention of photography. Thus Leonardo's notebook must be regarded to some extent as an illustrated treatise on the mechanical ideas in circulation in Northern Italy and Southern Germany during his lifetime. The common ascriptions of many of the devices he depicts are quoted to illustrate the obscurity of the actual origin of inventions, besides his own great originality and fertility. In many instances, inventions have been credited not to those who made them, or even made any considerable contribution to them, but had the leading part in their dissemination. From the social point of view, the effective disseminator of an idea performs a major service, and deserves his repute, if not exclusive credit.

Leonardo's sketches show that he must have spent much time in textile and engineering shops. He left a notable drawing of an arsenal foundry. His interest in machines inspired him to search for the laws that governed their operation. He made extensive attempts by observation, logic and experiment to derive the laws of statics and the elementary laws of motion from the study of tensions in pulley strings, inclined planes, collisions, sliding and falling bodies, etc. His notes on these problems, with their neat figures, resemble very much the familiar modern textbook on elementary mechanics, though the incidental comments are much more philosophical and personal. They have been analysed by Hart. In the course of the discussion of particular problems he enumerates laws of motion. He says: 'Nothing whatever can be moved by itself but its motion is effected through another.' Again, 'All movement tends to maintenance, or rather all moved bodies continue to move as long as the impression of the force of their motors remains in them.' He deduced this from the flight of birds.

While analysing the operation of the parachute, he remarks that 'an object offers as much resistance to the air as the air does to the object'. He investigated the fall of heavy bodies and stated that 'a weight which has no support falls by the shortest route to the lowest point, which is the centre of the world. In the air of uniform density, the heavy body which falls at each stage of time acquires a degree of movement more than the degree of the proceeding time'.

He dropped weights from a tower, and convinced himself that they did not fall vertically. He believed he could detect a small easterly deviation in the point of impact; and he ascribed this to the earth's rotation. He described the path of the falling body as 'a combination of a straight and curved line which joins it from [the point of fall] to the centre of the earth. It is a curved line in itself and in every point of the path'. This, and other examples, show he had some conception of the parallelogram of velocities. He also had some conception of the parallelogram of forces. He discussed the forces acting on a body lying on an inclined plane. He said 'that the weight of the body divides its gravity in two aspects, that is according to the line [along the inclined plane] and according to the line [perpendicular to the inclined plane]'.

He stated that the ratio of the rapidity of movement of a sphere sliding down an inclined plane to that of a body falling freely was as the height of the vertical fall to the length of the inclined plane.

In his analysis of the movements of weights on a system of pulleys he said: 'If a force carries a weight in a certain time through a definite distance, the same force will carry half the body in the same time through double the path.' This expresses the principle of work.

He had some conception of energy and power, as he noted that 'if a wheel is moved for a moment by a quantity of water, and if this water is not added to either by flowing or by quantity, or by a greater fall, the function of this water is finished'. He was quite clear on the impossibility of perpetual motion. He said: 'Oh speculators on perpetual motion how many vain projects of the like character you have created! Go and be the companions of the searchers after gold!'

He made experiments on the recoil of spheres from plane surfaces, perhaps from a desire to understand the effect of the percussion of cannon balls on the walls of fortresses. He concluded that 'the blow will be less powerful than its impulse according as the angle of its percussion is nearer the right angle', and he believed that the angles of incidence and rebound were equal.

Leonardo drew many of his theoretical conclusions from the analysis of difficult subjects, such as the movements of birds in flight, and the human figure. He said that 'Mechanical science is very noble and useful beyond all others, for by its means all animated bodies which have movement perform their operations, which movement proceeds from their centre of gravity'.

His advocacy of the study of mechanics as a key to the movements of living organisms is unusual, for according to the naïve view the movements of living organisms are governed by laws specific to living organisms, and different from those governing the movements of machines and dead matter. Leonardo even advocates the study of human anatomy in order to appreciate movements of the body as illustrations of the laws of mechanics.

He found the centre of gravity of a bird from experiments on a model. He noted that 'occasionally the centre of gravity is to be found outside of the body'.

He interpreted the manœuvres of flying birds from the relations between the varying positions of the centres of gravity and pressure. 'When the bird which is in equilibrium throws the centre of resistance of the wings behind the centre of gravity, then it will descend with its head downwards.' He deduced the functions of the tail and illustrated them by models.

He noticed the elements of streamline when he remarked that 'the wings being convex above and concave below, the air escapes more easily the percussion of the wings with elevation than with lowering'. He distinguished between apparent and effective wing surface. He advocated high flying to escape turbulence, and give time and space for recovery. He tried to deduce the principles of soaring, and made numerous exquisite sketches of soaring birds in various positions. This part of his programme was first solved by the German gliders after the war of 1914. They were prevented from military flying by the treaty of Versailles, so they concentrated on engineless gliders, on which there were no restrictions, and discovered how to soar and make long flights in them.

His lengthy studies of water and waves, eddies and pressures were inspired by the desire to understand the motion of the invisible air and its relation to flight. For the attainment of 'the true science of the movement of birds in the air it is necessary to give first the science of the winds, which we will establish by means of the movements of water'.

His interest in canalization and pumping also stimulated his researches on hydrostatics and hydrodynamics. His investigations of fluid flow, of wave-motion, of pressure in connected tubes, and the influence of pressure on rate of flow, contained observations later ascribed to Castelli, Newton, l'Emy, Pascal, Stevinus and Galileo. His proposal to drive a pump by a pendulum was later ascribed to Ramelli and Besson. His proposals for improvement in the details of pumps were later ascribed to Ramelli, and his water screw consisting of coiled pipes to de Rubeis. He also suggested the centrifugal pump.

Leonardo deduced the centre of gravity of solid figures. He

correctly calculated the centre of gravity of the tetrahedron. His result was later ascribed to Commandin and Maurolycus.

He made experimental investigations on friction and concluded that the amount of friction was independent of the areas in contact. He found that smoothing and lubrication reduced friction, and that if bodies had the same degree of smoothness, the friction was proportional to the pressure between them. He concluded from his experiments on the sliding of a variety of bodies on a horizontal polished surface that the frictional resistance to motion was equal to one quarter of the weight of the sliding body. He recognized the existence of the coefficient of friction, which seemed, according to his experiments, to be the same for all bodies on a polished surface. Hart states that this was 'the first presentation in scientific history of any laws of friction whatever.'

His experiments on the deflection of struts and beams are almost as interesting. They probably arose out of his architectural work. He showed that if one thousand rushes are bound together tightly, they will support more than twelve times the collective weight which could be borne when distributed on them singly. His theoretical analysis of bending under load was roughly correct.

He left an early example of the use of graphical methods in science. He found the relation between time and velocity in a falling body. Time was plotted vertically, and velocity horizontally.

Leonardo did not understand that force is proportional to acceleration and not to velocity. He said that 'if a force moves a body in a given time over a given distance, the same force will move half this mass through the same distance in half the time'. He did not recognize the principle of moments. He did not recognize the general principles of the parallelograms of forces and velocities, though he handled many particular cases correctly. His theory of the inclined plane was correct, but not complete, like that of Stevinus. He made some of the classical mistakes of students of mechanics. For instance, he believed that if the rope in a tug-of-war were held in equilibrium by the two contending parties, and each party were hauling with a force of four units, then the tension in the rope would be equal to eight units. He had forgotten that he had noticed in another problem that action and reaction are equal and opposite.

Though he said that 'there is no certainty in sciences to which one of the mathematical sciences cannot be applied, or which are not in relationship with these mathematics', he was a poor calculator, and made many errors in simple arithmetic.

50

The Eighth Month of Science

LEONARDO'S apprenticeship to painting led him to study anatomy, which assisted him to surpass his predecessors in giving life to his figures. His sense of mechanics, strengthened by his studies of industrial and military machinery, brought the dynamics of living matter to his attention, and predisposed him to combine physiological with anatomical investigations. He injected melted wax into a brain removed from the cranium, to discover the structure of the ventricles. He gave the instruction: 'Make two air-holes in the horn of the larger ventricle and inject the melted wax into it, at the same time making a hole in the *memoria* and fill through such a hole the three ventricles of the brain; and then when the wax has hardened, remove the brain and you will see the exact form of the three ventricles. But first insert the fine tubes into the air-holes, so that the air in the ventricles can stream out, giving place to the injected wax.'

Four centuries later, anatomists were still claiming priority in the invention of this method.

He discovered from experiments on frogs that the spinal cord was biologically prior to the brain. He said: 'The frog retains life for some hours after the head, heart, and intestines are removed . . .' but it 'instantly dies when its spinal cord is perforated . . . It thus seems that here lies the fundamentum of motion and of life'.

He noted in his studies of the lung that 'dust is injurious', and he seems to have conceived that it was the cause of lung diseases.

One quarter of his anatomical drawings deal with the heart. He made detailed experimental investigations of its structure and function. He showed that Galen's teaching that air is carried direct to the heart by the pulmonary vein, and that the heart has two cavities only, is wrong. He proved that the heart possesses four cavities, and he investigated the movement of blood through them by models. He made a wax cast over the ventricles and their vessels. He made a gypsum mould from the wax cast, and took an impression from it in glass. He examined through this glass model the vortices made by the blood when driven by the contraction into the arteries. He also showed that the valves allow the blood to flow in one direction only. His contract to make a great equestrian statue of Francesco Sforza had particularly stimulated his interest in the anatomy of the horse, and he noted that 'in order to compare the skeleton of a horse with that of a man, you must present the man on tiptoe, when portraying the bones'. He noted for further consideration 'the affinity, which the conformity of bones and muscles of animals have with the bones and muscles of man'.

Hopstock states that no one before Leonardo, so far as is known, made so many dissections on human bodies, and interpreted them so well. His account of the uterus was far more accurate and intelligible, and he was the first to give a correct general description of the human skeleton, and a correct picture of nearly all of the muscles in the human body. Besides his use of injections and casts, he was the first who employed serial sections. So far as is known, he was the first to have illustrated anatomy by drawings from the object.

Leonardo made sustained studies of meteorological and geological phenomena. He recognized the meaning of the existence of fossils on the tops of mountains, and estimated the age of geological processes freely in periods of hundreds of thousands of years. He noted the effects of erosion on the shape of the earth's surface. He even noted the increase of erosion through cultivation, now believed to be one of the causes of the decline of Graeco-Roman civilization.

'The rivers mature greater deposits of soil when near to populated districts than they do where there are no inhabitants because in such places the mountains and hills are being worked upon, and the rains wash away the soil that has been turned up more easily than the hard ground which is covered with weeds.

'The heights of mountains are more eternal and more enduring when they are covered with snow during the whole winter.'

He noted the deeper colour of the blue sky seen from the top of Monte Rosa, and said: 'The atmosphere acquires its blueness from the particles of moisture which catch the luminous rays of the sun.'

The blueness of smoke increases with the fineness of its particles. The whiteness of the smoke from burning wet green wood is due to the size of the particles, which are large enough to reflect light like a solid body.

Leonardo made sketches of apparatus for measuring the amount of steam produced by boiling a given quantity of water. He did not clearly distinguish between steam and air. This was first done properly by della Porta. He said that 'whether air can be compressed in itself is shown by the barber's vessel for supplying rose-water, in which it is doubled. Fire is quadrupled by the force of the place where it cannot increase'. Leonardo's work was inspired by at least three motives; the desire for gain, for fame, and for knowledge.

His desire for gain is seen in his design and construction of machines for polishing needles. He writes that 'early tomorrow, January 2nd, 1496, I shall make the leather belt and proceed to a trial'. He calculates that 'one hundred times in each hour 400 needles will be finished, making 40,000 in an hour and 480,000 in 12 hours. Suppose we say 4,000 which at 5 solidi per thousand gives 20,000 solidi; 1,000 lire per working day, and if one works 20 days in the month 60,000 ducats the year'.

His desire for fame is seen in the concluding paragraph of his treatise on flight. The machine was to be launched from a mountain named the Great Swan, so he writes: 'The great bird will take its first flight, on the back of its great swan, and filling the universe with stupor, filling all writings with its renown, and glory eternal to the nest where it was born.'

His love of truth is seen in his observation that 'though our spirit may have lying for its fifth element, nevertheless, the truth of things remains as the supreme nutriment for fine intelligences'.

After describing the qualities desirable in a dissection he says: 'As to whether all these things have been in me or no, the hundred and twenty books written by me will furnish sentence, yes or no, for in these I have not been hampered by avarice, or by negligence, but only by time. Vale.'

Leonardo's great fertility in research has inspired discussions on his method of work. Paul Valéry has attributed to him a method of experimenting with concepts. He says: 'It consists only in the throwing of one image—of one concrete mental relationship—amongst phenomena, amongst the images of phenomena, let us say, in order to be rigorous. Leonardo seems to have had knowledge of this kind of psychical experimentation, and it seems to me that during the three centuries after his death the method was recognized by nobody, though everyone used it—of necessity . . .' He quotes Leonardo's meditations on rays of light: 'The air is filled with an infinite number of straight and radiating lines, crossed and intercrossed, and never one of them coinciding with one another, and for each object they *represent* the true *Form* of their own reason.' Valéry contends that 'it was reserved for Faraday to rediscover the method of Leonardo as applied to physical science . . . He, too *visualized* systems of lines uniting all bodies, filling all space in order to *explain* phenomena of electricity . . .'

His comparison of the methods of Leonardo and Faraday is instructive, but did not the Ionian philosophers use the same method of experiment in the imagination, when they developed the atomic theory? Usher has discussed the mental process of invention according to the principles of Gestalt psychology. He considers that invention occurs in perception and in conception. The primitive inventions in crafts are of the first sort. They consist of modifications of familiar operations that occur while the inventor is watching and handling his tools. Though these inventions may be of the greatest significance, after they are made they appear trivial to the spectator. This explains why the names of the inventors of fire, the wheel, and other fundamental primitive inventions are not remembered.

The other type of invention depends on experimenting with concepts in the imagination. When general laws of nature have been discovered, the conceptual inventor can invent in his imagination machines which obey these laws. He can sketch them on paper, and because they obey the laws they will work. Leonardo described this as 'pre-imagining the imagining of things that are to be'.

This achievement is very impressive, and when it becomes possible, inventors are admired and remembered, because they seem to be creating practical machines by mere imagination.

Edison's invention of the gramophone in twenty minutes is a notable illustration of experiment in the imagination with general

scientific knowledge. Usher sees in Leonardo's work the transition from the perceptual to the conceptual mode of invention.
His interesting and valuable discussion of invention before and
after the creation of theoretical science helps to explain the
difference in the degree of the fertility of primitive and modern
invention, and gives one of the reasons why invention had less
prestige in ancient than in modern times. But it does not explain
why theoretical science was created. It cannot be expected to
explain a historical process, because it deals with psychological
and not with historical concepts. History is explicable only in
terms of theories of history and not in terms of theories of
psychology.

Freud's interesting analysis of Leonardo's psychology has the
same limitation. He has shown that his conduct and interests
were probably fixed by special infantile experiences. He was an
illegitimate child, and was reared by his mother alone until he
was five. The absence of his father increased the acuteness of the
normal infantile interest in his own origin, and established in
him a powerful investigatory habit. His lonely mother's exaggerated affection produced in him sexual prematurity. He overcame this infantile excess by an energetic repression, and the
repressed affection for his mother was expressed in idealized love
for boys. The energy that would have been discharged in normal
affections was sublimated through the investigatory habit, which
was thereby deepened and made permanent.

Freud suggests that Leonardo was able to find in Ludovico
Sforza a partial substitute for a father, and this explains the
greater normality of his art during his period in Milan. When
Sforza fell, and Leonardo had to leave him, he lost the substitute
father who had unconsciously helped him to escape from his
repressions. After this, the struggle against his repressions lapsed,
and the amount of energy sublimated through the investigatory
habit increased. Art was displaced still further by science, and
was resumed only through the stimulation of profound infantile
reminiscences. Freud suggests that the pictures of smiling
women, such as La Gioconda and Saint Anne, painted by
Leonardo in his later years, were due to the temporary release of
his repressions through his meeting with women who appealed to
his intense unconscious infantile reminiscences of his mother.

Freud's theory gives insight into the origin of Leonardo's
scientific habits, and of his inhibitions. His inability to complete

paintings, and to complete manuscripts for publication was related to the absence of completion in his sexual life, and the spread of repression from this part of his life into other parts. The extent of his scientific researches and their incompleteness are interpreted as sublimations of his persistent search for, and failure to achieve, a normal sexual life.

While Freud's theory throws light on the features of his work and into his motives for investigating nature, it does not deal with the problem of why science had developed to the particular stage which gave special scope to a person with his peculiar psychology. A scientific discovery is immediately due to the interaction of two factors, the body of science and the mental characteristics of a scientist. The type of mind which can interact successfully with the body of science at a particular epoch depends on the characteristics of that body at that epoch, for the characteristics of science at one epoch may be different from those at another. For instance, the body of science existing at the end of the nineteenth century was particularly suited for inter-action with a mind like Rutherford's. His exceptional insight into the particulate aspects of phenomena might have been much less effective at other periods. If Rutherford had become mature in 1850, when the idea of vibration in continuous media was most fruitful, his discoveries might have been less important. Leonardo was fitted to advance science at the particular stage it had reached in his day. Progress was made then by working out numerous particular cases, and this came most easily to those with multifarious interests.

He was entirely emancipated from submission to authority. He said: 'I do not understand how to quote as they do from learned authorities, but it is a much greater and more estimable matter to rely on experience, their masters' master.'

He drew up rules for the description of the movements of bodies, and tried to find mathematical statements for them. He said that 'mechanics is the paradise of the mathematical sciences because by means of it one comes to the fruits of mathematics'. Mechanics was valuable because mathematics became of social value through it, and it provided the way by which mathematics could become fertile in the investigation of nature. When a rule of mechanics had been discovered he said that 'before making this case a general rule, test it by experiment two or three times, and see if the experience produces the same effect'.

He had the three elements of the scientific method: observation, the reduction of the results of observation to mathematical rules, and the testing of these rules by experiment. The method was completed by his successors when they combined the three operations into one deliberate process.

Detailed knowledge of Leonardo's scientific researches had been acquired only during the last hundred years. One will ask how they could have had any influence on the history of science if they were not generally known soon after they had been made. His researches on human anatomy appear to have been entirely unread until recent times, and to have had virtually no influence on the progress of science. It was thought for a long time that his researches on mechanics, and mechanical invention, had had little more effect, but historical research has shown that these manuscripts were read by a few able men who plagiarized from them without acknowledgment. Jerome Cardan was one of the most notable. The treatise on hydraulics published by Castelli in 1621 owed much to Leonardo's researches.

The treatments of the centre of gravity given by Villalpond, and of the centre of pressure by Baldi, were taken by them from Leonardo. They led to Huyghens' theory of centres of oscillation through Roberval, Descartes and Fabry. Many of Leonardo's discoveries and inventions in mechanics had filtered anonymously into the body of mechanical knowledge at the beginning of the seventeenth century. Though the belief that Leonardo's mechanical researches had little influence is untrue, the inefficiency of the publication of his work is evident. This was not entirely due to his faults. The new technique of printing was developed during his lifetime, and the circulation of manuscripts was still the chief method of spreading knowledge. Many of the leading patrons of learning in the fifteenth century regarded printed books as vulgar and would not have them in their libraries. The printed book democratized learning and was as distasteful to many aristocrats then as the gramophone and the cinema have been to contemporary cultural aristocrats.

Leonardo himself esteemed printing very highly, and intended to print his notebooks, but his failure to do so had less serious effects in his lifetime than afterwards, when printing became the usual mode of publication.

The absence of scientific societies and scientific journals contributed much to the inefficiency of the publication of Leonardo's researches. Great discoverers are often averse to publication. The most famous example is Newton. Fortunately, there was a group of scientists who tactfully persuaded him to publish an account of his discoveries. There was no similar group to overcome Leonardo's hesitations. Failure to publish is not due entirely to the discoverer; it may also be due to the absence of necessary social mechanism.

Newton's *Principia* was published at Halley's expense. The cost of publishing Leonardo's notebooks would have been large. One of the inheritors of the notebooks attempted to arrange for publication, but could not secure sufficient financial aid. It was in fact scarcely practicable without the aid of a scientific society, and one may deduce that the non-publication of his work was chiefly due to the contemporary social organization. If a scientific journal had existed, Leonardo could conveniently have published his researches in a long series of short papers.

The incompleteness of his researches was connected with the absence of organized research laboratories. These were evolved after the factory system had developed, and owe much to it. Disciplined research workers, whose habits had been learned from the factory, would have enabled him to complete his investigations. He would then have expressed the laws of mechanics in the perfect modern form. He could not do this because the systematization of work, and hence of thought, had not proceeded far enough in the workshop of the artist and craftsman. A century later, the statement of the general laws of mechanics became easier, because the organization of work had evolved further towards the factory system, and systematic thinking became more habitual. Leonardo's inability to complete his researches was not due merely to psychological peculiarities. It was perhaps due, even more, to the particular nature of the contemporary mode of craft production, which was very individualistic.

When Leonardo's inventions and discoveries are summarized, they give an impression of extraordinary originality, but when they are seen against the five thousand pages of his notebooks, they appear in more correct relief. The bulk of Leonardo's work was not original. He read widely. Seventy-two medieval and classical authors are quoted by him, and he was familiar with the medieval researches mentioned in Section 43. He had read Albert of Saxony on gravitation, Jordanus on levers, and Roger Bacon on optics and flight. He had read Vitruvius, and sought translations of Archimedes. He was acquainted with Argyropoulos, the Greek scholar who translated Aristotle's *Physica* and *De Coelo* into Italian. He knew the writings of the great architect Alberti, who had improved the *camera obscura*, measured the depth of sea beds, invented a hygrometer and developed marine salvage. He collaborated with the architect Bramante, and met students of Aristotle, Avicenna and Averroes. He was friendly with della Torre, the professor of anatomy at Pavia. He read the works of Alkindi and Alhazen. The mathematician Pacioli, who was appointed to a chair of mathematics at Milan and accompanied him when he left Milan, was one of his best friends. Pacioli wrote the first textbook on arithmetic and algebra that was printed. It was published in 1494, and was based on the thirteenth century treatise by Leonardo of Pisa. Leonardo drew the diagrams for another treatise by Pacioli, which was on proportion. He also knew Toscanelli, who in 1474 had enthusiastically encouraged Columbus to sail to the west.

Leonardo was not a good linguist, and wrote in the style of a Florentine *bourgeois*. He could read Latin, but not Greek. There is little doubt that most of his mechanical inventions were improvements on machines he had seen or heard of, and his scientific discoveries were extensions of the researches of his medieval predecessors. His original contributions appear as a series of normal peaks on a high plateau of old knowledge.

One of the most striking features of his work, viewed as a whole, is its mark of experimental labour, which Leonardo continually praises. When Vasari tried to explain why art had flourished so splendidly in Florence, he ascribed it to three things. 'The first is censure, which is uttered freely and by many seeing that the air of that city makes men's intellects so free by nature, that they do not content themselves, like a flock of sheep, with mediocre works, but ever consider them with regard to the honour of the good and the beautiful, rather than out of respect for the craftsman. The second is that, if a man wishes to live there, he must be industrious, which is naught else than to say that he must continually exercise his intelligence and his judgment, must be ready and adroit in his affairs, and, finally, must know how to make money, seeing that the territory of Florence is not so wide or abundant as to enable her to support at little cost all who live there, as can be done in countries rich enough.

The third, which perchance is no less potent than the others, is an eager desire for glory and honour, which is generated mightily by that air in the men of all professions; and this desire, in all persons of spirit, will not let them stay content with being equal, much less inferior, to those whom they see to be men like themselves, although they may recognize them as masters—nay, it forces them often to desire their own advancement.'

In this explanation it is clear that the social prestige of the craftsman had become established in a mercantile society.

Vasari has described the conditions in Donatello's workshop. 'He was most liberal, gracious and courteous, and more careful for his friends than for himself; nor did he give thought to money, but kept his in a basket suspended by a cord from the ceiling, wherefore all his workmen and friends could take what they needed without saying a word to him.'

The social stigma of manual work, which had so long inhibited experimental science, was decreasing. The new ruling class of bankers headed by the Medici had undermined the feudal castes, but their revolutionary vigour soon declined. They adopted a literary Platonism which was at first inimical to science, but craftsmen, whose work was essential to merchants and exporters of luxuries, had been released from social subjection during the transference of power from feudalists to bankers. The establishment of the social repute of craftsmen created the condition in which experimental science could grow.

51

The Search for Precious Metals

THE evolution of a new type of society based on commerce, money and credit proceeded steadily until the fourteenth century. The organization of the old medieval society weakened as the new system grew. This process of disorganization was accelerated by constant wars, and by the epidemic Black Death, which killed about half of the population in the middle of the fourteenth century. The long wars between England and France had a particularly disturbing effect. They interrupted the trade route through France between Flanders and Italy. The raw cloth, woven from English wool in Flanders, could no longer be safely transported through France to Florence for finishing, and the Italian merchants could not safely travel through France to Flanders to supervise the management of the commercial side of the trade. The Italian and Flemish merchants diverted their route to the Rhine, and converted it into the highway of Europe. This founded the prosperity of the south German towns such as Augsburg and Nürnberg. The dangerous conditions stimulated the use of bills of exchange to avoid the transport of money. The devastation of the French towns weakened the commercial initiative of the French *bourgeoisie*. It looked to the king for help, and he exerted his aid through his own centralized authority. French industry and commerce became organized on national rather than civic lines, and the king's financial advisers acquired great power and riches. These men enabled him to raise funds without consulting any class in society. Jacques Coeur was one of a group which leased the minting of money from Charles VII. He learned the nature of the trade in metals, and in 1432 began to export silver to the East, and import gold, which he sold in France at an enormous profit. He leased the crown's mines in France, and engaged German miners to work them. He lent money to the French court at interests of 12 to 50 per cent. Though he was extortionate, he provided the king with the funds, and established regular taxes on trade, industry and agriculture, which enabled him to create the first regular army in 1439. Coeur left a fortune equivalent to about one million pounds in gold. And yet during his period the total volume of trade in France had not greatly increased. His accumulation was due to a transference of wealth from other members of society to himself.

The merchants in the south German towns profited from the diversion of trade to their cities. In Augsburg at the end of the fourteenth century two merchants named Fugger, who were the sons of a cloth dealer, began to import cotton from Venice, for finishing, and learned the principles of commerce from the Italians. Jacob, one of their sons, became master of the weavers' guild, and had seven sons. One of these sons, named Ulrich, engaged in international finance, and exported works by Dürer to Italy. Ulrich recalled his brother Jacob II from a theological college to work in the business. Jacob II proved the greatest of the family's financiers. Jacob II engaged in mining, and formed a partnership in 1505 with Hochstadter and Welser, to import three cargoes of goods direct to Germany from India, by the route newly discovered by Vasco da Gama.

Hochstadter borrowed the savings of the people and paid the depositors five per cent interest. He speculated with the deposits and became a monopolist of wood, corn, wine, copper and mercury, but ultimately failed.

The commerce between Europe and Asia was conducted by the export of silver, and the increasing scarcity of the precious metal produced a steady fall in prices, which was bad for trade. The Fugger transferred more of their attention to the precious metals to obtain ingots and money as security for lending. They encouraged prospecting and the development of the metal mines in the Tyrol, Bohemia and Hungary, and began to mine silver in 1487. They engaged in copper mining in Hungary ten years later, and cornered the copper market in Venice.

The supply of silver and other metals in Europe was considerably increased by this activity. German capitalists who had acquired wealth in trade entered many departments of the metallurgical industry, and Nürnberg capitalists established iron forges in Thuringia. Europe's supply of gold, and the spices necessary for seasoning food before the discovery of methods of preservation, came through Islam.

The Western Europeans aspired in the early Middle Ages to evade Islam and attack it in the rear by finding a direct route to the Indies, and a Genoese expedition led by the Dorias tried to discover the route around Africa in 1291. Genoese captains discovered the Canaries and Madeira. The mariners who explored the Atlantic coast of Africa returned with new knowledge, which they incorporated in charts free from the fancies of scholars. Their charts, which were simply guides to practice, were neglected by the theoretical scientists of the fifteenth and sixteenth centuries. The Portuguese became interested in the expeditions beyond their shores, and in about 1350 members of the royal house began to collect the new geographical knowledge and study the technique of navigation. One of them acquired an original copy of Marco Polo's narrative, and a valuable map, in Venice.

An expedition was sent from Lisbon in 1341 to search for western islands in the Atlantic. An Italian map was prepared in

1351, which apparently incorporated its results, and gave a remarkably exact forecast of the shape of Africa.

The Portuguese studies were continued by Prince Henry the Navigator. His father was King John I of Portugal and his mother was Philippa, the daughter of John of Gaunt. He was born in 1394 and distinguished himself at the capture of Ceuta from the Moors in 1415. Before King John died in 1433, he exhorted his son to accomplish the efforts to round Cape Bojador. Henry's captains brought the first slaves and gold dust from the Guinea coast beyond Bojador in 1441, and aroused boundless hopes of profit from geographical discovery.

Henry engaged Jacome of Majorca, and Arab and Jewish mathematicians to teach the rules of astronomy and the use of instruments to his navigators. He established an observatory at Sagres, near Cape St. Vincent, to make more accurate tables of the declination of the sun. His caravels or frigates were reputed the best sailing vessels afloat. Their seaworthiness and technical quality were essential for the success of the long coastal voyages.

Henry died in 1460. His work was extended by King John II, who employed his physicians Roderick and Joseph, and Martin of Bohemia as his committee on navigation. They calculated tables of the sun's declination, and improved the astrolabe, which he recommended as more convenient than the cross staff for observing the sun's declination.

The Spanish appointed a committee at this time for the instruction of pilots for voyages to the Indies. A record of their course exists. It was based on Sacrobosco's treatise on the sphere, Regiomontanus's spherical trigonometry and Ptolemy's Almagest; with exercises in the use of instruments and the observation of the movements of the heavenly bodies, and cartography. Regiomontanus's treatise was the first modern exposition of trigonometry, and was written in 1464. In it he used the sine and cosine, and applied algebra to the solution of geometrical problems. He was born at Königsberg in 1436, and his original name was Johannes Müller. He settled at Nürnberg in 1471, which was then a centre of trade and finance. He was invited by the Pope to reform the calendar, and died in 1476, shortly after his arrival in Rome. The methods of determining position at land, which had been developed considerably in antiquity, were applied very slowly to navigation. The difficulty of making observations on a moving platform was great, and the need for scientific navigation in the narrow Mediterranean sea was not imperative. The Muslims and the Chinese could cross the Indian and the China seas by following the monsoons, which blew very steadily in known directions.

When the desire for gold urged mariners to cross the Atlantic, they had to devise improved technique to deal with the more difficult conditions. A Portuguese writer of the fifteenth century said: 'Our discoveries of coasts and islands and mainland were not made without foresight and knowledge. For our sailors went out very well taught, and furnished with instruments and rules of astrology and geometry, things which all mariners and mapmakers must know.'

Christopher Columbus was born in 1446 in Genoa. His father was a wool-comber and he became a weaver before going to sea. As a mariner he visited England, and claimed to have been in Iceland in 1477. He became virtually Spanish and in 1478 married a daughter of one of the officers of Henry the Navigator. He studied his father-in-law's maps, and meditated on the possibility of reaching India by sailing westwards.

He prepared plans for a westward voyage based on the shape of the earth, the theories of geographers, and the rumours of mariners. His conception of the shape of the earth was inaccurate. He wrote in a letter to Isabella in 1498 after his discovery that 'the old Hemisphere has for its centre the isle of Arim, is spherical, but the other [new] Hemisphere has the form of the lower half of a pear. Just one hundred leagues west of the Azores the earth rises at the Equator and the temperature grows keener. The summit is over against the mouth of the Orinoco'.

The conception that the earth comes to a peak at Arim is Muslim. The attribution of the pear-shape implied that the Pacific Ocean would be small. He underestimated the size of the world and overestimated the size of Asia. This defective mixture of Ptolemaic and Muslim geography gave him false evidence for the ease of the western voyage to India.

He had heard that mariners had seen strange wood and canes in the western Atlantic, and if he had visited Iceland he may have heard of Leif Ericson's voyages.

He presented his plan to King John II of Portugal, who was keenly interested in the rival plan to reach India by a coastal route round Africa. The Bishop of Ceuta ingeniously suggested that Columbus's plan should be tried without his knowledge. A ship was accordingly sent to the west in secret, but it returned without success. The plan was offered to the court of France, and to Queen Isabella in 1486. Columbus's hopes were strengthened by Diaz's discovery of the Cape of Good Hope in 1488, and he sent his brother Bartholomew Columbus to England to try to interest Henry VII in his plan, but without success. Bartholomew tried again at the French court, but in the meantime, Ferdinand and Isabella had achieved success in their campaign to expel the Moors, and had time to receive Columbus again. He offered to lead an expedition to the west on the condition that he be appointed to the rank of admiral 'in all those islands, seas and continents that he might discover, the vice-royalty of all he should discover and a tenth of the precious metals discovered within his admiralty'. This condition was rejected, and he left for the court of France; Ferdinand and Isabella immediately changed their minds, and sent a messenger to bring him back, reaching him when he was six miles from Granada. He returned to the camp at Santa Fé, and signed the agreement on April 17, 1492. He sailed on August 3, 1492. On September 13 the western variations of the magnetic needle were observed for the first time. This frightened the crew. On October 12, 1492, one of his sailors sighted the New World.

Columbus collected specimens of slaves and gold, and sailed back to Europe, anchoring off Lisbon on March 4, 1493. Alexander Borgia, the Pope, issued bulls confirming the possession of all lands west of the Azores to Spain, as the African colonies had previously been allotted to Portugal. Columbus founded the West Indian slave trade on February 2, 1494, and established mining camps for gold on Haiti. Like so many men in the new commercial society, he hungered for gold. He said that 'Gold is the greatest earthly good. Its possessor can do as he will, even to despatching souls to paradise'.

He found the natives of Haiti gentle, upright and simple. When they resisted enslavement and fled, he hunted them with bloodhounds. Burney remarked that a 'man-hunt with bloodhounds was an unheard-of atrocity before Christopher Columbus invented it. It is more barbarous than cannibalism'. One third of the population of Haiti died in a few months. He had difficulties with his own men, and seven of them died under his tortures. News of these disorders reached the Spanish court, and an officer named Bobadilla was sent to Haiti to supersede him.

Bobadilla put Columbus and his brothers in chains and sent them back to Spain. Columbus insisted on wearing them throughout the voyage 'as relics and as memorials of the reward of his service'. His son said that he 'saw them always hanging in his cabinets, and he requested that when he died they might be buried with him'.

The Spanish court had, however, been justifiably shocked by his cruelty and avarice. It had been agreed that the seaman who first sighted land should receive a pension of ten thousand pieces of money. Columbus claimed this for himself, although he was not the first.

On his second voyage he suffered from nervous prostration through excessive exertion, and when he returned to Europe, he was wearing the garb of the Franciscans, the friars who took the vow of poverty.

52

Metal Mining

THE increasing demand in the fifteenth century for precious metals for coining, and for silver to pay for imports from the East, stimulated mining. The south German merchants, who were profiting from the Flemish-Italian trade, encouraged prospecting in the German mountains, and by the end of the century the requirements of the Fugger and others had created a mining boom. This was accompanied by a big improvement in technique.

As slavery had declined, one direction of this improvement was in appliances for saving labour.

Small notebooks on mining appeared at the beginning of the sixteenth century. These were written by practical men to refresh the memories of miners and metallurgists, and were not textbooks. The earliest known, *Ein Nutzlich Berg Buchlein*, was probably published at Augsburg in 1505. Another, named the *Probier Buchlein*, was published about 1510. These soon passed through several editions.

The Italian Biringuccio published a work at Venice in 1540, which contains the first printed account of the mercury process for extracting silver, the reverberatory furnace, and the liquation process, by which silver is separated from copper by keeping the temperature of the melt below the melting point of copper and about that of silver. He also appears to be the first to mention cobalt blue and manganese.

These were succeeded by Agricola's great Latin treatise on metals, published in 1556. An admirable annotated English translation of this was made by Herbert C. Hoover and his wife, Lou H. Hoover.

Agricola was born in Saxony, near the Erzgebirge, or Ore Mountains, in 1494. His original German name was Georg Bauer. He graduated at Leipzig University and was appointed to the municipal school at Zwickau, near his home, in 1518. He became principal in 1520, having as one of his assistants Johannes Forster, who collaborated with Luther on the translation of the Bible. He published in the same year his first book, which was a small Latin grammar. He left Zwickau in 1522, to lecture under his friend Mosellanus at Leipzig University. When Mosellanus died in 1524, he went to Italy at the age of thirty to advance his studies, and remained there about three years. Like Copernicus, Harvey and many other Northern European scientists of the period, his scientific inspiration and education was Italian, as he first began to concentrate on science while visiting the universities of Bologna, Venice and Padua. He specialized in medicine and began a revision of Galen. He became acquainted with Erasmus, who had settled at Basel as editor for Froben's press.

He returned to Zwickau in 1526, and in 1527 was chosen town physician at Joachimsthal, a booming mining camp founded only eleven years before, that already had a population of several thousands. Joachimsthal was in the midst of the Erzgebirge mining district, and within fifty miles of Freiberg, Schneeberg, Geyer, Altenberg and Annaberg and other well-known mining towns. When Elizabeth was improving British mining in 1565, she granted a patent to William Humfrey, Paymaster of the Mint, to bring to England 'one Christopher Shutz, an Almain born at St. Annen Berg'; a workman of 'great cunning' in finding and working calamin stone (zinc ore).

Agricola spent all of his time not devoted to medical duties in visiting mines and smelters, and reading all references to mining

8

in Greek and Latin authors. He learned mining technique from skilled miners, and cast one of them, named Bermann, as a speaker in a dialogue he composed on mining and mineralogy. This dialogue was published under the title, *Bermannus* by Froben in 1530, with a laudatory preface by Erasmus.

His mining knowledge now became profitable, for he acquired shares in the God's Gift mine at Albertham, discovered in 1530, which proved very rich. He wrote in 1545 that 'We, as a shareholder, through the goodness of God, have enjoyed the proceeds of this God's Gift since the very time when the mine began first to bestow such riches'.

His income from this mine seems to have enabled him to retire for a time from medicine, for he resigned from his post as town physician of Joachimsthal in 1530, and appears to have spent the whole of his time in visiting and studying mines. He was appointed city physician at Chemnitz in 1533, and resided there until 1555. He continued to have much time for mining. He published the first systematic works on physical geology and on mineralogy and both of these contributions to science were derived from his mining knowledge.

Agricola was a Catholic and retained his views through the Reformation, though he lived in the midst of an enthusiastically Protestant population. The social and religious conceptions of the miners were expressed by Protestantism better than by Catholicism, which was more suited to the southern European agricultural population. In fact, the energy generated by the expanded German mining industry was an important motive of the Reformation.

In spite of his Catholicism, Agricola was promoted by Protestant princes. He was appointed burgomaster of Chemnitz in 1546 by the Elector Maurice of Saxony, who, though a Protestant, collaborated with the Spanish Holy Roman Emperor Charles V against the league of German Protestant princes. The actions of Agricola and Maurice against their respective religious interests were probably due to the overriding influence of economic motives. The chief patrons of the German miners were the Fugger, who were Charles V's financial managers, so there were powerful reasons for finding an accommodation with the Catholic Emperor.

Agricola was a liberal Catholic who shared Erasmus's attitude. Like him, he was tactful, profound and competent, but was following a dwindling minority. He behaved with discretion in religious matters, so the Protestant mine-owners ignored his religious opinions, but made use of his expert knowledge. His views on class-conflicts were acceptable to them, for he writes of mining disputes that 'I always find that the owners who are abused have the best reasons for driving the men from the mines'.

Agricola spent twenty-five years collecting material for his treatise on metals. The text was completed in 1550, but five years passed before the illustrations were completed. These are one of the treasures of knowledge, for they are explanatory pictures of the contemporary methods and equipment of mining. Agricola was aware of the limitations of verbal descriptions of machinery, and he specifically expended so much expense and care on the illustrations for the benefit of posterity, who would be able to see at a glance from them the construction of machines. They have also provided an invaluable picture of the contemporary miners' mode of life, with its social implications. The printing had not been completed when he died in 1555, and the treatise was published in the following year.

Agricola starts his work with an apology for mining. One set of critics say that 'Scarcely one in a hundred who dig metals or other such things derive profits therefrom'. He answers this by asserting that the majority of miners are unskilled. They are men 'weighted with the fetters of large and heavy debts, they have abandoned a business, or desiring to change their occupation, have left the reaping-hook and plough'. As they are ignorant, they do not know how to find good veins and work them efficiently.

He replies to those who condemn the instability of mining compared with agriculture, that the gold and silver mines belonging to the communities of Chemnitz have been worked for eight hundred years, and 'are said to be the most ancient privileges of the inhabitants'. Though he does not wish to 'detract anything from the dignity of agriculture', he explains that 'the yearly profit of a lead mine in comparison with the fruitfulness of the best fields, is three times or at least twice as great'.

To those critics who condemn mining because 'the miners are sometimes killed by the pestilential air which they breathe; sometimes their lungs rot away; sometimes the men perish by being crushed in by masses of rock; sometimes, falling from the ladders into the shafts, they break their arms, legs or necks', and who assert that no compensation is sufficient for such dangers and loss of life, he replies that while he confesses that these occurrences are of exceeding gravity, and moreover, fraught with terror and peril, so that he would consider that metals should not be mined at all if they were frequent, 'things like this rarely happen, and only in so far as workmen are careless'.

He admits that mining destroys good agricultural land and forests and mentions an Italian law for the protection of fertile fields against mining. But he explains that mining is usually prosecuted in mountains unsuited to agriculture.

He admits that iron and bronze have increased the destructiveness of armaments, and gold has stimulated robbery, but the standard of civil life has been raised immeasurably by metal tools and machinery.

Finally, 'the metals are useful to merchants with very great cause, for, as I have stated elsewhere, the use of money which is made from metals is much more convenient to mankind than the old system of exchange of commodities [barter]'.

He then discusses the repute of mining, and whether it is 'honourable employment for respectable people'. He contends that while in the past it might have been dishonourable because miners were convicts and slaves, they are now free men, and 'receive pay, and are engaged like other workmen in the common trades'. Indeed, 'it would not be unseemly for the owners themselves to work with their own hands on the works or ore, especially if they themselves have contributed to the cost of mines'. The mine-owner should sometimes 'undertake actual labour, not thereby demeaning himself, but in order to encourage his workmen by his own diligence'. Manual work has become reputable even for owners.

Some men say 'that the scum of the miners exist wholly by fraud, deceit, and lying. For to speak of nothing else, but only of those deceits which are practised in buying and selling, it is said that they either advertise the veins with false and imaginary praises, so that they can sell the shares in the mines at one-half more than they are worth, or on the contrary, they sometimes detract from the estimate of them so that they can buy shares for a small price.'

As for such frauds, Agricola says, 'I concede it. But can they deceive anyone except a stupid, careless man, unskilled in mining matters?' He says that 'the miners themselves rarely buy or sell shares, but generally they have brokers who buy and sell at such prices as they have been instructed to give or accept'.

He starts his technical discussions with advice on prospecting. Clusters of wooded mountains are the most promising. If there is no forest for the supply of timber, then parts of the mountains near rivers, on which timber may be transported, should be chosen.

Low-lying plains should be avoided, owing to the difficulties of drainage and ventilation, and the construction of shafts. Gently sloping tunnels may be driven into the sides of mountains, and gravitation will assist the drainage of water and the transport of ore from the working places to the exterior. The presence of veins may be detected from the flavour of springs, by the warmth which liquefies hoar frost on their surface, by exhalations, and other signs. He gives a careful and illustrated account of the divining rod, and says that 'it ought to be examined on its own merits'. He explains that the movements of a forked twig are more difficult to follow than those of a straight twig. Cunning persons twist the twig, and simple ones move it involuntarily owing to the peculiar way in which they hold it. For these and other clearly-expressed reasons, a miner 'if he is prudent and skilled in the natural signs, understands that a forked stick is of no use to him'.

He suggests that 'the divining rod passed to the mines from its impure origin with the magicians', who used divining rods and incantations. 'When good men shrank with horror from the incantations and rejected them, the twig was retained by the unsophisticated common miners, and in searching for new veins some traces of these ancient usages remain.'

Robert Boyle, one century later, believed firmly in dowsing. His credulity was no doubt due to less direct experience of mineral prospecting.

Agricola generally shows a very high standard of clarity and material rationalism in explanation, derived from intense study of mining processes. Yet even he believed in mine demons. Hoover remarks that the widespread belief of miners in demons is due to the environment. He says, 'Neither the sea nor the forest so lends itself to the substantiation of the supernatural as does the mine. The dead darkness in which the miners' lamps serve only to distort every shape, the uncanny noises of restless rocks whose support has been undermined, the approach of danger and death without warning, the sudden vanishing or discovery of good fortune, all yield a thousand corroborations to minds long steeped in ignorance and prepared for the miraculous through religious teaching.'

The vertical and horizontal distribution of veins is described, and an account of the strata in the copper-bearing Harz mountains contains the first attempt at stratigraphic distinctions. Twenty strata are identified. The methods of forecasting the directions of strata are explained. These enable a miner to deduce the position of veins on his property from the known positions of veins on his neighbour's properties.

In another work, he gives the first satisfactory explanation of the origin of ore veins. He suggests that they are the sites of cracks and faults in the original rocks, which have been filled by deposition from waters and solutions circulating underground. This is the foundation of modern theory, and was expressed by Agricola more clearly than by any of his successors for two centuries.

He enumerates the sixty species of minerals already recognized, and added twenty new ores to the list. He was the first to assert that antimony and bismuth are metals.

He described the formation of mountains by erosion more fully and clearly than his predecessors.

He gave the first adequate account of the complicated methods and chemistry of assaying. His illustrations of furnaces show the degree of the advance in their design, and the numerous instruments used in conjunction with them. The products of the chemical analyses were weighed in balances protected from draughts, whose beams could be raised by a pulley for the moment of weighing, and then lowered until the pans rested on the base, so that the knife-edges were relieved from pressure when not in use.

Hoover states that his account of the assaying of lead, copper, tin, quicksilver, iron, and bismuth, and his explanation of the corresponding chemistry, is almost wholly new, and he would like to 'call the attention of students of the history of chemistry to the general oversight of these early sixteenth century attempts at analytical chemistry, for in them lie the foundations of that science'.

His illustrations show numerous wheelbarrows. These look as

if they had evolved from a hand-barrow carried by two men, through the substitution of a wheel for one man. The design of the supports for the axle of the wheel still resembles in shape the handles from which they were derived. This shows that the wheelbarrow was designed to increase the amount of ore that could be carried by a given number of labourers, rather than to reduce the amount of labour falling on each man.

A four-wheeled truck, with 'a capacity half as large again as a wheelbarrow' is described with a picture. 'A large blunt pin fixed to the bottom of the truck runs in a groove of a plank in such a way that the truck does not leave the beaten track. Holding the back part with his hands, the carrier pushes out the truck laden with excavated material, and pushes it back again empty. Some people call it a 'dog', because when it moves it makes a noise which seems to them not unlike the bark of a dog. This truck is used when they draw loads out of the longest tunnels, both because it is moved more easily and because a heavier load can be placed in it.'

The first known illustration of a mining truck running on rails was given by Munster in 1550. Wooden railroads had probably been in use in German mines for some time.

Agricola mentions that men worked in seven hour shifts, with one hour for walking in and out of the workings. They were not supposed to work more than one shift in succession, as they were liable to fall asleep on the second shift, or slip off home before the end of the second shift. If they had to work double shifts to deal with flooding or other accidents, 'to prevent themselves falling asleep from the late hours or from fatigue, they lighten their long and arduous labours by singing, which is neither wholly untrained nor unpleasing.'

As Agricola expresses it, the miner is allowed to work two shifts a day in some districts 'because he cannot subsist on the pay of one shift, especially if provisions grow dearer'.

The problems of ventilation are described, and the seasonal variation in the direction of the natural draught through the workings is noted. The inward draught is increased by ventilators that can be turned to catch the wind, and various designs of fans driven by hand, or by water wheels or windmills.

Large bellows are applied to the same purpose. These are also used for sucking bad air out of workings as much as twelve hundred feet long. He says that 'if machines of this kind had not been invented, it would be necessary for miners to drive two tunnels into a mountain' . . . and 'this could not be done without great expense'.

Agricola's descriptions and illustrations of hauling machines and pumps are particularly striking. He said that 'the depths of our shafts forced us to invent hauling machines suitable for them'. He depicts a large reversible winch driven by a water-wheel thirty-six feet in diameter. This machine requires five operations. The wheel contains two parallel sets of buckets with two movable troughs. The direction of rotation is controlled by an operator who raises or lowers the appropriate trough.

He depicts powerful rag-and-chain pumps which would raise water 220 feet and were used at Chemnitz to raise water 660 feet in three stages. These consist of a chain with leather balls spaced at distances of six feet. As the chain is pulled through the pipe, the balls act as primitive pistons and push the water before them. He gives a picture of a heavy chain of dippers rotated through gearing of the clock type, and the end bearing the heavy chain resting on a steel roller bearing.

He described seven species of suction pump. These were made from hollowed trunks, and their pistons were lifted directly by a labourer, or operated by water-wheels through cams.

'The seventh kind of pump, invented ten years ago, which is the most ingenious, durable, and useful of all, can be made without much expense.'

It consisted of a series of suction pumps. The inlet holes of the lowest pump were in the sump at the bottom of the mine, and the pumped water was delivered into an elevated tank. This acted as the sump for the second pump, and so on. All of these pumps were driven simultaneously by a water-wheel through a system of links.

These multiple-stage suction pumps evaded the problem of pressure raised by force pumps. It was possible to design force pumps that would theoretically raise water one thousand feet, but the wooden pipes which would have been used for carrying the water would not have stood the resulting pressures.

Experience vividly proved that water could not be raised more than a limited distance by one suction pump. Agricola says that it may raise water 'as much as twenty-four feet'.

53

The Effects of American Gold

T HE Italian Renaissance drew its strength from the stream of European commerce, which had been created in the main by the Italians, and converged in their country. At the time when the Renaissance was receiving its greatest expression, in the works of Machiavelli and Leonardo da Vinci, the decline of the commercial movement that fed it had already begun, and this was accelerated disastrously by the discovery of America.

The Augsburg merchants had noticed some time before that Atlantic navigation was damaging the Rhine trade route, and one eminent German merchant emigrated to Antwerp in 1474. The Venetian trade was declining, Genoa monopolized the wool trade, and Florence was cultivating a new southern trade with Morocco.

The Portuguese who had opened the direct trade with the East were too busy conducting the long voyages to attend to the distribution of their cargoes. These were reshipped from Lisbon to Antwerp, where the regulations for commerce were exceptionally free. Antwerp had antagonized the older towns by taking some of their trade, and was forced to develop on her own lines in self-defence. As she had long had a fair, she concentrated on this institution and made it continuous, so that the city could specialize in commerce. The older towns, with their intricate medieval regulations aiming at the exploitation of a small fixed market, were unfitted to deal with sudden changes in volume of business, due to the change of trade routes. Antwerp specialized in this commerce that other cities did not like and could not undertake. The German merchants, who had formerly imported goods through their offices in Venice, now established their houses in Antwerp, which became the centre for the distribution of the new ocean trade in gold, silver and spices.

The city became the greatest in Europe, and its large wholesale trade inspired improvements to the technique of commerce, such as the invention of commission business, and the modern bourse. The occasional fair is characteristic of medieval economy. The word 'bourse' comes from the name of the square in Bruges where the Florentine, Genoese and Venetian merchants had offices.

These developments required a new accuracy in standardization, before merchants could confidently deal in goods without seeing them.

America was owned by the Spaniards, and the unprecedented quantities of gold and silver found there belonged to them. The Spanish monarchy engaged the Fugger and other capitalists to manage the business. Gold was collected in the West Indies until 1516. Production in Mexico started in 1522, and in Peru in 1533.

The method of extraction with mercury was introduced in America in 1557. This greatly enhanced the value of the mercury mines at Almaden in Spain. The exploitation of these mines was entrusted to the Fugger, who also formed settlements in Peru, and connections in various parts of America. The Welsers were allowed to mine copper in San Domingo.

The Spanish colonists in America devoted themselves almost entirely to mining. They imported their food from Spain. This produced a rise in the price of food in Spain which hurt the people. The development of manufacture was neglected, and the imports of foreign manufactures, and even food, increased.

A Venetian ambassador reported that 'the Spaniard can only live through France. Hence he must import corn, textiles, paper, books, even to carpenters' work and must himself travel to the ends of the earth for gold to pay for them'.

The transport of the Spanish and Portuguese cargoes from the Indies from Lisbon to Antwerp was undertaken by Dutch fishermen. They returned to the Iberian peninsula with cargoes of salt-fish and cloth.

As the Spanish trusted to their supplies of gold, and neglected to cultivate their own agriculture and industry, they depended almost entirely on foreign countries for high-grade manufactured goods. According to Bodin they exported one hundred million pounds of gold, and two hundred million pounds of silver to France after 1533, which were enormous quantities at that time. It produced a great fall in values, and after the opening of the mines at Potosi in 1545, the fall was catastrophic. Feudal rents lost four-fifths of their value, charitable foundations, hospitals and schools were ruined, and the middle class bought many estates.

As financiers to the Spanish crown, the Fugger drew immense profits. They lent Charles V 310,000 florins to outbid Francis I of France for the title of Holy Roman Emperor. Charles pledged to them the whole of Antwerp, the greatest city in the world, as security.

The Spanish policy collapsed when the supply of gold from America began to contract. It left Spain without any permanent inheritance of improvement and skill. Philip II went bankrupt in 1575 and 1596. This crippled the Fugger, and other German and Genoese bankers, and afterwards the private capitalists no longer looked to the financing of kings' wars and policies for their largest profits.

The Spaniards turned on Antwerp and destroyed it in 1576, but they could not destroy the technical knowledge acquired by the Flemings. This became the foundation of the achievements of Stevin and Huyghens.

The wealth of the Spaniards passed increasingly to the Dutch, who were their bitterest enemies, through the Dutch ascendancy in navigation, technique and commerce.

54

Prince Maurice's Quartermaster General

THE concentration of world commerce in the Netherlands put an excessive burden on the local merchants. Their more intelligent members were impelled to seek quicker and simpler methods of calculation, which would save the labour of clerks, and increase the turnover of business. In response to this situation Simon Stevin, who was born at Bruges in 1548, and died at the Hague in 1620, invented the decimal system. He may have been unaware that he had rediscovered a method of the Babylonians, or that some others had previously made partial use of the idea of a decimal. He wrote the first treatise on decimals. This was published in Flemish and French in 1585. An English translation was made by Robert Norton in 1608. Norton's title is: *Disme: The Art of Tenths or Decimall Arithmetike.* Stevin salutes his public in the preface. He writes: 'To Astronomers, Land-meaters, Measures of Tapistry, Gaudgers, Stereometers in generall, Money-Masters, and to all Marchants, Simon Stevin wisheth health.'

He excuses his presumption in offering such a small book, which contains only a couple of dozen pages, to so many worthy people, asking them to reflect that they should not measure the merit of the book by comparison with their own great worthiness, but by comparison with 'human imbecility'.

'But what of that,' he asks. 'Is this an admirable invention? No certainly: for it is so meane, as that it scant deserveth the name of an invention: for as the countryman by chance sometime findeth a great treasure, without any use of skill or cunning, so hath it happened herein.'

He will 'speake freely of the great use of this invention; I call it great, being greater than any of you expect to come from me . . . the use and effects of which, your selves shall sufficiently witness by your continual experiences.'

He remarks that the world has become 'a Paradise, abounding in some places with such things as the Earth cannot bring forth in other'. This is due to 'computation Astronomicall', which has made world navigation possible by assisting the Pilot to determine the 'elevation of the Equator and of the Pole, by meanes of the declination of the Sunne', and 'to describe the true longitudes, latitudes, situations and distances of places'. 'But as the sweet is never without the sowre,' these things cannot be done without great 'travayle in such computations, namely in the busy multiplications and dimensions which proceed of the sixty progression of degrees, minutes, seconds, thirds &c. And the Surveyor or Land-meater knowth, what great benefite the world receyveth from his science . . . besides, he is not ignorant (especially whose business and imployment is great) of the troublesome multiplication of Roods, Feete and oftentimes of ynches, the one by the other, which not only molesteth, but often also (though he be very well experienced) causeth error, tending to the damage of both parties as also to the discredit of land-meater or surveyor, and so for the Money-masters, Marchants and each one in his business . . .'

Stevin says that his system 'teacheth the easy performance of all reckonings, computations, and accounts, without broken numbers . . .' Through it 'wee gaine the time which is precious', and avoid 'the paines, controversy, error, dammage, and other inconviniences commonly hapning therein'. Nor need it be accepted without test, for unlike certain inventions that 'at first seeme good, which when they come to be practiced, effect nothing of worth, as it often hapneth to the serchers of strong moving, which seeme good in small proofs and modells, when in great, or coming to the effect, they are not worth a Button: whereto we answer, that herein is no such doubt: for experience dayley sheweth the same: namely, by the practize of divers expert Land-meaters of Holland, unto whom we have shewed it, . . . who do use the same to their great contentment . . . The like shall also happen to each of yourselves using the same as they doe: meane while live in all felicity'.

Stevin advocated the introduction of decimal coinages and weights and measures. The invention of positional notation in the canalized region of Babylon and its re-invention in the canalized Holland is notable.

Stevin's decimal system was not adopted quickly. Though it was inspired by commerce, merchants did not immediately see its advantages. It does not follow that because inventions and science have been created through the demands of commerce and industry, they will be immediately adopted by commerce and industry after they have appeared. One of the paradoxes of history is that science is a product of human demands, and yet is not necessarily used when it becomes available. Science has evolved from crafts and industry, and has created new industries, and yet science is still starved by industries and governments. This is not difficult to understand. Inventors and scientists are the extrapolators of the social perspective in which they live. A man such as Stevin satisfied great needs, of which his less penetrating contemporaries were unconscious, or to which they were selfishly indifferent. Society does not advance at the rate of its most gifted members, and yet it determines the general direction in which they go; nor are its most creative activities free from frustration by selfish classes within its own structure.

Stevin started as a merchant's clerk in Antwerp, and owing to his knowledge of mechanics he was appointed director of land and water construction in Holland. Prince Maurice of Orange made him quartermaster general of the Dutch army. He introduced commercial methods of book-keeping into the management of the Dutch finances. This was the first time that the book-keeping of a State was conducted according to *bourgeois* conceptions.

Stevin was the technical organizer of Prince Maurice's successful resistance to Spanish domination. He was the leading military engineer of the day and superintended the construction of the Dutch fortifications. As a patriot he insisted on writing his works in his native language, because 'our own Flemish language is the richest, the most ornate and the most perfect of all languages'.

He constructed a land carriage propelled by sails, which carried twenty-eight people and outstripped galloping horses on the sea-shore.

He published a treatise on mechanics in 1586 in which he deduced the conditions of equilibrium from the behaviour of a continuous chain supported on a smooth triangular beam. It is known that such a ring will not slide round in perpetual motion, and yet the lengths of chain resting on the two supporting slopes may not be equal. Stevin deduced the tensions in networks of strings from the observation of the equilibrium of the chain, and implicitly used the parallelogram of forces. He deduced from pulleys the principle of virtual work.

His studies of hydraulics in connection with canalization led to equally valuable results. He demonstrated the hydrostatic paradox that the pressure on the bottom of a vessel of water does not depend on its shape but on its depth. He noted that one pound of water in a narrow tube could easily exert a pressure of one hundred thousand pounds on a broad piston, and discovered the principle of the hydraulic press. He proved by experiment the existence of upward pressures in liquids, and implicitly used the principle afterwards demonstrated by Pascal, that the pressure at any point in a liquid is the same in all directions. He found the total pressure on the side of a vessel by a method of limits which foreshadowed the integral calculus, and he investigated the equilibrium of floating bodies. He showed that if a floating body was stable, its centre of gravity was in the same vertical line as that of the displaced liquid, and he applied his result to the design of ships.

Finally he was the first to publish a clear experimental refutation of Aristotle's theory of motion. In his work of 1586 he describes an experiment made in collaboration with a brother of the jurist, Hugo Grotius. He writes (in F. S. Taylor's translation): 'The experiment against Aristotle is this: let us take (as I have in company with the learned H. Jan Cornets de Groot, most diligent investigator of Nature's mysteries) two leaden balls, one ten times greater in weight than the other, which allow to fall together from a height of thirty feet upon a board or something from which a sound is clearly given out, and it shall appear that the lightest does not take ten times longer to fall than the heaviest, but that they fall so equally upon the boards that both noises appear as a single sensation of sound. The same, in fact, also occurs with two bodies of equal size but in ten-fold ratio of weight.'

Through such men as Stevin, the commerce and industry of the small country of Holland annexed Spanish trade, and withstood the armies of the Spanish Empire.

55

Galileo Perfects the Method of Physical Science

THE method of research in physical science which has proved so successful during the last three centuries first appears in its complete form in Galileo's *Dialogues Concerning Two New Sciences*. This treatise was published in 1638, when the author was seventy-four years old, and had been collecting and developing his material for fifty years. The two new sciences that he claims to have invented were the theory of the strength of materials and structures, and the theory of motion.

Galileo himself has stated in the first paragraph of his treatise the social activity from which the theory of the strength of materials and structures was derived. He writes: 'The constant activity which you Venetians display in your famous arsenal suggests to the studious mind a large field for investigation, especially that part of the work which involves mechanics; for in this department all types of instruments and machines are constantly being constructed by many artisans, among whom there must be some who, partly by inherited experience and partly by their own observations, have become highly expert and clever in explanation.'

'You are quite right. Indeed, I myself, being curious by nature, frequently visit this place for the mere pleasure of observing the work of those who, on account of their superiority over other artisans, we call "first rank men". Conference with them has often helped me in the investigation of certain effects including not only those which are striking, but also those which are recondite and almost incredible.'

The Venetian arsenal was at least four centuries old in Galileo's time. It had been described three centuries before by Dante. He writes in the twenty-first canto of the *Divine Comedy* that the mariners:

> In the Venetians' arsenal as boils
> Through wintry months tenacious pitch, smear
> Their unsound vessels; for the inclement time
> Sea-faring men restrains, and in that while
> This bark one builds anew, another stops
> The ribs of his that hath made many a voyage,
> One hammers at the prow, one at the poop,
> This shapeth oars, that other cables twirls,
> The mizen one repairs, and mainsail rent,
> So, not by force of fire but art divine
> Boiled here a glutinous thick mass. . . .

Galileo also noticed the activities and experiences of the ship-wrights. He had learned from them that if a large ship was built in the same proportions as a seaworthy small ship, it was liable to collapse on the stocks. Similar experiences were drawn from architecture.

A nail driven into a wall supported very much less than half the weight supported by a nail of twice the thickness.

He showed that these effects follow from the uniformity of the tensile strength of the material, combined with its size and shape. When a big ship was made out of the same material as a small one, the strength of the material in both cases was the same, but the sizes were different. If the two ships had similar shapes, they could only have the same strength if the strengths of the materials of construction were in a due proportion. He derived approximate formulae for the strength of rods, and explained why tubes containing the same amount of material were stronger. He deduced the design of a beam thickening towards the middle, so that the flexion at all points should be the same.

He applied his results to the whole of nature. He explained that the size of trees was limited by the strength of their wood, and the proportions of big trees are different from those of small trees. Human giants are impossible because beings of similar shape made of the same materials would collapse. Whales could grow to larger proportions than land animals because their weight is supported by the water, and not by limbs. He explained that bones are usually hollow because this form gives the maximum strength with lightness. He sketched a bone for a hypothetical giant animal, making the changes in proportion necessary for providing the requisite strength, and showed that it would be impracticably clumsy.

He measured the tensile strength of materials, and discussed its origin. This led him to consider the theory that tensile strength is due to the vacuum. According to Aristotelian ideas, nature abhors a vacuum, so the constituent particles of a solid body might cling together in their anxiety to avoid a vacuum. Galileo measured the force with which very smooth plates in sliding contact stick together, and regarded it as due to the resistance to the vacuum.

He conceived a more satisfactory experiment to measure the resistance to the vacuum. He believed that water is without cohesion and is held together entirely by the resistance to a vacuum. The tensile strength of water is therefore a direct measure of the resistance to the vacuum. He made a smooth cylinder with a well-fitting plug. The plug contained a valve through which the cylinder could be completely filled with water. The cylinder was inverted, and securely suspended, and weights were attached to the plug. He had constructed a column of water which could be submitted to tension by weights like a brass wire. He had shown that all vertical rods suspended from the end break under their own weight, when they exceed a certain length depending on the tensile strength of their material. From this he advanced to the conception of a limiting length of a rod of water suspended from the top of his cylinder. He deduced from common experience with pumps what this length might be.

He describes how he had heard of a pump that 'worked perfectly so long as the water in the cistern stood above a certain level; but below this level the pump failed to work. When I first noticed this phenomenon, I thought the machine was out of order; but the workman whom I called in to repair it told me the defect was not in the pump but in the water which had fallen too low to be raised through such a height; and he added that it was not possible, either by a pump or by any other machine working on the principle of attraction, to lift water a hair's breadth above eighteen cubits'. That is, above twenty-four feet.

He concludes: 'and really is not that thing which is attracted in the pump a column of water, attached at the upper end and stretched more and more until finally a point is reached where it breaks, like a rope, on account of its excessive weight?'

As he believed water was without cohesion, he deduced that the resistance to the vacuum was equivalent to the pressure of a column of water twenty-four feet high.

Brass and other materials could not be held together exclusively by resistance to a vacuum, because the limiting lengths at which they broke under their own weight were vastly greater than the equivalent of twenty-four feet of water. He supposed that their extra strength was due to a viscous binding substance which held the constituent particles together with a force far greater than the resistance to the vacuum.

Galileo demonstrated that the resistance to the vacuum was limited, and equivalent to the pressure of a column of water twenty-four feet high, but he did not identify this resistance with the pressure of the atmosphere. Galileo's figure of twenty-four feet for the resistance of the vacuum is exactly the same as that given by Agricola in 1556, eight years before Galileo was born, for the maximum lift of a suction pump.

Galileo expounded his new science of motion in three sections, dealing with uniform motion, naturally accelerated motion, and the application of the theory of these two types of motion to the analysis of the flight of projectiles. His general theory is expressed in thirty-eight propositions, and various problems, lemmas and scholia cast in a rigid Euclidean form. This extended, systematic theory of motion was new, and also included many ingenious solutions of difficult theorems. But Galileo's philosophical comments were even more striking.

He says: 'It has been observed that missiles and projectiles describe a curved path of some sort; however, no one has pointed out the fact that this path is a parabola. But this and other facts, not few in number or less worth knowing, I have succeeded in proving, and what I consider more important, there have been opened up to this vast and most excellent science, of which my work is merely the beginning, ways and means by which other minds more acute than mine will explore its remote corners.'

The root of his achievement lay in his successful analysis of the motion of falling bodies. He explained his mode of approach. He would ignore discussions of the cause of motion and restrict himself to an investigation of how it occurred.

He says of proposed causes of motion that 'all these fantasies, and others too, ought to be examined; but it is not really worth while. At present it is the purpose of our Author merely to investigate and to demonstrate some of the properties of accelerated motion'. Galileo starts by recalling his observations of technical processes. He refers to the phenomena of pile-driving, which provides an example of a body falling freely.

'Tell me, gentlemen,' he says, 'is it not true that if a block be allowed to fall upon a stake from a height of four cubits and drives it into the earth, say four finger breadths, that falling from a height of two cubits it will drive the stake a much less distance. . . .' The decrease in effect must be due to decrease in speed of impact, and this must be related to the shorter distance of fall. What is this speed? After observing the common facts of falling bodies, a definition, or theory, of the law of increase of speed with fall must be propounded. He says:

'First of all it seems desirable to find and explain a definition best fitting natural phenomena. For anyone may invent an arbitrary type of motion and discuss its properties . . . but we have decided to consider the phenomena of bodies falling with an acceleration such as actually occurs in nature and to make this definition of accelerated motion exhibit the essential features of observed accelerated motion.'

He believes that, after repeated efforts, he has succeeded in doing this. He finds the proof from the consideration 'that experimental results are seen to agree with and exactly correspond with those properties which have been, one after another, demonstrated by us'. He states the intellectual principle which guided his invention of theories for experimental test. He says: 'Finally, in the investigation of naturally accelerated motion we were led, by hand as it were, in following the habit and custom of nature herself, in all her various other processes, to employ only those means which are most common, simple and easy.'

He adopted the principle of simplicity as the guide to the

formulation of theories for experimental test, which Dirac considers the characteristic intellectual method of the Newtonian period in physical science, in contrast with the principle of beauty, which was used to find the theories of relativity and quanta, needed to describe experimental observations of recent physics.

Galileo continues: 'When, therefore, I observe a stone initially at rest falling from an elevated position and continually acquiring new increments of speed, why should I not believe that such increases take place in a manner which is exceedingly simple and rather obvious to everybody?'

The first simple hypothesis that occurred to him was that the speed should be proportional to the distance of fall. He examined the logical implications of this hypothesis before he tested it experimentally, and fallaciously concluded that if it were true, falling would be instantaneous; which is in fact contradictory both to the hypothesis and to observation. Having rejected this hypothesis by fallacious logic, he considered the hypothesis that the speed is proportional to the time of fall. He examined its logical implications and could find none in contradiction to experience, so he proceeded to experimental tests. As he had no satisfactory apparatus for demonstrating directly that the speed is proportional to the time of fall, he deduced that the hypothesis implied that the distance fallen was proportional to the square of the time of fall. Even that was too difficult to test directly, owing to the speed of freely falling bodies, so he devised a method of retarding their rate of fall. He did this by rolling them down an inclined plane. This was made of 'a piece of wooden moulding or scantling about 12 cubits long'. He measured the time taken for a 'hard, smooth, and very round bronze ball' to roll down the plane, and then measured the times for one half, one third, one quarter and other fractions of the length. 'In such experiments, repeated a full hundred times, we always found that the spaces traversed were to each other as the squares of the times, and this was true for all inclinations of the plane.'

The intervals of time were measured by an accurate water clock, which would measure to within one-tenth of a pulse-beat.

The chief feature in this experiment was the systematic test, not by one, but by hundreds of experiments, for many varieties of experimental arrangement.

Galileo deduced the law for free fall from the law for inclined fall with the aid of the assumption that the speed at the end of any fall, vertical or inclined, would be the same if the height of the fall were the same.

He proved by logic and experiment that this assumption was true. If it were untrue, then a body could raise itself by its own weight. We must believe that if the motion of a body is suddenly reversed, the body will return to its original position. Now what would happen if two inclines of equal height but different slope were placed together, so that a body could be rolled down them like a switch-back? If the body were rolled down the slope which gave it the higher speed, it would be shunted up the other slope with a greater speed than it could have gained by falling down that slope. Hence it would rise higher than its original height.

In addition to this logical proof, Galileo provided an experimental proof. He fastened the string of a pendulum to a nail in a wall. He displaced the bob so that it could swing freely along the face of the wall, and noted that it always rose to the same height at each end of the swing. He then fixed a pin in the wall, vertically below the supporting nail, so that the string was caught half way through the swing. He noted that even then, the bob rose to the same height at the opposite end of its swing. The same result was obtained when the pin was placed at various points on the vertical line beneath the nail, so long as it was above the level to which the bob was swinging. Galileo explained that the various arcs traversed by the bob were equivalent to combinations of frictionless inclined planes, so the experiment proved that all combinations of such planes restored the fallen body exactly to the level from which it had fallen, and neither above nor below. Hence the speed at the end of a fall down any inclined plane depends only on the height.

Galileo deduced the law of uniform motion as the limiting case of accelerated motion. Suppose a body ran down an inclined plane and was shunted up a rising plane. Its deceleration up the rising plane would be the less the smaller the slope, and if the slope were zero, and the plane horizontal, the deceleration would be zero. Thus the body would continue for ever at uniform speed.

Galileo then states the two laws of motion in his analysis of the trajectory of a projectile, and compounds two velocities. He says:

'Imagine any particle projected along a horizontal plane without friction, then we know from what has been more fully explained in the preceding pages, that this particle will move along this same plane with a motion which is uniform and perpetual, provided the plane has no limits. But if the plane is limited and elevated, then the moving particle, which we imagine to be a heavy one, will on passing over the edge of the plane acquire, in addition to its previous uniform and perpetual motion, a downward propensity due to its own weight; so that the resulting motion, which I call projection, is compounded of one which is uniform and horizontal and of another which is vertical and naturally accelerated. We now proceed to demonstrate some of its properties. . . .'

He proves that the path of the particle must be parabolic, and deduces 45° as the elevation for the maximum range, and says that 'from accounts given by gunners, I was already aware of the fact that in the use of cannon and mortars, the maximum range, that is the one in which the shot goes farthest, is obtained when the elevation is 45°'.

He then illustrates how the establishment of a correct theory enables the scientist to discover facts previously unknown. He deduced from the properties of the parabolic path 'what has perhaps never been before observed in experience, namely, that of other shots those that exceed or fall short of 45° by equal amounts have equal ranges'.

Galileo had given a complete exposition of the nature and manipulation of the method of scientific research, and he had evolved it primarily from the analysis of facts provided by shipwrights, builders, gunners, and other technicians; and from the work of predecessors who had derived their knowledge from similar sources.

56

Galileo Opens the Window of the Universe

GALILEO achieved far more fame during his life by his contributions to astronomy than by his perfection of scientific method. He was born in Pisa, and was the son of a musician whose family had been prominent in Florence for centuries, until the Florentine Republic was overthrown. His father was a musician who considered himself a nobleman, but was impoverished. He earned little from music, so he desired his son to enter the wool trade. As Galileo early showed intellectual ability, his prospective career was changed to medicine. He was given a thorough literary education in a Benedictine monastery and sent to study at the University of Pisa. He transferred his interest to physical science, but his first discovery was due to his combination of medical and physical interests. He noted the constancy of the time of oscillation of the pendulum, by comparing it with his pulse, and applied it to the measurement of the pulse. At the end of his life he prepared a design for a pendulum clock.

He investigated the centre of gravity of solid bodies on the suggestion of the Marquis Guidubaldo, who was an enthusiastic mathematician. By Guidubaldo's aid, and his own strenuous soliciting, he was appointed professor of mathematics at Pisa with an annual salary equivalent to £13. He was not comfortable at Pisa and, in 1592, secured the chair of mathematics at Padua, again through Guidubaldo, who exerted his influence with the Venetian senate, which controlled the university. His annual salary was fixed at the equivalent of £32. Lectures on artillery and fortifications were an important part of his professional duties. He wrote a treatise on fortification, and invented the proportional compasses or sector, which were of great value to military engineers. The Venetian senate made much use of Galileo's knowledge of engineering for its defensive and offensive armaments. Owing to this, he received an invitation in 1604 from the Duke of Mantua to become his military engineer.

Galileo made many of his investigations in mechanics while he was at Padua. He organized the manufacture of the instruments he had invented, and lectured on their use.

Audiences of two thousand persons attended his lectures, and his fame spread. Kepler probably sent him a copy of his *Prodromus Dissertationum Cosmographicum*, as a letter of thanks from Galileo exists. This was written in 1597, and in it Galileo says: 'Many years ago I became a convert to the opinions of Copernicus, and by that theory have succeeded in fully explaining many phenomena, which on the contrary hypothesis are altogether inexplicable. I have drawn up many arguments and confutations of the opposite opinions, which however, I have not hitherto dared to publish, fearful of meeting the same fate as our master Copernicus, who, although he has earned for himself immortal fame amongst a few, yet amongst the greater number appears as only worthy of hooting and derision; so great is the number of fools. I should indeed dare to bring forward my speculations if there were many like you; but since there are not, I shrink from a subject of this description.' Kepler replied that he should continue his speculations and publish in Germany his defence of the Copernican theory. Galileo did not follow this advice, nor in later years did he show any appreciation of Kepler's discoveries of the laws of planetary motion.

Galileo heard a rumour in 1608 that some Dutchmen had invented an instrument with two lenses which magnified distant objects.

The printing of books, which was a fairly new industry in Europe, had grown with exceptional rapidity in Holland, owing to the greater freedom of opinion. This was accompanied by an increase in the number of readers, and in the demand for spectacles. Dutch opticians created a flourishing lens industry to meet this need. Casual experiments with combinations of lenses were made, and two mechanics at Middelburg, Jansen and Lippershey, discovered at some time between 1581 and 1608, that lenses could be combined to form microscopes and telescopes. Lippershey received a secret order from the Dutch government on October 2, 1608, for a telescope.

Galileo meditated on the rumour. He soon worked out the optical principles of the instruments, and presently made a telescope that would magnify more than ten diameters.

He was commanded to show it to the Doge of Venice. He has left a description of one of his demonstrations to the nobility. He said:

'Many gentlemen and senators, even the oldest, have ascended at various times the highest bell-towers in Venice, to spy out ships at sea making sail for the mouth of the harbour, and have seen them clearly, though without my telescope, they would have been invisible for more than two hours . . . Perceiving of what great utility such an instrument would prove in naval and military operations, and seeing that his Serenity greatly desired to possess it, I resolved to go to the palace and present it to the Doge as a free gift.'

Galileo did this, and his professorship at Padua, which he had held for seventeen years, was made a life appointment and his annual salary was raised to 1,000 florins.

Bernal has quoted Galileo's letter to the Doge in which he remarked that the new instrument was of inestimable benefit to every maritime and terrestrial affair. 'One is able to discover enemy sails and fleets at a distance greater than customary, so that we can discover him [the enemy] two hours or more before he discovers us, and by distinguishing the number and quality of the vessels, judge of his force whether to set out to chase him, or to fight; or to run away. . . . Also on land can one look into the squares, buildings, and defences of the enemy.'

He directed his instrument to the heavens, and was astounded by his observations. He had found that he had, as it were, opened a window into the outer universe. Without the telescope, the heavens had appeared like a surface ornamented by stars. With it, the vast depth of the universe was revealed. The three-dimensional outer universe had been a mathematical deduction; now the third dimension was revealed in observation.

'Being infinitely amazed thereat,' he wrote to Vinta, the secretary of the Grand Duke of Tuscany, 'so do I give infinite thanks to God, who has been pleased to make me the first observer of marvellous things, unrevealed to bygone ages.' He had discovered the ridges on the moon, and estimated their height from the length of their shadows. He had found that the Milky Way consisted of myriads of stars, and that the number of fixed stars was at least ten times as many as those visible to the naked eye. He presently saw the discs of the planets for the first time, and noted the phases of Venus. He discovered independently sun spots, and the rotation of the sun.

'But the greatest marvel of all,' he said, 'is the discovery I have made of four new planets.' These were satellites of Jupiter.

Galileo had been seeking before these events to secure an invitation to the Medicean court at Florence. In spite of his fame and activity in Padua, he wished to return to Tuscany. He accepted the permanent appointment to the Paduan chair only because the Florentine negotiations were stationary, and, as he described it, 'Fortune's wings are swift, but those of Hope are drooping.'

His pupil, Prince Cosimo de' Medici had recently inherited the dukedom, so Galileo started his discreet soundings. Before he had constructed his telescope, he wrote confidentially to personages at Florence that 'having now laboured for twenty years, and these the best years of my life, in dealing out, so to speak, by retail, to all who chose to ask, that small portion of talent, which, through God and my own labour, I have gained in my profession; my desire would be, to possess such rest and leisure as to be able to conclude three great works which I have in hand, and to publish them before I die.'

He did not believe that he could obtain more leisure than he possessed at Padua, if he had to continue to lecture to support his family.

'It is impossible to obtain from a Republic, however splendid and generous, a stipend without duties attached to it; for to have anything from the public one must work for the public, and as long as I am capable of lecturing and writing, the Republic cannot exempt me from this duty, while I enjoy the emolument. In short, I have no hope of enjoying such ease and leisure as are necessary to me, except in the service of an absolute prince.'

Soon after writing this letter, he made the astronomical discoveries, and decided to name the satellites of Jupiter the Medicean stars. Keen interest in him was now aroused in Florence, and he was offered an appointment without routine duties at an annual salary equivalent to £200. He wrote that he proposed to earn his emolument by writing. The profusion of his ideas did him harm and many of them could be of use only to princes who 'alone make war', and 'erect fortresses'. The works he wished to finish were 'two books on the system of the universe; an immense work full of philosophy, astronomy, and geometry, three books on locomotion, a science entirely new, no one, either ancient or modern, having discovered any of the marvellous accidents which I demonstrate in natural and violent motion'.

He would write three volumes on statics which would contain four times as much as was known to his predecessors.

'I have also various treatises on natural subjects, on sound and speech, on sight and colours, on the tide, on the composition of continuous quantity, on the motions of animals, and others; besides, I have also an idea of writing some books on the military art, giving not only a model of a soldier, but teaching with very exact rules, all which it is his duty to know that depends on mathematics, as for instance, the knowledge of encampment, drawing up battalions, fortifications, assaults, planning, surveying, the knowledge of artillery, the use of various instruments, etc.'

He wishes to prepare a new edition of his tract on the sector, and mentions that several thousands of the instrument have been sold. He also wishes to work out the periods of Jupiter's satellites. Finally, he wishes to be named philosopher, besides mathematician to the Duke, because he professed 'to have studied a greater number of years in philosophy than months in pure mathematics'.

Galileo left the Republic of Venice for the despotism of Florence in 1610. He became the intellectual ornament of the Medicean court. He visited Rome in 1611 under the auspices of the Grand Duke, and exhibited his telescopes to the ecclesiastical dignitaries, amid great applause.

The discovery of Jupiter's moons provided strong evidence for the Copernican theory. If Jupiter was the centre of a miniature planetary system, then it seemed by analogy that the great luminary of the sun should also be the centre of its planetary system.

The arguments for and against the Copernican system were discussed in high excitement at many places, including the Grand Ducal court. Scientists were invited to the Grand Ducal table to assist in the discussions. Castelli was one of these. He supported the Copernican theory enthusiastically. The Grand Duchess was keenly interested, but feared the theory was heretical. Castelli wrote to Galileo describing his discussions, and Galileo, happy at the august interest, replied with incautious enthusiasm in a letter written in December, 1613. He wrote that the Grand Duchess had spoken well when she said that the Holy Scriptures could not err, and 'that the decrees therein contained are absolutely inviolable'. But he would have added that 'though Scripture cannot err, its expounders and interpreters are liable to err in many ways'. The most grave errors arise from literal interpretation. If this is accepted, God would have limbs and passions, forgetfulness and lack of foresight. Many propositions in the Scriptures are accommodated to the capacity of the vulgar. But 'for those few who merit to be separated from the plebeian crowd, it is necessary for wise expositors to produce the true meaning'. This is especially necessary in the interpretation of matters involving mathematics. Holy Scripture and nature are both emanations from the Divine word. The first has to be accommodated to the vulgar. 'But Nature being on the contrary inexorable and immutable, and caring not one jot whether her secret reasons and modes of operation be above or below the capacity of men's understanding, it appears that, as she never transgresses her own laws, those natural effects which the experience of the senses places before our eyes, or which we infer from adequate demonstration, are in no wise to be revoked because of certain passages of Scripture.'

When an apparent discordance between Scripture and observation occurs, it is the business of wise expounders to investigate whether the conventional interpretation is correct. He believes that it would be 'prudent if men were forbidden to employ passages of Scripture for the purpose of sustaining what our senses or demonstrated proof may manifest to the contrary. Who can set bounds to the mind of man? Who dares assert that he already knows all that in this universe is knowable?'

He believes that the 'articles concerning salvation and the stability of the faith' are the core of religion, and that no unnecessary assertions about the world should be added to them, even by persons who, though they may be divinely inspired, yet we see clearly that they are destitute of the intelligence necessary, not merely to disprove, but to understand those demonstrations by which scientific conclusions are confirmed. . . .'

The Dominicans secured a copy of this letter, and forwarded it to the Inquisition. Galileo travelled to Rome, with a personal letter of introduction from the Grand Duke to one of the cardinals, to define his doctrine. In spite of his powerful arguments and influence, he was not exculpated. He was admonished, and instructed not to promulgate the Copernican theory by writing or in any other way. Copernicus's treatise, and all other works supporting his theory were banned.

Galileo returned to Florence and continued his preparation of the *Dialogues on the Two Systems of the World*.

In 1618 three notable comets appeared. These inspired a tract on comets, written by a pupil under Galileo's supervision. It contained strictures on the views of the Jesuit Grassi and increased the order's enmity towards Galileo.

Cardinal Barberini, who had been one of Galileo's most sympathetic supporters among the prelates, was elected Pope in 1623. Galileo and his friends hoped he would remove the prohibition against the Copernican theory. He visited the new Pope in 1624 and was very well received.

He continued writing his *Dialogues on the Two Systems*, and

presently, in 1630, these were finished. He had now to secure a
licence from the Pope for their publication. He travelled to Rome
in May, and was informed that the Pope would give the permission if it were plainly stated in the book that the Copernican
theory was merely a hypothesis, and if the book were concluded
with an argument against the theory composed by the Pope
himself. Galileo agreed, and the manuscript was returned to him
with the licence. The work was published in Florence in January
1632.

57

Science and Freedom

THE Inquisition suddenly ordered in August 1632 the
sequestration of all copies of the *Dialogues on the Two
Systems of the World.*

Galileo was astonished, and complained to the Grand Duke of
Tuscany, who instructed Niccolini, his ambassador in Rome, to
express his surprise, and register a protest. The Pope snubbed
Niccolini, and desired him to inform the Grand Duke that he
expected help and not hindrance from him in matters concerning
theology.

Galileo was summoned to the office of the Inquisition for
examination. After delays, he arrived in Rome in 1633. His
affairs were conducted with great skill by Niccolini, who was one
of the few among Galileo's friends who understood the Roman
political currents. The ambassador was supporting the reputation
of a great countryman, and was unwilling to see him degraded.

Galileo was frail, and sixty-nine years old, and knew he was
intellectually in the right. He had a lively temperament, and had
difficulty in restraining it. Niccolini advised him to be completely
submissive and recommended him to agree even to deny the
Earth's motion. He reported that 'this advice of mine has
afflicted him extremely: so much so, that ever since yesterday he
has been in such a state of prostration that I have my fears for
his life'.

The Inquisition felt that there were already too many independent thinkers in Florence. Besides this political opposition to Florence, the Pope's personal feelings had been ruffled. He had been informed that his argument had been put into the mouth of Simplicio, the Aristotelian butt in the *Dialogues*. He was also convinced that Galileo's doctrine was bad, and that Galileo certainly believed his own doctrine.

Niccolini continued his entreaties, but the Pope told him he must do what was necessary for the furtherance of the Christian faith.

Galileo was treated by the Inquisition with a consideration unexampled in its history. He was allowed at first to stay with Niccolini, instead of being cast, like all former prisoners, including princes, prelates and noblemen, into the dungeons.

Even when he was removed to the Office for questioning, he was not put in the dungeons, but was accommodated in the officers' quarters. But the separation from his friends upset him, and he was very miserable.

The Commission of Cardinals that conducted the examinations was apparently not unsympathetic, and interceded with the Pope for his release from the Office. The Pope consented to a conditional release, and he was allowed to return to Niccolini's house.

When Galileo was examined for the third time, he discovered that he had misunderstood the admonishment of 1616. He had not realized that it limited his liberty to write, and he had transgressed this limitation.

He had believed he would be liberated shortly, and now he found himself 'vehemently suspected of heresy', and condemned. He was menaced with torture, and whether or not it was to be applied, he expected it, for he replied:

'I am in your hands; do as you please with me.' The minute of the examination states: 'And as nothing more could be got from him he was remanded.'

He was commanded to abjure his heresies, which he did. He was sentenced to imprisonment during the pleasure of the Inquisition, and was detained at Siena, and then in his own house at Arcetri.

None of the documents relating to the trial of Galileo is officially ratified by the Pope. The decree of 1616 and the sentence of 1633 are merely the fallible judgment of an assembly of cardinals.

Galileo's friends burned as many of his private papers as they could find after his condemnation. He was continually watched by spies. When he was first summoned to Rome he became despondent and wrote that he detested the remembrance of all the time he had consumed in study. After the trial, he said that he had lost interest in research. 'The pleasure which I have taken hitherto in making observation on new phenomena are almost entirely gone.'

He wrote in 1636 to Peiresc, the French ambassador at Rome, who had attempted to assist him: 'I have said, my lord, that I hope for no alleviation; and this is because I have committed no crime. If I had erred, I might hope to obtain grace and pardon; for the transgressions of the subject are the means by which the prince finds occasion for the exercise of mercy and indulgence. Wherefore, when a man is wrongly condemned to punishment, it becomes necessary for his judges to use the greater severity, in order to cover their own misapplication of the law.'

According to his lifelong habit, he continued to work, though without enthusiasm. His greatest achievement, the *Dialogues on Two New Sciences*, were finished in 1636, and published in 1638.

He discovered the librations of the moon in 1637, just before he went blind. He wrote of this: 'I have observed a most marvellous appearance on the surface of the Moon. Though she has been looked at such millions of times by such millions of men, I do not find that any have observed the slightest alteration in her surface, but that exactly the same side has always been supposed to be represented to our eyes. Now I find that such is not the case, but on the contrary that she changes her aspect, as one who, having his full face turned towards us, should move it sideways, first to the right and then to the left, or should raise and then lower it, and lastly incline it, first to the right and then to the left.'

He noted that these variations were daily, monthly and yearly.

Galileo's condition at that time was noticed by Milton, who visited him about 1638, and referred to the occasion in his pamphlet *Areopagitica*, on the freedom of the press. He wrote:

'I could recount what I have seen and heard in other countries, where this kind of inquisition tyrannizes, where I have sat among their learned men, for that honour I had, and bin counted happy to be born in such a place of Philosophic Freedom, as they suppos'd England was, while themselves did nothing but bemoan the servil condition into which Lerning amongst them was brought; that this it was which had dampt the glory of Italian wits; that nothing had been there writt'n now these many years but flattery and fustian. There it was that I found and visited the famous Galileo, grown old, a prisner to the Inquisition, for thinking in Astronomy otherwise than the Franciscan and Dominican Licencers thought.'

Galileo still bargained with the powers for the sale of his method of determining longitudes at sea from Jupiter's satellites.

Bernal has drawn attention to an interesting feature of this bargaining. In 1616 he had offered it to the King of Spain at the price of a grandeeship and a large sum of money, with the remark that he has 'neither ports nor islands, nor provinces nor realms, nor even ships to go visiting there. It is the enterprise for a great monarch . . . No other crown in the world today is more fit for that than Spain'. His offer was not accepted. Then in 1637 he offered it to the States-General of Holland. He said: 'I have chosen to present it to these illustrious gentlemen, rather than to some absolute prince, because when the prince alone be not capable of understanding this machine, as almost always happens, having to rely on the advice of others, very often not very intelligent . . .' The matter is not understood and the offer rejected. 'But in a republic, when the deliberations depend on the opinion of many, a small number and even a single one of the powerful rulers, moderately knowledgeable about the proposed matter, may give the other courage to lend their consent.' But the States-General also failed to accept his offer. The method was not, in fact, as practicable as Galileo believed.

Galileo became head of his family in 1591. His brother and his own son were wastrels, and he had to pay his sister's dowry. He was never married, but had three children by a Venetian woman of lower social class. He secured a special dispensation from the Church to put his two daughters into a nunnery before they were sixteen years of age. He persuaded the Grand Duke of Tuscany to legitimize his son.

Though Galileo had a strong sense of family duty, he appeared to have no sense of political duty. He did not foresee that his departure from the relative freedom of the Republic of Venice for the deceptive attractions of his own country, and payment without duties under an absolute prince, would ruin his happiness and self-respect.

The Papacy feared to attack Venice because the Venetians astutely flirted with the Protestant powers, and if menaced might have introduced the Reformation into Italy.

If Galileo had had political understanding, he would have remained there, or at least have returned there in 1616, after the first admonishment by the Inquisition. He did not perceive that the Medicean Grand Dukes could not protect him in the last resort, because they were politically bound with the Papacy. Nor did he understand that his conflict with the Inquisition was a social and political, and not an intellectual matter. The disorder of the Papacy, which had culminated in the pontificate of the Borgia, had led to reorganization. The Commission of Cardinals in 1537 had reported on its condition, and the order of the Jesuits was in process of formation. The Inquisition was renewed in 1542, and in 1559 the Index Expurgatorious was begun. These were the weapons of the Counter-Reformation.

Giordano Bruno was burned in Rome in 1600, for supporting the Copernican theory, and other heresies, when Galileo had already achieved fame. Galileo had grown up in Tuscany under Francesco de' Medici, who inherited the dukedom in 1574. One hundred and sixty-eight murders occurred in Florence during the first eighteen months of his reign.

Italian society was declining through the transfer of power to the Atlantic countries. Its governing class, which had risen to power as merchants in the Middle Ages, had declined into a corrupt leisured class, whose economic roots were decaying. It assisted the Spaniards in the creation of the Counter-Reformation and the renewed Inquisition, as an effort to preserve its political power by force. The Spaniards did not need freedom, because they could obtain power by importing gold. Their North European opponents could obtain gold only by labour and invention. They were therefore in favour of the freedom conducive to industry and invention.

Galileo, who had grown up in a decaying society, did not understand that his independent intellectual attitude, which had been appropriate to a rising commercial class struggling for power against feudalism two centuries earlier, was no longer serviceable to the leisured class into which the successors of the earlier Italian merchants had been transformed. His attitude was appropriate only to merchants and individualists of Northern Europe, who were the new aspirants for power. He did not see

9

this. He did not understand that service under the Medicean prince was bondage.

Milton has described such a situation in his own moral terminology:

> But what more oft in nations grown corrupt
> And by their vices brought to servitude
> Than to love bondage more than liberty,
> Bondage with ease, than strenuous liberty.

Galileo believed that science could be separated entirely from religion, and also from politics and commerce. He seemed to believe that its economic value, of which he was keenly aware, was accidental.

Galileo's views have been typical for scientists during the last three centuries, not only on scientific method, but also on the relations between science, religion and politics.

The position in which Galileo's views placed him has been described. Up to 1939 nearly all scientists shared such views, and then many of them found themselves in a similar position. The majority of scientists still believed that there is no necessary connection between science, religion and politics, and many trusted statesmen compromised with those who had once more revived the Inquisition for the preservation of a declining governing class.

Those who revived the Inquisition, like the Pope in Galileo's time, had a better understanding of politics, and realized that in crises the possession of power is more important than the cultivation of intellectual freedom.

The progressive class in Western Europe in Galileo's time also understood very well that force must be used to preserve and extend its power. The Elizabethans fought like bandits, and Milton's friends also knew how to use force in the service of progress.

The danger and value of such action depends on whether it is used on behalf of a reactionary or a progressive governing class.

Cromwell's dictatorship limited the power of the old landed aristocracy, with its hankering for absolute monarchy and papism. He restricted freedom to free a new governing class. Because this class was rising, it needed freedom and free thought, and when it secured power, it raised them to a degree not hitherto seen in the world. The distinction between the use of force for the preservation of a declining class or in support of a rising class is of the utmost importance.

The failure to make this distinction exacerbated those who used force in the interests of progress. The greatest service that can be rendered to science in a period of crisis is to assist the struggle of the progressive class for power, so that this can be completed with as little trouble, and as quickly as possible.

Milton's protest against inquisitory methods was correct, but the determination of the Cromwellians to win was more correct.

Freedom in itself has little meaning. It exists in the main only in so far as it is in the interest of some powerful social class. As Pirenne has remarked, Liberty is the device under which the commercial and industrial classes have fought for power. Freedom is advantageous to a rising class because they are on its side, so that knowledge of them strengthens its cause. During progressive periods, it is convenient to detach the conception of freedom from the prevailing social conditions, and advocate its cultivation as an independent good. But this abbreviation of definition is permissible only when conditions are improving. The advocacy of the extension of freedom after the improvement has ended may be disastrous. Freedom was extended as good in itself in the Weimar Republic, while the social system was decaying. It temporarily assisted the growth of science, but at the same time provided the freedom under which the protagonists of a decaying system could seize political power.

On the whole, freedom in the Weimar Republic did more harm than good, owing to the social conditions of the period. Freedom in Ionia, after emancipation from Babylonian and Egyptian theological domination, and freedom in the Atlantic countries after the limitation of the power of the landowners, was beneficial. Freedom and control are social techniques of the same sort, but contrary direction. Sometimes one, and sometimes the other, and sometimes a combination of both, as under Cromwell, is justified. Freedom is beneficial to science when it provides opportunity to a rising class. Control is beneficial to science when it protects a rising class. Freedom is inimical to science when it assists reactionary elements to gain power, and control is inimical to science when it preserves the power of a declining class. The definition of a progressive class depends on political understanding and judgment. If the scientist wishes to enjoy freedom, he must be able to choose the progressive side. For this reason the scientist must study politics.

Galileo's career is a classical demonstration of what happens when a scientist ignores politics, for his conflict with the Church was in essence a political affair. He trusts to his personal ability in intellectual persuasion, and to the political protection of reactionary powers, instead of seeking the protection of progressive powers, who will fight for him as well as argue, if necessary.

58

Freedom in the Interest of Skill

THE Spaniards believed that the gold of America would enable them to conquer the world. They already ruled Italy, Austria and the Netherlands, besides their own country, and the New World belonged to them.

The outlook for England, with her small population of six million, and its backward development, was bad. Elizabeth, Cecil, and their colleagues planned to improve it. British industry and commerce could not supply the materials for the new warfare.

Saltpetre, sulphur and metals came from Catholic ports under Spanish influence, and were not sold freely to Protestant customers.

Mining in England was undeveloped, and iron and copper could not be easily bought abroad. Alum, which was of importance to the textile trade, came from Ischia, which belonged to the Pope.

The plan of development adopted by Elizabeth and Cecil had features which foreshadowed the plans of the government of the Soviet Union in recent times. They founded industries to provide munitions, including metal mining, brass-founding, and wire-drawing. They engaged the Augsburg capitalists as technical advisers to supervise these innovations.

As Cunningham writes: 'Most important of all was the skill of

German engineers; their methods of pumping water were introduced, and rendered mining possible where it had never been
practiced before.'

Copper mines were started at Keswick, and lead mines were
operated at Colbeck in 1564 by German miners. But no capital
for these developments was borrowed from the Augsburg
capitalists. It was subscribed within the country.

Agriculture was encouraged for military reasons, so that the
country could supply strong, well-nourished soldiers. The
fisheries were encouraged by compelling the population to eat
fish on three days in the week, so that large numbers of skilled
seamen would be available to man ships of war.

Capitalists were encouraged to found glass, paper, starch and
soap industries by the grant of monopolies.

While Cecil refused to allow the import of foreign capital, he
encouraged the import of skilled refugees.

Freedom was encouraged, not so much as an abstract good,
but as a means of increasing the national capital of industrial
skill. By it, large numbers of skilled workers who had been persecuted in the Spanish Netherlands, Greece, Italy and Spain, were
attracted to England. In fact, the England of Elizabeth, with its
population of six million, absorbed more refugees than the
England of the 1930s, with its population of forty-five million.
The English people disliked these refugees, but were compelled
by Cecil to absorb them. Their presence was advantageous to the
governing class.

As a result of this policy, the English people and industry at
the end of Elizabeth's reign were relatively prosperous, and the
crown was relatively poor; whereas in Spain the crown was rich
and the people and industry poor. Unlike Spain, England was
able to supply her colonies with food and cloth without disor-
ganizing her economy, and she had enough sailors, soldiers and
munitions to resist aggression.

Holland increased her technical development still further, and
for a century led Europe. The skill of her artisans gave her
flexibility in adopting profitable new processes.

While the English crown developed industry by the encouragement of private capitalists, the French crown directly created new
industries. The English policy strengthened the middle classes
and encouraged their initiative, but the French policy created
uniformity of organization and opinion, which gave corporative

strength, but hindered private initiative, and led to the absolute state of Louis XIV.

The economies of each country were unified, and completed the coalescence of their peoples and cities into nations.

History became the economic and political affairs of nations, and the state became supreme in politics when capitalism became supreme in wholesale trade.

The economic change transformed the *bourgeoisie's* outlook. As Pirenne remarks, the *bourgeois* of the Middle Ages was privileged by law, and the city was the centre of his life, but the modern *bourgeois* was privileged by virtue of his economic situation, and the city is merely his business centre and residence, while his interests are spread through the world.

This is the chief cause of the unsatisfactory nature of modern urban life.

59

To the Effecting of All Things Possible

THE rapid increase in wealth and possibilities brought by the expansion of commerce and the discovery of the New World inspired optimism. Those classes that benefited most from the developments were the most optimistic. Their hopes were expressed by many writers. George Best, who was Martin Frobisher's lieutenant on two of his voyages, published *A True Discourse of the Late Voyages of Discoverie* in 1578, in which he praised the inventions that made these achievements possible, and forecast from the increasing rate of invention and discovery an increase in human command over the earth. In particular, he gave evidence that the tropics and arctic regions were not uninhabitable by man, and might become a new human dominion. He believed that his 'time only may rightely bee called the liberall and flourishing age', because science and technique, 'especially now in these later dayes', has been so much improved 'by continuall practise, and the exercising of good wittes', that the 'pleasure and profite' of the world is rapidly increasing. He instanced printing, the compass, and navigation as inventions that had transformed human knowledge, and he believed others equally potent could be found.

The most famous exponent of the new optimism in the possibilities of technique was Francis Bacon. He was born in 1561. His father was one of Elizabeth's great statesmen, and he and his brother, Anthony, were educated for the law. Anthony Bacon secured for Richard Boyle the introductions which assisted him to make his fortune and provide the means that his son, Robert Boyle, later put to such good use for science.

Bacon was obstructed in his career by his kinsman Lord Burleigh, who wished to promote his own son, Robert Cecil. He was conscious of his extraordinary talents, which increased his ambition. After the death of Elizabeth, he secured promotion by obsequious attention to the Duke of Buckingham, James I's favourite. He was appointed Lord Chancellor in 1618. James had evaded the recall of Parliament since 1614, and in 1621 the demand could no longer be withstood. The infuriated Parliamentarians indirectly attacked the king by exposing irregularities in the conduct of his chancellor. Bacon was convicted of bribery, and dismissed. The elucidation of this affair is not simple. Bacon believed in authoritative rule by the crown in favour of the poorer classes, whereas his chief opponent, Coke, was the leader of the *bourgeoisie*, and believed in government by the commercial and landed oligarchy. Bacon was not scrupulous with money, but was concerned with profound political problems. Coke was very astute, but shallow-minded. His copy of the *New Organon* was inscribed with the lines:

> It deserveth not to be reade in Schooles,
> But to be freighted in the Ship of Fooles.

Bacon was insensitive on questions of personal morality, but his conduct is not adequately summarized by Pope's 'wisest, brightest, meanest of mankind'. The qualities of his opponents were different, but equally unbalanced.

Bacon dictated a tract, *Of the Interpretation of Nature*, some time in 1603, the year of Elizabeth's death. The manuscript, with corrections in his small firm handwriting, is in the library of the British Museum. It contains the leading ideas of his later writings. He notes in it that his age is distinguished by 'the opening of the world by navigation and commerce, and the further discovery of knowledge'. He believes that these techniques have cured the limitations of the home-bred wits of primitive man. Speaking in the *New Organon* of the human need to conquer nature, he says: 'Even if the breath of hope which blows on us from the New Continent were fainter than it is and harder to perceive; yet the trial (if we would not bear a spirit altogether abject) must by all means be made'. He found that 'there is hope enough and to spare, not only to make a bold man try, but also to make a sober-minded and wise man believe'. He considered what this hope might inspire. 'To speak plainly and clearly, it is a discovery of all operations and possibilities of operations, from immortality, if it were possible, to the meanest mechanical practice'. He expresses this aspiration in the *Interpretation*. In the later *New Atlantis* he says that 'the end of our foundation is the knowledge of causes, and secret motions of things; and the enlarging of the bounds of human empire; to the effecting of all things possible'.

Bacon adopted the method of a lawyer in pleading for this programme. He attempted to justify it by appeals to the beliefs of his readers. He attempted to show that it had been forecast in Biblical prophecies, and could be convincingly deduced from the dogmas of the Christian religion. He suggested that Daniel's prophecy that 'many shall pass to and fro, and science shall be increased' referred to his own times. One may make a quite different deduction from it. Had Daniel in his Babylonian experiences noted that science was born of commerce and navigation? Were the agents that produced science in Babylonia analogous to those that were producing science in the sixteenth century?

Bacon thought that 'howsoever' Daniel's prophecies may be, 'religion should clearly protect all increase of natural knowledge' because it leads to the greater exaltation of the glory of God, and because it is 'a singular help and a preservative against unbelief and error'. The value of studies of archaeology and prehistoric anthropology is of interest in connection with this opinion. These studies provide good ground for optimism concerning the future of humanity. They show that primitive man has survived extreme perils of extinction, so one may justly hope that modern man will face comparable dangers with equal success.

As God 'hath set the world in man's heart', man has been specially fitted to understand it. Having received 'so large a charter from God', he must put it to the use 'for which God has granted it, which is the benefit and relief of the state and society of man'.

'And therefore,' he says, 'it is not the pleasure of curiosity, nor the quiet of resolution, nor the raising of the spirit, nor victory of wit, nor faculty of speech, nor lucre of profession, nor ambition of honour or fame, or inablement for business, that are the true ends of knowledge.' Some of these are more worthy than others, but all are inferior to the true end, which is the restitution of man to his state before the fall. Science and technology are to be used to restore man to the condition of Adam, who was created lord of the world. Bacon's confidence in these agents was such that he did not forbear to hope that they would reveal how life may be made immortal. Compared with this, pure curiosity was a trivial motive for the pursuit of science. 'And therefore knowledge, that tendeth but to satisfaction, is but as a courtesan, which is for pleasure, and not for fruit or generation.' Knowledge 'that tendeth to profit or glory, is but as the golden ball thrown before Atalanta . . .' to hinder her in the race. Particular in contrast with general theory is like Harmodius, who put down one tyrant, rather than Hercules, 'who did perambulate the world to suppress tyrants and giants and monsters in every part'. Though man cannot, as yet, escape the curses of death and labour, he can use the latter for the restitution of man's state. Bacon drafted a plan and proposed a method for accomplishing this. He named his plan '*The Great Instauration*'; that is, the restoration of man from his fallen state to his original leadership of the world, as described in the Biblical account.

The Great Instauration was to be composed in six parts, containing an enumeration of the sciences, a method for interpreting nature, a natural history of the universe as a foundation for science, an improved method of intellectual analysis, anticipations of the new philosophy, and an exhibition of the new philosophy. Bacon completed the second part under the title of the *New Organon*, and made notes for some of the others, but he said that the completion of the sixth part, to which the others were preparatory, was above his strength and beyond his hopes. But he had made a beginning, and 'the fortune of the human race will give the issue'. He believed that this might be extraordinary beyond the present imagination of men. 'For the matter in hand is no mere felicity of speculation, but the real business and fortunes of the human race. For man is but the servant and interpreter of nature: what he does and what he knows is only what he has observed of nature's order in fact or in thought; beyond

9*

this he knows nothing and can do nothing. For the chain of causes cannot by any force be loosed or broken, nor can nature be commanded except by being obeyed. And so those twin objects, human Knowledge and human Power, do really meet in one; and it is from ignorance of causes that operation fails.'

No excellence of method can supply the mind with the material of knowledge. Those who do not aspire to guess the divine, but to discover and know 'must go to facts themselves for everything'. This labour cannot be replaced by any genius or meditation, 'no, not if all men's wits could meet in one'.

He believed that Democritus and the Ionian Greeks had a deeper insight than Pythagoras and Plato into the nature of science. He noted that philosophies of the Platonic type appealed to the 'ambition of the understanding', and did not improve upon the model. In them 'the proceeding has been to fly at once from the sense and particulars up to the most general propositions' and to deduce various consequences from them. 'A short way, no doubt, but precipitate; and one which will never lead to nature, though it offers an easy and ready way to disputation.' He proposes to use a new form of induction, in which he will proceed from one axiom to another, so that the most general notions are not reached until the last. It is different from the logician's induction, 'which proceeds by simple enumeration', and 'is a puerile thing'. His induction will 'analyse experience and take it to pieces, and by a due process of exclusion and rejection lead to an inevitable result'.

Science cannot be based merely on sense-impressions and empirical information, for sometimes the senses give no information or false information. He has therefore sought 'to provide helps for the sense', and has endeavoured to do this by the use of experiments rather than instruments.

The eye is subject to illusions, and the constituents of things are beyond the resolving power of the most powerful microscopes. But 'the subtlety of experiments is far greater than that of the sense itself, even when assisted by exquisite instruments', if the experiments are skilfully devised to test the point at question. He does not give much weight to the immediate perception of sense, but contrives 'that the office of sense shall be only to judge of the experiment, and that the experiment itself shall be the judge of the thing'.

His improved form of induction, assisted by experiment, would be sufficient to interpret nature if the mind itself were not defective. But the innate ideas, and those that enter the mind from without, distort its operation, and make it 'far more prone to error than the sense is'. The intellect must be purged to enable it to qualify for dealing with the truth. The false ideas entering it from the old philosophies must be refuted. The logical method must be improved, and allowance must be made for the effect of innate ideas that cannot be eradicated. When this has been done, the 'lawful marriage between the empirical and the rational faculty' will have been established for ever. His method 'is not an opinion to be held, but a work to be done'. He aims at the invention of technique and not of arguments. He does not try to deduce the nature of things from principles, but to discover general principles from things. The former method enables one 'to command nature in action', for axioms, or scientific laws, 'once rightly discovered', lead to results 'not here and there one, but in clusters'.

Bacon followed the inspiration of the development of machinery. He had noted that the mechanical arts have 'in them some breath of life', and are 'continually growing and becoming more perfect', whereas philosophy, on the contrary, stands like a statue, worshipped but not advanced. He wanted to introduce into mental operations a quality of growth analogous to that observed in technique, and he believed it could be done if the mind was given suitable tools, as the naked hands of the craftsman are assisted by tools. He wanted 'the entire work of understanding to be commenced afresh', and provided with a method that enabled it to proceed 'as if by machinery'. His philosophical method was parallel to the machine. As the machine assists the mechanic of moderate gifts to do good work, so his philosophical method or machine will enable persons of moderate intellect to make useful contributions to science. As for his own work, it is a child of the times 'rather than of wit'. He is merely a guide 'to point out the road; an office of small authority, and depending more upon a kind of luck than upon any ability or excellency'. He had happened to appear at a strategic moment in the history of science. Time would show that those who joined him in the use of his method, which consists not of extracting 'experiments from experiments (as an empiric), but from works and experiments to extract causes and axioms, and again from those causes and axioms, new works and experiments', would reveal technical inventions as remarkable as the 'new-found world of land'. Existing science will seem as barbarous compared with these new inventions as the inhabitants of the New World appear in comparison with those of the Old.

He wished that the 'arts and sciences should be like mines, where the noise of new works and further advances is heard on every side'. If one turns 'from the workshop to the library', he will be astonished at the 'poverty and scantiness of the subjects which till now have occupied and possessed the minds of men', when compared with the admirable variety of products in the former. One should introduce the methods of the workshop and the mine into mental operations.

But other agents are also necessary for the progress of science. 'Efforts in this field go unrewarded,' because those who advance science are great wits, while the rewards are 'in the hands of the people, or of great persons', who are generally not learned, and cannot understand their achievements. For the same reason, scientists do not even receive popular applause. 'And it is nothing strange if a thing not held in honour does not prosper.'

But he considered that men's tendency to 'despair and think things impossible' is 'by far the greatest obstacle to the progress of science'.

Bacon gave one illustration of his method. He applied it to the analysis of the nature of heat. He made a list of phenomena exhibiting heat, including the sun's rays, meteors, flames, hot solids, liquids and vapours; 'all bodies rubbed violently', quicklime dissolved in water, oils that burn the teeth, alcohol that hardens the white of egg, herbs that burn the tongue, etc.

Then he made a list of phenomena, parallel, item by item to those in the first list, in which heat is absent. These included moon rays, 'rotten wood, which shines by night, and yet is not found to be hot', the *ignis fatuus*, the sparkle in sea water when struck by oars at night, etc. He could not think of any body whose heat was not increased by attrition. The ancients had fancied that the stars were heated by attrition of the air. He would like experiments made to see whether cannon balls were heated by attrition of the air. Wind, or air in motion chills, but 'motion of this kind is not so rapid as to excite heat, and is the motion of a mass, and not of particles; so that it is no wonder if it does not generate heat'.

His third step consisted of an analysis of the degree of heat in the bodies itemized in the previous lists. He notes that 'in solid and tangible bodies we find nothing which is in its nature originally hot'. Animal heat is increased by motion and exercise. The heat of the heavenly bodies is never great enough to set fire to wood or straw, but 'it is however able to extract vapour from moist substances'. There are many degrees of strength in the heat of flames, but that of powerful lightning exceeds all others, for it melts 'wrought iron into drops, which those other flames cannot do'.

Motion increases heat, as may be seen in the use of furnace bellows. 'An anvil grows very hot under the hammer, insomuch that if it were made of a thin plate it might, I suppose, with strong and continuous blows of the hammer, grow red like ignited iron. But let this be tried by experiment,' etc.

He then applied his method of induction to the facts in these three lists. He rejected in each item qualities not present in it, and therefore responsible for its heat, though they may be present in other hot items. As the sun's rays are hot, heat cannot be matter. Heat cannot be of the same nature as the heavenly bodies because common fires are hot. Heat cannot be light, because boiling water and other dull substances are hot. As iron does not visibly swell when heated, heat cannot be due to the expansion of the body as a whole. Heat cannot have a destructive nature because all bodies are heated so easily. Heat could not exist in the nature of things positively, as, 'on account of heat being kindled by the attrition of bodies', it is the effect of an 'antecedent nature'.

Bacon now abstracted those features of heat common to all the items. He said: 'From a survey of the instances, all and each, the nature of which Heat is a particular case appears to be Motion. This is displayed most conspicuously in flame . . . it is quite clear that heat causes a tumult and confusion and violent motion in the internal parts of a body, which perceptibly tends to its dissolution.' He noted that 'heat is one thing, heating another', as 'heat is produced by the motion of attrition without any preceding heat'. He concluded 'that heat is a motion of expansion, not uniformly of the whole body together, but in the smaller parts of it . . . Heat is a motion, expansive, restrained, and acting in its strife upon the smaller particles of bodies'.

Bacon gave only one example of the application of his method, but it was remarkably successful, for it led him to propose the dynamical theory of heat.

His method was not the same as that used by Copernicus, Gilbert, Galileo, and their successors. He was critical of their achievements. He complained of Gilbert that after he had most laboriously investigated the properties of magnetism, he 'proceeded at once to construct an entire system in accordance with his favourite subject'. Galileo's observations of Jupiter's satellites, etc., were 'all indeed noble discoveries', but he regarded demonstrations of this kind with suspicion, because 'the experiment stops with these few discoveries, and many other things equally worthy of investigation are not discovered by the same means'. He explained that the advance of learning was impeded by the splitting of special sciences from universal knowledge. The specialists lost a broad perspective, and were unable to correct theories consonant with their own science, but not with the general background of knowledge. For this reason, he opposed Copernicus's theory, because repugnant to general experience, though consistent in itself. He rejected Galileo's theory of the tides, which was based on the supposition of relative motion between the seas and the rotating earth, because he did not believe the earth moved.

He believed there was a connection between the moon and the tides, and that it was due to actions operating at great distances. He believed that these powers which act at distances are 'all finite and fixed in the nature of things', and their limits are set by 'the mass or quantity of matter in the bodies acted on', or by media, or other agencies.

While he said that 'inquiries into nature have the best result when they begin with physics and end in mathematics', he also said that mathematics should 'only give definiteness to natural philosophy', and should not 'generate or give it birth'. He had in mind the Platonists and Pythagoreans, who believed they could deduce the properties of nature from numerical speculations and coincidences. The Baconian induction was successful in deriving the dynamical theory of heat, and Darwin used a similar method in deriving the theory of evolution from a multitude of biological particulars.

Bacon proposed and made many experiments. He suggested that the time kept by a clock at the top of a steeple and at the bottom of a mine should be compared, to find whether 'we may take the attraction of the mass of the earth as the cause of weight'.

He had found that the specific gravities of all solids and liquids lay within a ratio of 1 to 21; 'so limited is nature, or at any rate that part of it with which we have principally to do.' He investigated the ratio of the specific gravities of vapours to liquids. He completely filled a glass phial, which would hold about one ounce of liquid, with alcohol. He weighed the filled phial, and tied a flattened bladder to its neck, so that there was no free space over the liquid. He placed the phial on a chafing dish of hot coals. The alcohol began to evaporate, and presently filled the bladder, and he pricked the latter before any of the vapour could condense. He measured the quantity of alcohol lost from the phial, and as he knew the volume of the bladder, he could calculate what volume of vapour was obtained from the volume of the lost liquid. He 'computed the results; which showed clearly, that the body had acquired by the change a degree of expansion a hundred times greater than it had had before'.

Bacon showed by experiment that water is virtually incompressible. He filled a leaden sphere with water, sealed it, and had it heavily pressed. The water 'exuded through the solid lead like a fine dew', and the deformation of the sphere was slight, so he concluded that water resists compression.

He was not an incapable experimenter.

Besides restating the aim of science, and elaborating a method of research, Bacon described in his fable, the *New Atlantis*, an organization for advancing science. He imagined an undiscovered island in the Pacific, named Bensalem, whose inhabitants had organized a rational society based on advanced science and technique. They concealed their existence from the rest of the world to prevent the incursion of less civilized people, but they sent out secret expeditions to acquire all new knowledge.

The institute that organized the rational society and research was named Solomon's House. Its members were named fellows, and had specific duties. Twelve sailed secretly into foreign countries, to bring information of books and plans for experiments. Three fellows made notes of all experiments recorded in books. Three collected all information on mechanical crafts and experimental science, and on processes not yet adopted by the crafts. Three fellows 'try new experiments', and another three analyse their results and attempt to deduce new laws from them.

Three fellows consider how these new laws and results may be applied to 'use and practise for man's life and knowledge'.

All of the fellows discuss together the results of this programme, and three more consider what new lines of research are suggested by them. Yet another three fellows follow these new lines; and finally, there are three who extract the most general conceptions from the previous activities, and are named 'interpreters of nature'.

The fellows were assisted by a staff of apprentices, or research students, and a large number of assistants.

Their house had 'two very long and fair galleries', with statues of the principal inventors and discoverers. 'There we have the statue of your Columbus, that discovered the West Indies', and of the inventors of ships, ordnance, music, writing, printing, astronomy, metals, glass, silk, wine, corn, sugar, etc. The inventor of any valuable new process is given 'a liberal and honourable reward'.

The growth of commerce and discovery, that had directed Bacon's interest towards science, impelled many more men in the same direction during the first half of the seventeenth century. When these men came together, and sought for a means of incorporating their interest, they followed Bacon's plan for a Solomon's House. They formed a society of scientists, and tried to organize its activities according to Bacon's pattern. This society presently became the Royal Society of London, and its members are named fellows, after the Baconian title.

The duties of the fellows of Solomon's House were not restricted to their headquarters. They had 'circuits or visits of divers principal cities of the kingdom; where, as it cometh to pass, we do publish such new profitable inventions as we think good'. This was the pattern of the British and American Associations for the Advancement of Science, realized two centuries later.

There is much confusion concerning Bacon's contribution to science. The professional scientist notices his technical limitations. And yet it is evident that Bacon's scientific writings are very important. The core of Bacon's work was not science, but the social relations of science. He was virtually the first, and a very great, writer on this subject.

Bacon's criticisms of Gilbert, Galileo and Copernicus are not so unfounded as is generally supposed. He did not greatly esteem

Galileo's method of abstracting problems entirely from their general and social context. The limitation of Galileo's conception of science, which was exposed by his inability to understand the nature of his conflict with the Church, was nevertheless rarely grasped until recent times. Scientists have followed Galileo for three centuries, piling up discoveries in regions of research artificially isolated from the general body of knowledge and social affairs. The fate that overcame Galileo is now threatening the scientists who have followed him. They, like him, have failed to understand the relations between science and society, so they are finding themselves in dangerous perplexities.

Harvey said that Bacon wrote on science like a lord chancellor. It may be retorted that Harvey, who had probably attended Galileo's lectures at Padua, conceived science in the limited Galilean manner, and found himself in the camp of Charles I instead of Cromwell's.

If scientists are to save mankind and themselves now, they must no longer be pure Galileans, but become also Baconians, and remember that 'knowledge, that tendeth but to satisfaction, is but as a courtesan', and its proper use is for 'the benefit and relief of the state and society of man'.

60

The Mayor of Magdeburg

MAGDEBURG owed its importance to its site on the River Elbe. The trade between northern and southern Germany crossed the river most conveniently by the city, and the trade between east and west naturally travelled along the river to Hamburg, and the North Sea. Owing to these connections, Magdeburg was a member of the Hanseatic League. The city was only one hundred miles from Chemnitz, the centre of the mining industry so well described by Agricola. It was on one of the routes by which the precious metals, and other products of this industry were transported to Holland, the centre of the commercial world in the seventeenth century.

Magdeburg was of strategic importance in the Thirty Years' War. The Catholic armies under Tilly, and the Protestant armies under Gustavus Adolphus both wished to possess it. In 1631 Tilly threatened it with siege, if it did not surrender. The mass of the population were strongly Protestant and wanted to resist, but a section of the rich men who governed the city, though Protestant, feared the destruction of their wealth, and wished to make terms with Tilly. Gustavus Adolphus was very anxious that Magdeburg should resist, because it provided him with a bridge across the Elbe, and access to the south. He was unable to send reinforcements and munitions immediately, and in fact desired to borrow the city's own military store. He offered them in return promises of extensive future help. When the city councillors showed unwillingness to accede to this request and proposed to compromise with Tilly, Adolphus's agents threatened to appeal to the citizens over their heads. The council then decided to lend their stores to Adolphus. Tilly advanced on the city, but Adolphus was still unable to come to its aid. The defence of the city, with its depleted stores, fell mainly on the citizens, under the military leadership of a Swedish general. Two defence officers were appointed by the city council, one of whom was Otto von Guericke. This young man belonged to a leading family in the city. He was born in 1602, and was twenty-nine years old when appointed officer of defence.

He had been prepared from his youth to take part in the government of the city. He was an only son of wealthy parents and every aid was lavished on him. He had been sent at the age of fifteen to study law at the University of Leipzig, and continued his studies at Helmstedt and Jena. He was then sent to Leyden, where he attended lectures on science and military engineering. Military science was often the core of university science courses at that date. The separation of physics, chemistry and biology courses, as known today, came at a later date.

He visited England and France and returned to Magdeburg when he was twenty-three. He had married, and immediately became a leading citizen.

As defence officer and military engineer, he designed fortifications and armaments and superintended their construction. The lack of stores, and especially of gunpowder, was very serious, so he organized the manufacture of powder from the supplies of nitre in the single apothecary's shop in the town.

In spite of his energy and ability, Magdeburg fell, as Gustavus Adolphus failed to come to its aid, and it could not hold out long against Tilly's superior forces. The city was burned and completely destroyed. Guericke nearly lost his life, and all his property. He was saved through the intercession of a leading citizen who happened to be friendly with one of Tilly's generals, and he and his family were presently ransomed by the Protestant friends of Magdeburg.

After his release, Guericke was appointed quartermaster general to Gustavus Adolphus, following the example of Stevin in becoming the technical organizer of resistance by the Protestant leaders of commercial powers against the Catholic landed and financial powers.

Gustavus counter-attacked, and presently recaptured the site of Magdeburg. After this had been achieved, Guericke was released from his quartermaster generalship, and returned to supervise the reconstruction of the city. He designed new bridges, fortifications and buildings, besides taking a leading part in politics. As the city was poor, it could not pay him enough for a livelihood, so he had to increase his income by farming and brewing.

He was appointed burgomaster of the city in 1646, and retained a leading official position during the rest of his long life, which ended in 1686.

Much of his time was given to diplomatic negotiations on behalf of the city at Vienna, Prague, Regensburg and other capitals.

Guericke's early training in, and continual practice of, science and engineering continually kept the problems of the properties of matter before him. While he kept this aspect of nature in mind, he also followed the scientific discussions of the day on the structure of the universe.

He tried to interpret theology by combining his scientific and religious interests. He attempted to determine the location of heaven and hell, and to harmonize Joshua's account of the suspension of the motion of the sun with Copernican theory. These problems brought him to the consideration of the properties of outer space, which he supposed was a vacuum. How could he obtain a piece of vacuum and see what the properties of outer space, and of heaven and hell, were like?

As an experienced executive engineer, and a man who had

acquired the habit of solving problems by action and improvised research, he approached the problem of the vacuum in an active practical attitude. He decided to try to make a vacuum, and investigate its properties by experiment, besides speculation. He was accustomed in his brewery to handle liquids and gases and to use pumps, and he knew how to empty trenches and put out fires, which also involved knowledge of pumps. A good deal was known about these at Magdeburg, owing to the proximity of the city to Chemnitz, the centre of the region where miners had been forced to learn much about pumps, and had acquired more knowledge on this branch of engineering than was possessed by any other group of engineers in the world.

Guericke conceived the plan of filling a vessel completely with water, and then removing the water with a suction pump. He thought that if the water could be removed, a vacuum would be left in the vessel. He filled a wooden barrel from his brewery with water, and then tried to pump out the water with a suction pump, which consisted of a barrel about one foot long and several inches in diameter, with a piston that could be drawn out directly by hand.

The defender of Magdeburg, who had no doubt put out many fires during the siege of his city, was probably very familiar with fire engines. It is not surprising that he adopted the forcepump of a fire-engine, which acts as a suction pump on the inlet stroke, for the removal of the water from the barrel. He found that after the first few strokes, great force was needed to pull out the piston, and he had to strengthen all the joints and fastenings. But he found that with three strong men hauling on the piston, the water could be removed.

A noise came from the barrel as if the remaining water was boiling, and it was noticed that air was leaking in; a phenomenon ever since so familiar to employers of vacuum technique. Guericke covered the barrel with pitch to stop the leaks, and repeated the removal of water, but again the air leaked through the crevices even when covered with pitch. He then submerged the whole barrel in water, and found the leakage was much reduced. But this was still unsatisfactory, so he made a roughly spherical large copper vessel which would not leak. He did not bother to fill it with water, but attached the pump to it directly, and found the air inside could be directly removed. When the sphere was nearly exhausted, it suddenly collapsed with a loud report. Guericke perceived that it had collapsed owing to its imperfect sphericity, so he made a more perfect copper sphere. This did not collapse after exhaustion. He found that when the stop-cock was opened, air tore in with great force. His skill in handling large copper vessels was derived from his experience in his brewery.

He now constructed 'a special machine for making a vacuum'. This was the first air pump. He recognized the necessity for preventing leaks and reducing the amount of dead space inside the pump to a minimum.

He began a long series of entirely new investigations with this machine. He used glass spheres with wide necks and ground joints for observing vacuum effects. He found that the smallest quantity of air was expansible beyond the limits of observation. He noted that when the air was being exhausted, it expanded of itself into the pump cylinder. He noted the rapidity with which equalization of pressure occurs in a long tube that is being exhausted, and observed that the gusts of air were sufficient to blow bolts and nuts along the inside of the tube. He deduced from this that atmospheric storms are due only to differences in air pressure, and forecast a big storm from a big drop in atmospheric pressure. He noted the clash of water inside a vacuum, which produces the water-hammering effect. He directly measured the specific gravity of the air by weighing a glass globe full and exhausted, and recognized that the result depended on pressure and temperature.

He showed that light could travel through a vacuum, but sound would not. He found that candles went out, and animals died, when placed in a vacuum, and he concluded that fire obtains something from the air which enables it to support combustion. He enclosed a burning candle in a volume of air held over water, and found that the candle consumed one-tenth of the air before it was extinguished. His large scale experiments with vacua were not less remarkable. He showed that even fifty men could be hauled by a piston in a cylinder which had suddenly been connected with a large vacuum chamber. He constructed large hemispheres which required teams of twenty-four horses to pull them apart when exhausted, but which fell apart without effort when air let in by opening a tap.

Guericke first made these experiments at Magdeburg about 1650. He was appointed diplomatic representative of the city at the Reichstag at Regensburg in 1654, and it is said that he repeated the experiments before the Emperor of Germany and the assembled princes, though this has been questioned.

His diplomatic task was to secure the freedom of Magdeburg from ducal protection. The demonstration of the 'Magdeburg Hemispheres' at Regensburg, if it did occur, was no doubt intended to secure prestige for Magdeburg by exhibiting the genius of its citizens, and thus secure favourable consideration of her diplomatic aims. It was a form of cultural propaganda. There is little doubt, too, that Guericke was proud of his own ingenuity. His apparatus was expensive in spite of the workshop resources of his brewery, and he increased its cost by decorations with precious inlaid ornaments. This attempt to use science as a means for political propaganda failed. Guericke did not secure the freedom of his city, though he increased his personal fame.

His researches were not restricted to vacua. He constructed the first electrical machine. It consisted of a large ball of sulphur which could be rotated on a horizontal iron axis by a crank.

Electrification was produced by holding the hand against the sulphur sphere while it was rotated. The engineering scale of this machine was again of fundamental value, and provided results that could not be obtained with small laboratory apparatus.

He could create large electric charges, and these enabled him to discover the phenomenon of electrical repulsion. With a copy of Guericke's machine, Leibniz in 1672 consciously produced electric sparks for the first time.

Robert Boyle first heard of Guericke's invention of the air-pump in 1657. With Hooke's assistance he immediately constructed an improved pump, and began a series of experiments described in his book on *New Experiments Physico-Mechanical, touching the Spring of the Air*. This contains three hundred pages, and the experiments and their description were completed in two years.

Boyle made many experiments on flames and animals in air under reduced pressure, and approached the discovery of oxygen. He noted the views of Paracelsus and Drebell, that 'it is not the whole body of the air, but a certain quintessence or spirituous part of it, that makes it fit for respiration'. He is favourable to this opinion, 'for we see, that in our engine the flame of a lamp will last almost as little after the exsuction of the air, as the life of an animal . . .' and 'our engine thus shows us a new kind of resemblance betwixt fire and life'. Experiments on the dissolved air in water, which is released by reducing the pressure, led him to conjecture 'that there is wont to lurk in water many little parcels of interspersed air, whereof it seems not impossible that fishes may make some use'.

He observed the boiling of warm water at reduced pressure, and deduced from it 'that the air, by its stronger or weaker pressure, may very much modify (as the schoolmen speak) divers of the operations of that vehement and tumultuous agitation of the small parts of bodies, wherein the nature of heat seems chiefly if not solely, to consist'.

He discussed the expansion of air as evidence for the atomic constitution of gases, and while writing with keen interest, excuses himself from offering an answer, as the question is so difficult.

His account of the experiments, which was in 1660, when he was thirty-four years old, was adversely criticized by Hobbes and others. In a second series of experiments to confirm and extend the first, he described the discovery and proof of the celebrated law named after him.

The air-pump is the most important technical invention in the history of science, because it provided a means for investigating gases, which present the phenomena of matter in their simplest form. As the human body is not a good material on which to start the investigation of nature, because it is too complex, so solids and liquids are at first less helpful than gases as guides to the constitution of matter. The expansibility of gases made their atomicity seem probable, and the law discovered by Boyle provided the data for the first successful deduction from the atomic hypothesis by mathematics. This was made by Newton when he showed that Boyle's law could be mathematically deduced from an atomic conception of gases.

The successful deduction converted the atomic hypothesis into a scientific theory, and provided a theoretical foundation for chemistry. John Dalton recorded that he drew his inspiration from Newton's incursion into the atomic theory of gases.

Guericke's spectacular experiments with the big hemispheres revealed the possibility of a new source of power. For the first time since the harnessing of water and wind, a new form of motive power was discovered. Newcomen succeeded in harnessing the power of the vacuum by his steam engine, and this led to the development of steam power.

The study of the steam engine produced the science of thermodynamics, and this, when combined with the atomic theory of gases, produced statistical mechanics and the quantum theory.

The investigation of the electrical properties of gases at low pressure, made possible by Guericke's air-pump and his electrical machine, led to the discovery of the electron, and the electrical constitution of matter.

61

The Father of Chemistry and Uncle of the Earl of Cork

R OBERT BOYLE remarks at the end of his first book on the spring of the air that though he had intended it to be only a short letter describing his results, it had expanded into a volume, 'yet the experiments already mentioned in it are so far from comprising all those that may be tried by the help of our engine, that I have not yet been able to try all these, which, presently occurring to my thoughts, upon my first seeing the working of it, I caused to be set down in a catalogue within less than half an hour.'

Boyle here reveals one of the most important parts of scientific method. It consists of the invention of a new instrument or technique. When this has been done, the subjects for a lifetime of research may be written down in less than half an hour. Speculation is idle until the experimental means of testing it have been invented.

The experimental means were derived from the mechanic's workshop. The air-pump constructed by Hooke and Boyle was about three feet over all. Its size was typical of the industrial machines of the day, and the sort of skill required to handle it depended on practical acquaintance with the mechanical processes by which it had been constructed.

Boyle was aware of the necessity of studying industrial processes in order to acquire the orientation which sets the mind towards experimental discovery, and he discussed the problem repeatedly. He advocates in his long treatise on the *Usefulness of Natural Philosophy* the need for personal experiment, even with the most disagreeable materials. He says that he is not too squeamish to experiment on the nature and use of dungs. 'And though my condition does (God be praised) enable me to make experiments by others' hands; yet I have not been so nice, as to decline dissecting dogs, wolves, fishes, and even rats and mice, with my own hands. Nor, when I am in my laboratory, do I scruple with them naked to handle lute and charcoal.' He explains that natural philosophy teaches not only the knowledge of nature, but 'in many cases to master and command her'. The true scientist not only knows many things which other men ignore, 'but can perform many things, which other men cannot do', and is enabled by his skill 'not barely to understand several wonders of nature, but also partly to imitate, and partly to multiply and improve them'. He discusses the usefulness of mathematics, and of mechanics to natural philosophy, and explains 'that the Goods of Mankind May be much increased by the Naturalist's insight into Trades'. He says that he will show that 'insight into trades may improve the naturalist's knowledge', and that the naturalist, 'as well by the skill thus obtained, as by the other parts of his knowledge may be enabled to improve trades'. He agrees that industrial processes are a part of the history of nature. It will not 'suffice to justify learned men in the neglect and contempt of this part of natural history, that the men from whom it must be learned are illiterate mechanics . . .' This social objection, he says, 'is indeed childish, and too unworthy of a philosopher, to be worthy of a solemn answer'. He believes that the progress of natural philosophy has been hindered by the 'haughtiness and negligence', and 'superciliousness and laziness' too often learned in 'schools'. These social attitudes have damaged the true interest of mankind by keeping 'learned and ingenious men . . . strangers to the shops and practices of tradesmen'.

The phenomena of industrial processes are particularly instructive because they show nature in motion, and 'that too, when she is (as it were) put out of her course, by the strength and skill of man, which I have formerly noted to be the most instructive condition, wherein we can behold her'.

He recommends scientists 'to disdain, as little as I do, to converse with tradesmen in their work houses and shops', and takes leave to say that 'he deserves not the knowledge of nature, that scorns to converse even with mean persons, that have the opportunity to be very conversant with her'. The scientist may often obtain very instructive information from those 'that have neither fine language nor fine clothes to amuse themselves'.

Craftsmen have a thorough knowledge of the materials they handle because they lose trade if their products are inferior. Owing to 'want of subsistence' their wits are sharpened, and they are forced to invent more economical tools and processes, for 'necessity' was ever 'the mother of invention'. He had noticed that craftsmen are familiar with many substances not mentioned by the classical authors, and he records that he has 'learned more of the kinds, distinctions, properties and consequently of the nature of stones, by conversation with two or three masons, and stone-cutters, than ever [he] did from Pliny or Aristotle, and his commentators'.

Craftsmen's theories and opinions were based on frequently repeated experiences, whereas scholars usually restricted themselves to a few experiments. As craft was often passed down from father to son, a family might learn of slow effects, which may take twenty years or longer to develop, and which could not be noticed in a short experiment. He wished to 'carry philosophical materials from the shops to the schools'. He desired gentlemen and scholars to converse with tradesmen, for 'it will qualify them to ask questions of men, that converse with things'. From this knowledge of the processes of craftsmen, scientists should be able 'to meliorate the inventions of illiterate tradesmen'. He considers 'that in many cases, a trade differs from an experiment not so much in the nature of the thing, as in its having had the luck to be applied to human uses, or by a company of artificers made their business, in order to their profit, which are things extrinsical, and accidental to the experiment itself'.

Boyle describes scientists like himself as 'commercers with nature'. He exhibits the introduction of the psychology of the trader into man's attitude towards nature. The scientist approaches nature in the attitude of an entrepreneur.

Mathematics and mechanics are useful to him because they assist him 'to frame theories, or to make observations and experiments'. The study of geometry and machinery, with their 'lineal schemes, pictures and instruments, assist the imagination to conceive many things, and thereby the understanding to judge of them, and deduce new contrivances from them'.

He explains that one of his motives for studying nature is his ardent desire to benefit his fellow men, and he believes that natural philosophy should 'afford them both curious flowers to satisfy their curiosity, and delight their senses, and excellent fruits, and other substantial productions, to answer the necessities, and furnish the accommodations of human life'.

Boyle acutely criticized the Aristotelian theory of the elements, which had been accepted for two thousand years. He said that he could 'not look upon any body as a true principle or element, which is not perfectly homogeneous but is further resolvable into any number of distinct substances'. He first propounded the modern theory of chemical elements, and also of systematic chemical analysis. He believed that 'matter and motion' were the most primary 'principles of things', and directed scientific thought towards atomic theory.

Boyle's effort to establish the social repute of the systematic study of craft and engineering processes, and to break the social barrier between gentlemen and craftsmen, was of the greatest service to science. He and his followers transformed the attitude of the governing class towards the study of nature and annexed the knowledge of craftsmen and engineers for the benefit of this class. Science began to advance rapidly when the motive power generated by the interests of the governing class was more consciously applied to it. Besides appreciating that successful research depended on the orientation of mind derived from the craftsman and merchant, Boyle explained to his 'dear nephew', the heir to the Earldom of Cork, that he hoped to 'indear' experimental philosophy 'to hopeful persons of your quality', because the 'effectual pursuit' of it 'requires as well a purse as a brain'.

The rise of Boyle to great wealth was very recent, and was accomplished by Richard Boyle, the father of the scientist. The family had been obscure English country gentlemen for many generations, and Richard Boyle, who was born in 1566, was educated at Cambridge, and had intended to study law, but had not the means. He says that he 'resolved to travel into foreign kingdoms, and to gain learning, and knowledge, and experience abroad in the world'. He sailed for Ireland in 1588, and when he arrived in Dublin 'all my wealth was twenty-seven pounds three shillings in money', a diamond ring given him by his mother, and some changes of clothes, 'with my rapier and dagger'.

He married a lady with an estate of £500 per annum in 1595. She died in childbirth in 1599. Richard Boyle records that her inheritance was 'the beginning and foundation of my fortune'.

He engaged in estate speculations, and his wealth grew rapidly, so rapidly that the jealousy of Sir Henry Wallop, the lord treasurer of Ireland, and others, was aroused. These influential persons informed Queen Elizabeth that he could not have obtained all this wealth without receiving payments from foreign princes, as he had been poor when he had arrived in Ireland.

A rebellion in Munster postponed the discussion of this matter, and Richard Boyle's land was wasted in the fighting. He returned to London to resume the study of law, and was engaged by the Earl of Essex. When Essex was appointed governor of Ireland, Wallop's anxiety concerning Richard Boyle revived. Richard states that he had sundry papers which showed 'a great deal of wrong and abuse done to the queen in [Wallop's] late accounts'.

Wallop feared that Richard would use these papers to blackmail him, so he again denounced Richard to the Queen, who ordered his arrest. After four months' investigation, he secured his acquittal, and recorded later that the Queen had commented: 'By God's death, these are but inventions against this young man, and all his sufferings are for being able to do us service, and those complaints urged to forestall him therein. But we find him a man fit to be employed by ourselves, and we will employ him in our service, and Wallop and his adherents shall know, that it shall not be in the power of any of them to wrong him; neither shall Wallop be our treasurer any longer'.

The Queen appointed him clerk of Munster, and he bought Sir Walter Ralegh's ship, the *Pilgrim*, to sail again to Ireland. 'And this was the second rise, that God gave to my fortune.' He was very active in the suppression of Irish revolts. Some time later Sir Robert Cecil persuaded Ralegh to sell his Irish estate to Richard Boyle, as it was 'then altogether waste and desolate'. While this powerful politician represented to Ralegh that his Irish estates were virtually without value, Richard Boyle states that through the purchase 'my assurances were perfected, and this was the third addition and rise to my estate'. He married the only daughter of Fenton, the secretary for Ireland, who presented him with 'one thousand pounds in gold' as a wedding present.

He presently acquired the titles of knight, Lord Boyle, Baron of Youghall, Viscount Dungarvan, and Earl of Cork; and was Treasurer, and one of the two Chief Justices, of Ireland. His estate became the 'greatest in the memory of the last age'. He built many villages and towns, and his constructions subsequently received Cromwell's praise, who is reported to have said that 'if there had been an Earl of Cork in every province, it would have been impossible for the Irish to have raised a rebellion'.

The first Earl of Cork was the richest of the new rich of his age. He had a great eye for business.

Robert Boyle was his fourteenth child and seventh son, and was born in 1626 at the great house of Lismore in Munster. He was Irish only by place of birth. He explains that as the younger son of a great nobleman he was in a happy position to pursue scientific studies. He was not called to manage the estate and affairs of the family, and yet he had an adequate income.

He could afford to be pious and kind, independent and even eccentric.

The first Earl of Cork exhibited the mastery of business and common affairs characteristic of the new class of Tudor mercantile noblemen. Robert Boyle's orientation towards crafts was derived from their outlook. His father, in contrast with the feudal nobility, believed that children should be reared simply, on rough but wholesome food. This strengthened their constitutions and gave them some knowledge of the common people and their occupations, which, incidentally, was the best preparation for future business. Robert Boyle had been sent as soon as possible to a peasant nurse and was reared for years in the country. He has recorded his gratitude for this early toughening. He was not over-bred, in spite of his birth and the fineness of his mind. Owing to his fortune, he did not need to use the exploiting habits acquired through his descent to make money.

He could find a more urbane exercise for them in restless acquisition of natural knowledge and in the analysis and improvement of trading processes. His nobility, though very recent, had much influence on science. The ordinary member of his class was too busy acquiring riches to advance beyond the degree of acquaintance with technique necessary for its exploitation, and had not yet learned to understand and respect it. This could not be done until the new sort of gentlemen personally studied crafts and mixed with craftsmen. Only a great nobleman could advocate that without loss of caste. Boyle helped to establish the social repute of craft processes, and thus made the source of experimental science worthy of the personal attention of gentlemen, and of the governing class. As soon as these processes had acquired as much social repute as the mental operations of scholars and gentlemen, practice and theory could be harmoniously combined and so provide the condition for the rapid development of modern science.

Robert Boyle made such an important contribution to this development because he had a strategic social position. He became 'the father of chemistry' because he was the son of his father, and 'uncle of the [third] Earl of Cork', besides having great talent.

62

The Royal Society

WHEN the dominance of the mercantile classes became confirmed, their interests determined the perspective of intellectual and other endeavour. The problems of trade and manufacture were accepted as of the highest importance. They were studied by those directly engaged in them, and by others who derived incomes from them even if not directly engaged. Thus men of business and leisure were interested in the same problems. A sharp division between the trading and the leisured classes could not be drawn. Traders meditated on the scientific aspects of their problems in working and leisure hours, and men of leisure dabbled in inventions which they thought might draw big dividends.

Men with these interests had occasionally appeared ever since the revival of trade at the beginning of the Middle Ages, but their number increased rapidly with the growth of the power of the mercantile classes. There were enough of them in several countries in the first half of the seventeenth century to form considerable groups of men of ability. These men were brought together by their common interests and at first unconsciously formed themselves into clubs and societies. The English group became the parent of the Royal Society of London.

As this society was not consciously invented by an individual, and came into existence through the impulse of prior impersonal social forces, its origin cannot be defined precisely. The original members of the Royal Society, which was approved by Charles II in 1660 and granted a royal charter by him in 1662, gradually became conscious in the forties of the seventeenth century that they were forming a definite group. The mathematician John Wallis has described how he joined in conversations in London in 1645 on the new experimental philosophy.

A group of persons met weekly for the performance and discussion of experiments. These were made in the lodgings of one of their members, or in a tavern, or in Gresham College. This institution had been founded on endowments bequeathed by Sir Thomas Gresham in 1575. He was financial adviser to Elizabeth and Cecil, and one of the greatest mercantilists of the age. He founded his college for the instruction of the people of London, believing that the new interests of society, which were mercantilist, had created a need for the general education of the people. Seven professorships, presently held by men such as Wren and Hooke, were established: in divinity, astronomy, music, geometry, law, physics and rhetoric.

Wallis said that the meetings of his friends were first suggested by Theodore Haak, a German resident in London; and that John Wilkins, the brother-in-law of Oliver Cromwell, was prominent in them. Wilkins wrote on mechanics, and was interested in the rationalization of language and the means of communication.

The group tabooed theology and politics, and discussed medicine, anatomy, geometry, astronomy, navigation, statics, magnetism, chemistry, mechanics and general natural phenomena. They met in the optical workshop of one of their members, to have materials and instruments at hand for experiments, or at the lectures of the Gresham professor of astronomy, accompanying him to his lodgings after he had finished his lectures, to continue discussions.

Robert Boyle joined the group in 1646, when he was twenty years old. He wrote to his French tutor that he had been studying 'natural philosophy, the mechanics and husbandry, according to the principles of our new philosophical college that values no knowledge, but as it hath a tendency to use'. He would be grateful if 'good receipts or choice books on any of these subjects' could be sent from abroad, and these would make the sender 'extremely welcome to our *invisible college*'.

These meetings began near the end of Charles I's reign, during a period of extreme theological and political tension. To their participants they appeared as a refuge where discussion was restricted to apparently neutral subjects, in which persons of differing theological and political opinions could join without antagonism. The group wished to be unnoticed by the theological and political contestants, and held its meetings in modest obscurity. Perhaps for that reason Boyle described it as the 'invisible college'. Sprat said that 'their first purpose was no more than only the satisfaction of breathing a freer air, and of conversing in quiet one with another, without being ingag'd in the passions and madness of that dismal age'.

As the tension in London grew, some members migrated to Oxford. They held similar meetings there, which were fostered by Wilkins, Petty, Willis, Boyle, and others. They met at first in Petty's lodgings, because he lived in the house of an apothecary, whose drugs and apparatus were available for experiments; and then at Boyle's house, because he had constructed a laboratory. Members who remained in London continued to meet until 1658, when their place of meeting was commandeered as a quarter for soldiers.

The meetings were revived at Gresham College after the restoration of the monarchy. The members now sought a more formal organization. They discussed rules for regulating their proceedings, and electing new members, at their meeting after Wren's lecture on November 28, 1660. Wilkins was chairman, and others present included Boyle, Petty, Wren, Brouncker, and a Scottish nobleman named Moray, who had accompanied Charles during his exile. They compiled a list of forty-one persons suitable for membership, and proposed that members should subscribe one shilling weekly towards expenses. Moray informed Charles of the design for the new society and reported at the next week's meeting that the King 'did well approve of it, and would be ready to give encouragement to it'. Moray was appointed the first president. During the following year the title of 'Royal

Society' was apparently suggested by John Evelyn in conversation with Charles. The Society petitioned the King in 1661 for a royal charter, and received it in 1662. Brouncker was the first president of the incorporated society, and the council included Boyle, Petty, Wallis, Wilkins and Wren; and the German scholar Henry Oldenburg was appointed secretary. The members were to be named fellows. A second and extended charter was granted in 1663, and one hundred and fifteen fellows were elected.

The Society flourished extraordinarily. A history of it was written within five years of its first charter. Abraham Cowley composed a poem on the Society, in which he said that:

> None e're but Hercules and you could be,
> At five years Age worthy a History.

The history was compiled by Thomas Sprat, later Bishop of Rochester, and published in 1667. Sprat had access to the minutes of the meetings and was supplied with material by other fellows. His work is a personal interpretation, supported by much co-operative help. Sprat explains the Society as a product of the 'inquiring temper of the age'. He believes that this arose from the liberty of thought encouraged by the Reformation. He could not carry the origin of the Society many years back, 'yet the seeds of it were sown in King Edward VI's and Queen Elizabeth's reign'. Ever since that time, experimental learning had 'retained some vital heat', though it had not the opportunities for ripening that it now enjoys. He concludes that the Church of England is the mother of this sort of knowledge, and should therefore give it all nourishment and support.

He explains the objects of the Society, though he feels that 'some of Bacon's writing' gives a better account of them than anything he can compose.

He notes that the Greeks exercised their wit and imagination about the works of nature more than was 'consistent with a sincere inquiry into them'. The fellows of the Royal Society, on the contrary, avoided the artifices of words, and sought 'a bare knowledge of things'. Their description required a clear and precise language, so the fellows aimed at polishing and standardizing English, and using it 'to make faithful records of all the works of nature or art'.

They wanted to establish a system for perpetually increasing

10

the knowledge of nature. He says that scientists 'have the advantage of standing upon' the 'shoulders' of their predecessors, and anticipates or inspires a famous remark of Newton's.

The Society was to be international because it was to 'found a philosophy of mankind', and not merely of Englishmen's interests. They would 'make the Royal Society the general bank, and free port of the world. A policy which whether it would hold good, in the trade of England, I know not but sure it will in the philosophy'.

Men of all sorts and professions were admitted. When the social status of John Graunt, the celebrated author of the *Observations on the Bills of Mortality* and founder of demology, was mentioned as a bar to membership, the King himself said that 'if they found any more such Tradesmen, they should be sure to admit them all, without more ado'. Sprat says that this incident will show the attitude of the Society to the manual arts.

Nevertheless, the majority of the fellows were gentlemen under no compulsion to work. This had the advantage of preventing too much attention to particular profit and exploitation. Persons who busy themselves too much with the exploitation of a particular process are like the guards who let the prisoner escape and lost the ransom, through pausing to pick up some small coin dropped from the prisoner's pocket. 'It busies them about possessing some petty prize; while Nature itself, with all its mighty treasures, slips from them.' There is a similarity in this passage and another famous phrase of Newton's, about the undiscovered sea of knowledge.

Their work in laboratories was superior to study in schools, because experimenters co-operate, while students sit and listen. Struggling with experiments teaches modesty, whereas quick memorizing produces slickness and arrogance. Those who take their opinions from others are generally less open to reason than the original discoverers. The free method of inquiry produced greater results than the formal. Sprat suggested that philosophical training was not necessary for experimental work. Indeed, the intelligent amateur could surpass the formal professional, as was shown by the superiority of Cromwell's soldiers.

The knowledge of nature acquired by scientists enabled them to equal and improve upon traditional technique. If they were excluded from surgeries, or from the workshops of mechanics, they would nevertheless, with the help of better instruments, more materials, more hands, and a more rational understanding of medical and manufacturing processes, restore the old processes and discover 'many more of far greater importance'.

Sprat points out that the settled conditions after the restoration encouraged manufacture and trade. The Society intended to provide a philosophy suitable for such conditions. It was to be 'for the use of cities, and not for the retirements of schools'. The Society was 'to resemble the cities', which are 'compounded of all sorts of men, students, soldiers, shopkeepers, farmers, courtiers and sailors; all mutually assisting each other'. The Society had broken down the partition wall, or class barrier, between 'all conditions of men' to encourage the study of their techniques, and the exchange of their technical knowledge. The Royal Society 'goes to the root of all noble inventions, and proposes an infallible course to make England the glory fo the western world'.

England, as one of those lands that border on the seas, was 'most properly seated' to receive the matter which provides new science. Owing to her situation, she was an exchange for universal knowledge. Her climate and air, 'the influence of her heaven', the 'composition of the English blood', and the 'disposition of her merchants' should, under the leadership of the Royal Society, qualify her for the headship of a philosophical league directing the civilization of Europe.

The fellows of the Royal Society 'escaped the prejudices that used to arise from authority, from inequality of persons, from insinuations of friendship' and other subjective relationships because they were in the habit of attending to things. It was 'in vain for any man amongst them' to strive to shine by wit, for the results of their experiments were esteemed, rather than acute comments. As Veblen has since remarked, the attention to things and processes has directed conceptions away from principles of dominance to impersonal relationships.

The work of the Society was a 'painful digging and toiling in nature', and less easy and fine than teaching. Consequently, 'strict punctilios' of conduct were an incumbrance to them, just as an artificer's best suit is an encumbrance to him when working in his shop. For similar reasons, their fellows avoid eloquence in the description of their experiments. This quality is 'fatal to peace and good manners'. They have resolutely rejected all extravagance in expression, all 'amplifications, digressions and swellings of style'. They aim at a 'return to the primitive purity, and shortness, when men delivered so many things, almost in an equal number of words'. The fellows are expected to use 'a close, naked, natural way of speaking; positive expressions; clear senses; a native easiness: bringing all things as near the mathematical plainness, as they can: and preferring the language of artisans, countrymen, and merchants, before that of wits, or scholars'.

It will be noticed that the influence of science on philosophy and literature was expressed very clearly before Newton and his work were known. The characteristics of thought and writing at the end of the seventeenth and the beginning of the eighteenth centuries were not due to Newton's achievements, though they were heightened by them. Newton's modes of thought were rather the efflorescence of a social movement that preceded him.

The new grasp of the nature of experimental science gave Sprat and his contemporaries a better insight into ancient science. He said that Greek physics was utterly useless for the good of mankind. The Greeks regarded physics as an occupation for the private meditations of their wise men. 'What help did it ever bring to the vulgar? What visible benefit to any city, or country in the world? Their mechanics, and artificers (for whom the true natural philosophy should be principally intended) were so far from being assisted by those abstruse doctrines; that perhaps scarce any one of those professions, and trades, has well understood Aristotle's *Principles of Bodies*, from his own time down to ours.'

This had had unhappy consequences. Whereas arts and manufactures had tended steadily to improve, mental philosophy had been subject to severe vicissitudes. When empires fell, their mental culture dissolved, though their crafts tended to survive. This was due to the divorce of mental philosophy from the crafts. It was cultivated to a degree which placed it beyond the understanding of those unable to devote the whole of their lives to it, and was therefore incomprehensible to men of business. This led to the belief that it was useless. If it had been kept nearer to material things and processes, it would have survived better, like ploughing and iron-making, through the periods of social turmoil. 'By bringing philosophy down again to men's sight, and practice, from whence it was flown away so high: the Royal

Society has put it into a condition of standing out, against the invasions of time, or even barbarism itself.' By 'establishing it on a firmer foundation than the airy notions of men alone', that is, 'upon all the works of nature', and 'by turning it into one of the arts of life of which men may see there is daily need, they have provided that it cannot hereafter be extinguished', as in the past, 'at the loss of a library, at the overthrowing of a language, or at the death of some few philosophers'; for 'men must lose their eyes, and hands, and must leave off desiring to make their lives convenient, or pleasant, before they can be willing to destroy it'.

Sprat says that while the Royal Society had been considering methods of improving building materials, and the design of houses, roofs, chimneys, drains, wharves and streets, the disasters of the Plague and Fire of London had occurred. These had provided a motive for redoubling their labour on research into the constitution of nature. Improved technique provided the means for the quickest recovery from these disasters. It was the best source of encouragement, and for this reason, it seemed that 'the shops of mechanics' provide the best moral besides natural philosophy. Wren, Hooke, and their colleagues had the inspiration of building a new city on the most advantageous site in 'all Europe for trade and command'. They could plan a new world centre for trade and culture. The Royal Society set out to make a 'universal, constant, and impartial survey of the whole creation' as a contribution to that aim. Its international aspects were cultivated by correspondence with the leading scientists in all nations, during peace and war. The King gave special permission for the Society to continue its correspondence with Huyghens during the Anglo-Dutch war.

The mixture of merchants with scholars added an 'industrious, punctual and active genius' to the quiet and reserved temper of men of learning. It led to sustained efforts to improve technique. The Society's first endowed lecture was on the subject of mechanics. 'The noise of mechanic instruments' was heard in the King's palace at Whitehall. Chemical experiments were conducted there at his command. He increased the privileges of the College of Physicians, and planted a new garden for medicinal herbs. He considered planting fruits and trees, and an observatory, in St. James's Park. He encouraged improvements in the design of ships, sails, keels, etc., and was very ready to 'reward those that shall discover the meridian', i.e. shall show how to discover longitude at sea. He presently founded the Royal Observatory at Greenwich.

Sprat found the source of the energy which inspired all this activity in the social movements of the Reformation and Civil War. Few experiments had been made in Elizabeth's time because the classics were not yet assimilated, and the Reformation was not yet complete. But the Civil War 'stirred up men's mind from long ease and a lazy rest, and made them active, industrious and inquisitive'. The relics of antiquity were mastered, and men became weary of religious disputes, and 'not only the eyes of men, but their hands' are open and prepared to labour.

The fellows were asked to make a survey of treatises and descriptions of the natural and artificial products of all countries. They scoured the world for technical knowledge and ideas, like the planners in the Soviet Union. They started a catalogue of all trades, works and manufactures, noting the processes, instruments, tools, engines and manual operations employed. They started a catalogue of all the natural things, animals, plants and minerals, found in England. They began a survey and map of the stars and planets. They studied 'the way of finding the longitude of places by the Moon'. They studied methods of improving the manufacture of tapestry and silk. They sought how to improve saffron and the cultivation of potatoes. They attempted to discover how to make 'iron with sea-coal', one of the technical processes fundamental for modern industry and the development of England, as it relieved the iron smelter from the dependence on wood fuel, in which England was deficient. They attempted to use 'the dust of black lead instead of oil in clocks', and forecast the modern use of graphite lubricants. They studied the smelting of lead ore, and the use of pit coal. They attempted to change the taste of edible flesh by altering the feed of the animals from which it was procured. They tried to make wine out of sugar, so that an over-production of sugar in the West Indies might be utilized to replace expensive imported wines.

Hooke outlined a scheme for systematic meteorological observations. Petty designed and built a double-bottomed ship. Brouncker studied the recoil of guns, by full-scale experiments in the courtyard of Whitehall. His precise analysis of the phenomena led towards the distinction between energy and momentum. Graunt 'deduced many true conclusions, concerning the gravest, and most weighty parts of civil Government, and human nature' from the bills of mortality which had passed through the hands of every tradesman for many years without profit to anyone, 'except only to the clerks that collected them'. Hooke invented the watch spring. Wren invented a constant temperature furnace, and a thermostat for hatching eggs, and keeping at a constant temperature watches for finding longitude. He also investigated the mechanics of rowing, sailing, swimming and flying, and experimented on the transfusion of the blood. Descartes had based his conceptions of the laws of motion on experiments with tennis and billiard balls. Wren continued experiments with balls, and made the dynamics of collision clear for the first time. He studied the vibrations of pendulums, and conceived an arrangement which would simulate the movements of the solar system. He speculated on the law of gravitation, and his discussions with Hooke and others provided an important background of ideas for Newton's thoughts. Sprat said that Wren could 'lay peculiar claim' to the 'doctrine of motion, which is the most considerable of all others, for establishing the first principles of philosophy, by geometrical demonstrations'. He attempted to improve the use of terrestrial magnetism for navigation, and he invented rotating drums for continuous wind and temperature records.

Wren's talent, like Leonardo da Vinci's, was wonderful, but its chief significance lies not in its individual fascination as a magnificent flower of human ability, but in its integration of many arts and sciences. The indivisible relationship of all human activities is explicit in a career like his, and the impulse that science owes to practical and social interests is exemplified.

Sprat discusses the influence of the Royal Society's activities on the methods of education. He complains that the classical education unfits a man for business. It follows the 'preposterous course' of teaching general rules before particular things, and it makes students 'witty in objecting', rather than 'ready in resolving, and diligent in performing'. The young should be educated through the senses and memory, and not through the intellectual judgment. The best remedy for the defects of literary education is experimental training. All men are equal before the facts of nature, and the scientist 'looks on everything standing equal to it, and not as from a higher ground'. He does not see the world in terms of personal authority, and the conceptions of social rank. The upper classes cannot gain a deeper insight into nature merely by virtue of rank.

The experimenter does not always 'handle the very same subjects that are acted on the stage of the world; yet they are such as have a very great resemblance to them'. The experimenter receives a training appropriate for practical life, and his experience fits him to live in England, rather than 'Athens or Sparta'. His careful attention to facts and measurements cultivates the prudent habits characteristic of the *bourgeois*. 'The course of things goes quietly along', according to the even law of cause and effect, nature plodding on like a patient and industrious workman. One might also draw the reverse conclusion that *bourgeois* habits prepare men for work in experimental science, and when a *bourgeois* society has come into existence it may tend to cultivate experimental science.

Sprat, like Bacon, is at pains to prove that there is no conflict between science and religion. He instances Christ's miracles as divine experiments. In his own time, the piety of tradesmen has been particularly conspicuous. He points out that the English Church and the Royal Society have the same head, in the person of the king. They are both reformist, for one has reformed religion, while the other has reformed philosophy. 'They both follow the great precept of the apostle, of trying all things,' and holding fast to that which is good. If the English religion were otherwise, and 'an enemy to commerce, intelligence, discovery, navigation, or any sort of mechanics; how could it be fit for the present genius of this Nation?' Providence had indeed exhibited its benevolence by arranging this happy compatibility.

In these circumstances, it was legitimate to expect that the technique of manufacture would be improved. It would in fact be necessary to consider the results of improvements, and foresee whether 'they will not ruin those trades that are already settled'. He is confident that they will not, by appeal to a labour theory of value. 'The hands of men employed are true riches: the saving of those hands by inventions of art, and applying them to other works, will increase those riches'. Artisans should therefore not fear unemployment through the introduction of technical inventions.

The Dutch had particularly encouraged the invention of labour-saving devices, and immigration. This explained why they were more prosperous than the English.

The most rapid development of trade and industry would arise from direction by experimental philosophers. They would invent new trades. Modifying Plato, one could forecast that when mechanics had mental training, and philosophers had mechanics' manual skill, philosophy would attain to perfection.

The discovery of new worlds was to be expected from the invention of a reliable method of determining longitude at sea. As the Royal Society was studying this problem with 'peculiar care', its solution 'cannot now be far off'. The microscope had already revealed a far greater number of things than were contained in the universe visible to the naked eye.

Agriculture could be improved by the introduction of new plants. It was probable that the cultivation of flax could be established in Ireland, where many vast tracts of ground were 'now only possessed by wild beasts, or Tories almost as wild'.

In the past, technical inventions had been due mainly to the demands of 'luxury, or chance, or necessity'. The rate of development in expensive building and clothing had been fast, but there had been no improvement in building materials. Nor had there been any improvement in fundamental productive inventions, such as the cart and the plough. This division in direction of improvement reflected the circumstances of the origin of technique; 'the riches and dominion, that were at first in common, were unequally divided: the great, the wise, or the strong obtained a principal share; and either persuaded, or constrained all the rest to serve them with their bodies. Thence sprung all the arts of convenience, and pleasure, while the one part of men would not be content to live according to the first plainness of Nature: and the other were compelled to work with their hands, for the ease, and pleasure of their masters' lives, and the support of their own'.

The inventions of peace, war, cities, palaces, food, clothing and recreation sprang from this source, which is 'the most natural method of the foundation, and progress of manual arts'. They might improve by the discovery of new materials and processes.

The necessary research could not be undertaken without expenditure. The poets say that moral wisdom throve best in poverty, but it is certain that natural wisdom did not. It was fortunate that an unusual number of gentlemen in England were prepared to spend money on experiments. This was due to the protection of the sea. Her trade and forces were on the sea, and manned by working men. This enabled her gentlemen to stay at home and enjoy leisure. They lived in country houses, where there was much opportunity for observing nature. The gentlemen of continental nations such as France, Spain, Italy or Germany, were

10*

shut up in castles or cities, or engaged as officers in the big armies, and had less leisure and opportunity for experimental inquiry.

The English also had the benefit of changed social manners. The former governing classes talked only with their servants and travelled little. The new governing class was more affable, which increased the exchange in ideas. The gentry could no longer be averse from promoting trade through fear of social debasement. 'For they are to know that traffic and commerce have given mankind a higher degree than any title of nobility, even that of civility, and humanity itself.'

Sprat published his remarkable book four years before Newton's, and eleven years before Halley's, election to the Royal Society. A great scheme for the development of science to the benefit of mankind had been conceived, and to a considerable degree put into operation by the fellows of the Royal Society before those great men joined their ranks. The scope of the plans and the profusion of experiments and achievements show that the development could have been due only to a powerful social movement, and not to the accidental inspiration of a few talented men. The century preceded the genius in the 'century of genius'. Newton clarified and worked out with unparalleled ability some of the conceptions and methods emerging from the movement that led to the formation of the Royal Society. But the degree of his success had some unfortunate, besides advantageous, effects. It helped to concentrate scientists' attention on particular problems, and to professionalize the Royal Society. The Society's early enthusiasm with planned research for the benefit of mankind, which it had learned from Bacon, and the social movement that had inspired him, gradually declined in favour of technical virtuosity. It is probable that the social planning of research, and the conduct of particular researches, could not easily be done together, and that they separated through necessity. The Society's interest in the social utilization of science dwindled, and even the quality of particular researches, as described in its transactions, declined at the end of the seventeenth century. Hamilton has pointed out that the decrease of the rate of development of science at the end of the seventeenth century is parallel to the first halt of the general rise of prices since the discovery of America. Trade remained very profitable until the end of the century. This provided the optimism, and the motive for the enterprise, of the founders of the Royal Society.

Merton has made a very interesting and able analysis of the correlation of the development of science in the seventeenth century with industrial development, and especially with the growth of Puritanism. He has demonstrated in detail the inseparable development of science, technology and religion in this period, and has shown that the general themes of science were set by the sociological conditions, while interest in particular subjects within these themes varied according to the success and ability of talented individuals. For instance, Boyle, Hooke, Newton, Huyghens, Wren and Halley produced a special interest in physics by their remarkable achievements, but even they did not produce more than an extra expansion of a vigorous, pre-existing development.

In 1667 the Royal Society was only five years old. In 1939 it was 277 years old. Its long career has been packed with fascinating scientific events, but its record has never been more brilliant than in its first thirty years. The best features in the surviving Society had already been formed in that time; but some of the most important original features have withered for two centuries. The insight into the social relations of science shown by Bacon and the founders had virtually been forgotten until recently. The revival of this insight is connected with contemporary social changes, which rival or surpass the great social changes that occurred in England in the seventeenth century. The Royal Society's relative lack of interest in the social relations of science since the end of that century until recently is a reflection of an unchanging conception of the relation of science to society in the intervening period.

63

The Great Problem of the Shipping Period

ANDREW MACKAY wrote in his treatise on Longitude, published in 1810, that 'in every commercial state, any work that has for its object the improvement of the art of navigation, will always be favourably received'. The growth of ocean trade provided a powerful motive for improving the science of navigation. This depends on the determination of position on the surface of the ocean. If land is in sight, and landmarks are recognizable, the position of the ship may be determined by consulting a chart of the place observed, but if the ship is on the open sea, this method cannot be used. Position is given most conveniently in terms of latitude and longitude, so the ocean navigator requires methods of determining these when out of sight of land. As he is on a rolling and pitching ship, which sails through climates of varying temperature and pressure, he needs methods that will give accurate results in spite of these disturbances. Latitude is fairly easily determined from the altitude of the sun and stars. During the Middle Ages this was done with the elementary astronomical instrument, the cross staff. Its use was superseded by the sextant. This was introduced by Hadley in 1731, and was independently invented by Newton in England and Godfrey in America. Hooke preceded these with the invention of a similar instrument. Thus the sextant was independently invented almost simultaneously, in different parts of the world, by several persons. Its essential feature consists of mirrors which enable the observer to bring the images of two observed stars to coincidence, and thus accurately measure the angle between the stars. It is equally useful for finding the angle between the sun's lower limb and the apparent horizon. It gives a direct and quick result, which is accurate even when the instrument is held in the hand.

The problem of determining longitude was far more difficult. The direct way was by dead reckoning. The speed of the ship was estimated, or measured by casting a log overboard at the prow of the ship, and noting the time the ship, whose length was known, took to sail past it. The distance travelled east or west could then be computed, and this would give the longitude. When Columbus sailed back to Europe from the discovery of the New World, he disputed with his lieutenant whether they were approaching Madeira or the Azores. Each was skilled in the known methods of navigation, but their estimates of longitude differed by six hundred miles. In fact, neither knew where they were. Columbus had inspired his crew by falsely persuading them that he could accurately determine the ship's position. His calculation of longitude was so erroneous that he believed that

Cuba was part of Asia, and forced his crew to sign an affidavit to that effect. As Gould remarks, he attempted to abolish the Pacific Ocean by legislation.

The inability to determine longitudes led to very serious losses at sea. Between 1691 and 1721, England alone lost five naval squadrons from this cause.

When a ship sails along a parallel of latitude, the heavenly bodies preserve a constant altitude, but cross the meridian, and rise or set, earlier or later, to an observer on the ship. The longitude of the ship may be determined from the difference between local time on the ship, and standard time, on some fixed meridian of reference, such as that which passes through Greenwich.

The first theoretically satisfactory method of determining local time was proposed by Galileo. The eclipses of Jupiter's satellites, which occur frequently, and at very approximately the same time for observers at all points on the earth, may be predicted. Longitude may therefore be determined by comparing the time of an eclipse on a known longitude with the local time of the eclipse as observed on the ship. The method proved to be impracticable because the eclipses could not be steadily observed if the ship had the slightest movement, and for other technical reasons.

The most promising method of determining local time from the heavenly bodies is provided by the moon. It moves relatively rapidly across the sky, covering about twelve degrees in twenty-four hours. This gives changes of position large enough for accurate measurement. Hence, if the position of the moon could be accurately predicted, its place relative to the stars would give local time. Great efforts were made to collect accurate observations of the moon's motion. The Greenwich Observatory was founded in 1675, chiefly for this purpose. Flamsteed was instructed by Charles II, when appointed the first Astronomer Royal, 'to apply himself with the utmost care and diligence to the rectifying the tables of the motions of the heavens, and the places of the fixed stars, in order to find out the so much desired longitude at sea, for perfecting the art of navigation'.

The production of a theory of the moon's motion based on the new observations required the discovery of a general theory of planetary motions. This was given by Isaac Newton twelve years after the founding of the Greenwich Observatory, in his theory of universal gravitation. He said that this was the most difficult problem he had ever attacked, and was the only one that gave him headaches. The moon is attracted by the sun and planets, besides the earth, so its motion is extremely complicated.

The method of determining longitude from the moon's motion was suggested by Werner in 1514, but even Newton, two centuries later, had not perfected it beyond an error of two or three degrees, or from one to two hundred miles.

Another method, proposed by the Flemish astronomer Frisius in 1530, was the use of a very accurate watch. Portable clocks driven by coiled springs had been invented some thirty years before. Slow progress was made with this suggestion, owing to the difficulty of making accurate watches. The Nürnberg 'eggs', or watches, varied about quarter of an hour a day, while a variation of less than two or three seconds was necessary for satisfactory determinations of longitude. Huyghens was the first to construct a timekeeper designed to give longitude at sea. This clock, which was made in 1660, was regulated by a pendulum to provide more exact running. In order to perfect his clock, Huyghens analysed the mathematical theory of the pendulum, and discussed the influence of the rotation of the earth, and the shape of the earth, on its motion. This analysis, which contains the first correct theory of circular and wave motions, was published in 1673, and greatly assisted Newton in his creation of the general theory of planetary motions. If the period of the pendulum varied at different places on the earth's surface, it could not be of assistance in determining longitude. Hence experimental and theoretical knowledge of the pendulum, and its related problems of variation of gravity, of the shape of the earth, and the theory of circular motion, became of the first importance in connection with the possible determination of longitude. An expedition was sent in 1660 by the French Academy of Sciences to measure the period at Cayenne, in South America, of a pendulum that beat seconds at Paris. It was found to be slower. In 1672 Richet observed that a Paris seconds pendulum lost two minutes twenty-eight seconds daily at Cayenne. Newton deduced from this that the earth bulges at the Equator, and a spheroid whose diameters are as 230:229. The King of France ordered a direct measurement of the shape of the earth by survey. Expeditions were sent to Peru and Swedish Lapland about 1735, and returned with figures that confirmed Newton's prediction.

The *Principia* may be regarded, to a large extent, as a theoretical synthesis of the problems set in gravity, circular motion, planetary and lunar movement, and the shape and size of the earth, by the demand for better navigation. But it did not provide satisfactory practical answers. Newton said in 1713 that lunar theory would not then reliably give position within two or three degrees, or one to two hundred miles. 'A watch to keep time exactly' would do, 'but, by reason of the motion of a ship, the variation of heat and cold, wet and dry, and the difference in gravity in different latitudes, such a watch hath not yet been made'.

The British Government established in 1712 a Committee on Longitude. A bill was passed offering a reward of up to £20,000 for 'such person or persons as shall discover the Longitude', and sanctioning expenditure on encouragement and experiment. The Commission on Longitude lasted until 1828, and in 115 years considered a number of practical proposals and innumerable suggestions from cranks. Swift satirized these in his 'Ode for Music, on the longitude'. It expended altogether about £101,000 on aids and rewards to discoverers of longitude. Prizes were also offered by other governments. Philip II of Spain offered the first in 1598, perhaps through memories of the navigational disasters to his Armada.

The competitors for the English prizes concentrated on the lunar theory, or on the construction of accurate watches. The astronomer Halley studied tables of lunar observations and discovered a periodicity of eighteen years eleven days in the lunar motion. This enabled him to determine the moon's motion within two minutes.

Lunar theory was gradually improved, and Mayer in 1755 produced tables which gave a result correct to within half a degree. He died in 1762, and his widow was awarded a prize of £3,000 by the Commission of Longitude. The mathematician Euler received £300 for discovering the improved theory upon which Mayer's computations were based. The tables were tested on voyages to St. Helena and the West Indies. Mayer's tables were published in 1766 by the Commissioners, as the first issue of the *Nautical Almanac*, which has appeared annually ever since.

While the astronomers were struggling with the lunar theory, clock-makers attempted to construct watches unaffected by motion, temperature, humidity and gravity, which would keep time accurately enough to give the longitude to within half a degree. The problem was first solved in 1764 by John Harrison, the Yorkshire carpenter, after forty years of experiment and construction. He spent six years on his first machine, which was completed in 1735, and weighed 72 lb. It was tested on a voyage to Lisbon, and gave a promising performance. He was awarded £500 to construct a second machine. This was completed in 1739 and weighed 103 lb. He received a further £500 for a third machine, and seventeen years passed before it was finished in 1757. It weighed 66 lb. He now proposed to construct a time-keeper like a large watch. This fourth machine, which he named a chronometer, was about five inches in diameter, and beautifully finished. It was not supported on gimbals to keep it horizontal in the ship, and was merely laid on a cushion in a case.

It was tested on a voyage to Jamaica in 1761, and gave the longitude correct to less than two minutes of a degree. Harrison was entitled to the prize, if he could prove that the performance was not accidental. This was difficult, and a long wrangle began. The contemporary Astronomer Royal, Maskelyne, was biassed in favour of the lunar theory method, and had advised the acceptance of Mayer's tables. A second test of Harrison's chronometer showed that it would measure time correct to fifteen seconds in five months. He was now doubly entitled to the prize, but the Commissioners would not give it to him until he had shown them the works, which was not part of the original offer. But he received the balance of the first half of the £20,000 in 1765, when he was seventy-two years old. He had to make two more chronometers to prove that they could be repeated. The Board still procrastinated, and proposed very severe tests for them. Harrison was now seventy-seven, and still had not received the second £10,000. But George III became personally interested in the machines. The tests on one of them were made at the King's private observatory at Kew, and George took a sporting interest in the performance. He attended the daily observations, and was keenly interested to see how they kept inside the record. He finally used his influence to force Parliament to give Harrison the remaining half of the prize. This was achieved in 1772, when Harrison was seventy-nine.

He had proved by patience and fine workmanship that successful chronometers could be made. His machines were soon superseded by those of Le Roy, who had a more ingenious conception of the principles of chronometer design, and could think out problems that Harrison solved empirically. The problems of the industrial production of chronometers at reasonable prices were solved by the end of the eighteenth century.

The chronometer remained the standard instrument for determining longitude at sea until the twentieth century. It was then superseded by the radio time signal, that gives standard time virtually instantaneously at every point on the earth's surface.

The lunar theory became the chief scientific problem of the eighteenth century. It received intense intellectual study. The late Astronomer Royal, F. W. Dyson, has written that up 'to the present day, distinguished mathematicians of England, France, Germany and America have given large portions of their lives to the Lunar Theory. More arithmetic and algebra have been devoted to it than to any other question of astronomy or mathematical physics'.

This attention is not due to a peculiar curiosity of scientists about the moon, but to the former importance of lunar theory for navigation. In the seventeenth and eighteenth centuries, when English society was based on ocean trade and navigation, astronomy, which through lunar theory was the science most closely connected with navigation, became the senior science in universities. Its prestige was not surpassed by that of other branches of physics until the middle of the nineteenth century, when heat and electricity became the leading physical sciences. The amount of arithmetic and algebra devoted to the theory of electricity must be approaching, or already have surpassed, that devoted to lunar theory. This is not because scientists now find electricity more curious than the moon, but because electricity is of more interest than lunar motion to a society in which the problems of industrial production have become more important than those of ocean trade. Yet even this position is not final. The development of space research since the Second World War has stimulated an intense revival in planetary theory and computation. The problems of the navigation of space have given a strong impetus to the development of the computer, and all that that signifies.

64

The New Slave

TRADE and manufacture necessarily grow together, and exert a mutual influence, but in some periods trade has the chief initiative, and in others, manufacture. Trade possessed the chief initiative in the fifteenth to the seventeenth centuries. The feature of this period was the expansion of trade, which stimulated the production of raw materials and finished goods. Ancient technical methods of agriculture, mining and handicraft were strained to the limits of their possibilities in the effort to supply the new demand. The water wheel and the windmill were improved, and increased in size until they became unwieldy, and liable to excessive breakdowns for repairs. But these machines could not meet the increasing demand for mechanical labour. The number of convenient sites possessing water-power was limited, and the wind was fickle and weak. Some producers deserted this line of development, which had been followed steadily since the end of the dark ages, and turned back to slavery for an increased supply of power. The growth of negro slavery in the West Indies and the southern English colonies in North America provided the most striking example, but there were many others. Slavery was revived in Europe in the eighteenth century by the landowners of Eastern Prussia. Pirenne has commented on the great influence of this event on modern European history. It affected the tradition of these landowners, who provided a large number of the officers of the German army and civil service. When Germany became a modern industrial nation in the second half of the nineteenth century, she inherited this governing class, with its dictatorial tradition. Her foreign policy, which was an important contributory cause of the war of 1914, was formed by this class. The same class helped to restore authoritarian government after the war by assisting Hitler to seize political power.

The social conditions in the eighteenth century were not, in general, favourable to a return to slavery. The improvement of machinery seemed to offer a quicker route to increased profits. At that time machines were generally small, and evidently subordinate aids to the workman. The best way of improving the machine was to encourage the workman who was its master. Far-sighted social thinkers advocated initiative for the workman, as the best way of improving machinery and increasing production. This tendency, combined with centuries of Christian agitation for respect for the individual, made a general return to slavery unprofitable. Invention became the most promising source of increased production.

The industrial growth that followed the period of the great navigations is exemplified in the British coal industry. London became a great port, with a rising population of East India traders, and industries connected with them. The supply of English wood for domestic fires, industry and shipbuilding was insufficient, and substitutes were required. The situation was reflected in the increase in the price of firewood. While general prices rose by a factor of three from the middle of the fifteenth to the middle of the seventeenth centuries, the price of firewood rose by a factor of eight.

The new demand for fuel was met by increasing the imports of coal from Newcastle. This emancipated London from dependence on the naturally meagre English wood supply, and allowed population and industry to rise to a new degree of concentration.

The effect of this development on the production of coal in the Newcastle district is seen in the figures compiled by Nef and quoted by Merton. The annual export to the London district rose from 22,000 tons about 1550 to 690,000 tons about 1680, an increase of thirty times. The total annual output rose from 65,000 tons to 1,225,000 tons in the same period. The annual output of the whole British industry rose from 210,000 tons to 2,982,000 tons.

This prodigious rise of coal production was not an exceptional industrial phenomenon. The output of the salt and glass industries increased about fifteenfold. There were comparable advances in the alum and copperas, saltpetre, soap and brewing industries. A great industrial revolution occurred in the century preceding the *Principia*. It was followed by a century of slower progression. The annual output of coal rose from 2,982,000 tons about 1680 to 10,295,000 tons about 1780, or only threefold in comparison with the fourteenfold of the previous century. In contrast, the output rose to 241,910,000 tons about 1900, so that during the nineteenth century the increase was about twenty-fourfold. The rate of scientific discovery shows a parallel variation. It was very rapid until the end of the seventeenth century, then relatively slow until the end of the eighteenth century, rising again during the nineteenth century. The growth of science in the seventeenth century was associated with an industrial revolution little less great than that which occurred at the end of the eighteenth century.

The increase of coal production between 1550 and 1680 involved a qualitative besides a quantitative change in the industry. Hitherto, it had been a local hand industry, where men picked a few tons of coal from outcrops in hills or on the sea shore. Now it had become a national industry, in which large quantities of material were transported over great distances. It provided conditions for the growth of capitalistic organization, and the invention of mining machinery that would increase production.

The preoccupation of inventors with mining problems at this time is reflected in the patents issued. Nef states that seventy-five per cent of the 317 patents issued in England between 1561 and 1688 were directly or indirectly connected with mining. Forty-three of these were devices for improving the drainage of mines. Twenty per cent of all the patents issued between 1620 and 1640 dealt with water-raising and drainage. The problems that Agricola had discussed so well in the middle of the sixteenth century in connection with metal mining became more acute than ever through the rapidly increasing demand for coal and ores. The exhaustion of outcrops made the drainage of deep mines the most pressing technical problem. The ancient types of vacuum and force pump could no longer provide adequate service. Other ways of raising water were sought. Inventors tried to find new methods of blowing water up pipes. Hero of Alexandria had employed the expansive force of heated air for driving water through fountains. The inventors of the Renaissance tried to use steam for the same purpose. They did not clearly distinguish between hot air and steam. Leonardo da Vinci had investigated the pressure produced by steam, and the Italian della Porta, who followed in his tradition, published in 1606 the first description of a machine for raising water by steam pressure. The water to be raised was held in a tank with a rising pipe, and was forced up the pipe by admitting steam to the tank from a boiler.

Another source of propulsion was gunpowder. Accurate knowledge of the properties of gunpowder was one of the chief interests of the military monarchs who founded the Royal

Society and the French Academy of Sciences. When Huyghens was engaged by the latter body at its foundation in 1666, he directed researches on the possibility of using gunpowder as a motive for an internal combustion engine. He engaged Denis Papin to assist in this work. Papin found that he could not make the gunpowder engine work because 'a fifth part of the air' remained in the cylinder after each explosion, and prevented the formation of a perfect vacuum. He sought a working substance that left no residue, and reflected that this could be obtained from steam, which may be completely condensed into water, and in this form conveniently removed from the working cylinder, leaving a perfect vacuum. Papin embodied this idea in a machine. He constructed a vertical cylinder with a piston, and with heat applied to the base of the cylinder. The water turned into steam and forced the piston up, where it was held by a catch. The machine was allowed to cool, so that a vacuum was formed under the piston. When the catch was released, the piston was forced down by the pressure of the atmosphere, and could be used to do work. Papin published a description of this machine, which is the essential part of the steam vacuum engine, in 1690. While he had been advancing towards the piston engine, Thomas Savery, a native of Devonshire, employed della Porta's method of raising water by direct steam pressure in a practicable machine. He was awarded a patent in 1698 for a 'new invention for raising of water and occasioning motion to all sorts of mill work by the impellent force of fire, which will be of great use and advantage for draining mines, serving towns with water, and for the working of all sorts of mills where they have not the benefit of water nor constant winds'. He wrote a tract entitled *The Miner's Friend*, in which he showed how his engine could be used to drain mines. It seems that he conceived that his water-raising engine would be used to keep water mill-wheels running in dry weather by pumping the water back from the tail race. Savery may have received hints for his invention from the work of the Marquis of Worcester, who left obscure accounts of engines in his *Century of Inventions*. According to a work published in France in 1664, the Marquis made a machine which would raise four large buckets of water forty feet in one minute.

Savery demonstrated his machine to the King and the Royal Society in 1699. It consisted essentially of a tank connected by a pipe with a water sump. Steam was admitted to the tank, and then condensed. The vacuum so formed caused the water to be pushed up through a non-return valve from the sump into the tank. Fresh steam was now let into the tank, and the pressure forced the water through a vertical delivery pipe.

Savery was able to make one horse-power pumps, which would raise water about fifty feet, for about £50. His larger pumps were unsuccessful, owing to the engineering difficulties of making good pressure tanks and joints. When these became surmountable by improved engineering technique, his principle was employed successfully, and was embodied in the pulsometer pump introduced in 1876, and still used.

Savery apparently dropped his inventions as soon as he was appointed to a sinecure in 1705.

Another Devonshire man, Thomas Newcomen, was also working on the invention of steam pumps. He was an ironmonger in Dartmouth, who supplied iron tools to the Devonshire tin mines. During his business visits to the mines, he noticed the heavy cost of the horse-driven drainage pumps, and sought to invent a fire-driven pump to replace them. Newcomen was at work on this engine in 1698, before he had heard of Savery, and he experimented for ten years before he had solved his problem. This was mechanical, and consisted of making the operation of a Papin's cylinder self-acting. The history of his procedure is quite unknown. There is no evidence that he had read any account of Papin's works, and the story that he had been advised by Robert Hooke is discredited.

He had to make several first-rate inventions in the course of his achievement. He invented valve-gear, which, apart from the watch, was the first self-acting mechanism. He introduced the internal spray for cooling the steam inside the cylinder with the maximum speed, and the important snifting valve which released the obstructive dissolved air driven out of the boiler water by the heating.

He presently found that he could not patent his engine because Savery's patent covered all engines deriving their power from fire, so he went into partnership with Savery. They built a machine near Dudley Castle in 1712 for draining a mine in the Staffordshire coalfield. This was the true occasion of the birth of the steam engine. A description of the machine mentions no less than fifty-six parts. It raised water 153 feet at a rate of 120 gallons a minute.

Newcomen engines were in use in seven English counties by 1715. The first engine used abroad was erected in 1722 at Chemnitz, the centre of the mining industry described by Agricola. As early as 1725, an engine costing more than £1,000 was built in Scotland. The chief item of expense was the working cylinder. This was cast in brass, and cost about £250.

The increasing demand for metal goods had stimulated research on processes for cheapening the production of iron. The ancient method of smelting used charcoal, but the supply of this, especially in England, was inadequate and expensive. Repeated attempts were made to use coal, but were industrially unsuccessful until 1713, when Abraham Darby mastered the technique of smelting with coke made from coal. Whereas the pig iron made from charcoal had been converted into wrought iron, the pig iron made with coke was cast into vessels and pipes. The cost of cylinders for Newcomen engines fell from £250 to £25 when they could be cast in iron instead of brass.

The technical difficulties of iron founding are considerable. Cast iron varies greatly according to composition and preparation. Its properties, and the general processes of the steel industry were studied scientifically by Réaumur, who began a series of researches on these subjects in 1711. He published the trade secrets of the steel industry, which were two thousand years old. He identified the various sorts of cast iron by the microscope, and classified them into ten grades. He knew that grey iron was the best for casting, and that it tended to become white and brittle when reheated. He devised tests for strength and hardness, and in general founded modern scientific metallurgy.

Réaumur was acquainted with coke iron smelting independently of Darby, but in spite of this, and his great scientific contribution to metallurgy, the French iron industry failed to utilize his achievements. The economic pressure for the development of the iron industry was greater in England, and technical development followed the pressure of economics rather than the guidance of a scientist in advance of his economic environment. The history of Réaumur's metallurgical work shows how pure science tends to wither unless it is in robust connection with social needs.

The Newcomen engine saved the Newcastle coal industry. Disastrous flooding had started at the end of the seventeenth century, and without powerful new pumps many mines would have been permanently drowned out. The engine was a success in the mining industry, though very inefficient, because it could be fired with low grade unsaleable pit-head coal. It was less successful in metal mining districts such as Cornwall, where coal was imported and expensive.

No great improvement on the Newcomen engine was made for fifty years. The decline in engineering invention accompanied the general decline in rate of technical progress in the first half of the eighteenth century, which has already been mentioned. It seems that the Newcomen engine, like the *Principia*, belongs to the seventeenth century burst of technical development. When that burst was exhausted, no great innovation in engines occurred until a new social growth demanded it. The new industrial development started in the middle of the eighteenth century, and was associated particularly with the textile industry. By 1765 an improved engine was overdue. In that year James Watt invented his engine with a separate condenser, and at one stroke reduced engine fuel bills by about 75 per cent.

Watt was an instrument maker attached to Glasgow College, or University. He was asked to repair a defective model of a Newcomen engine used in demonstrations to the students of natural philosophy. He experimented with it and made it work, and was struck by its very large consumption of steam. He found that the volume of steam used in each stroke was several times that of the cylinder, and he noticed that this was due to the alternate heating and cooling of the cylinder during each stroke. This led him to an experimental study of the properties of steam. He found that steam is about 1,800 times as bulky as water at the boiling point. When the temperature was raised above the boiling point, its pressure rose in a geometrical ratio. If steam was passed into cold water, the volume of the water increased by one-sixth before it began to boil. This meant that the heat in a pound of steam was able to raise the temperature of six pounds of water to the boiling point. He was puzzled by this phenomenon, which was explained to him by James Black, the professor of chemistry in the college, who had just discovered latent heat. Seeing that one cause of the high consumption of steam, and hence of fuel, in Newcomen engines was due to the alternate heating and cooling of the cylinder during each stroke, he thought intensely of how it might be evaded. The solution shot into his mind during a Sunday walk on Glasgow Green. 'As steam was an elastic body it would rush into a vacuum, and if a communication was made between the cylinder and an exhausted vessel, it would rush into it and might be there condensed, without cooling the cylinder.'

He designed an engine with the working cylinder enclosed in a steam casing connècted with the boiler. This kept the working cylinder steadily at the temperature of the boiler steam. The top of the piston, instead of being exposed to the atmosphere, as in the Newcomen engine, was also exposed to steam from the boiler through a separate valve. The bottom of the piston, and the empty cylinder below it, were connected to the external condenser, and were therefore in connection with a vacuum. Owing to the difference in pressure between the boiler steam and the vacuum, the top side of the piston was pushed down the cylinder by the steam. Watt had, as it were, substituted steam for the atmosphere in a Newcomen engine, and now the steam pressure instead of the air pressure did the work.

As the working steam in the Watt engine was at first a substitute for the atmosphere, steam at very little more than atmospheric pressure was used. This reduced the difficulties of boiler design and made the engine safe. Watt subsequently obtained an increase of efficiency by cutting off the steam supply to the piston early in the stroke, so that the steam could do further work by its own expansion. But he obstructed the development of the high-pressure steam engine with or without condensers.

The industrial exploitation of Watt's improved engine was undertaken by the magnate Matthew Boulton. This manufacturer had a large works at Birmingham, in which factory and mass-production methods were being evolved. Handicraftsmen were leaving their home workshops to be organized in factories. These conditions stimulated sub-division assemblies of machinery. Boulton was keenly aware of the increasing demand for mill engines, and reported in 1781 that 'the people in London, Manchester and Birmingham are *steam mill mad*'. He formed the grand conception of patenting the Watt engine in all countries, and drawing tribute from the industry of the whole world. He had the capitalist idea of conquering the world by industrial instead of military power.

Boulton and Watt drew their patent royalties in the form of a percentage of the saving of fuel through the efficiency of their engine. This led to careful measurement by Watt of the work done by engines. He measured the average work done by horses and fixed a unit of horse-power, and gave the performance of his engines in terms of this unit. As a part of this scientific rating of the performance of his engines, Watt invented the indicator for registering the changes in steam pressure inside the cylinder during the stroke. The indicator consisted of a small piston pressed by the steam from the cylinder against a spring. The amount of compression was recorded by a pointer, which consequently gave the variations of pressure in the working cylinder. In 1796, Watt's colleague, James Southern, arranged that the pointer should carry a pencil bearing on a board connected with the main piston. As this moved backwards and forwards, and the pointer moved upwards and downwards according to the variations in steam pressure inside the cylinder, the pencil traced out on the board a closed curve which gave a complete history of the pressure changes inside the cylinder, and provided the data from which the work done in the cylinder by the steam could be calculated. This is the famous indicator diagram.

The Boulton & Watt firm kept the indicator as secret as possible, and it was not generally known until travellers brought back in 1826 a specimen used by the firm's men in Russia.

The young French physicist, Sadi Carnot, either learned of the existence of the indicator diagram, or rediscovered it. He set out to discover from a theoretical analysis of the diagram the maximum quantity of power that could be obtained in a Watt engine from the production of a defined quantity of heat in the boiler. Carnot assumed that heat was a fluid, and did work in the heat engine by falling from a high to a low temperature, by analogy with the water wheel. Together with this partly erroneous analogy, he had noted that the transmission of heat from a hot to a cold body through the medium of an engine led to the production of work, while the flow of heat from the hot to the cold part of a conductor did no work, so he concluded that the work done by the engine must have been derived from the changes in volume or state produced by the heat in the water. Hence the power was produced by the repeated addition to, and subtraction of heat from, the water, and was due to a cycle of operations. He then pointed out that the degree of reversibility was one of the conditions that determined the efficiency of a heat engine.

The greater the losses by conduction of heat, friction and leakage during the working stroke, the less is the approach to reversibility, and the less the efficiency. The other factor governing the efficiency was the difference in temperature between the boiler and the condenser. Carnot remarked that his assumption that the amount of heat in the steam was the same at the beginning and the end of the stroke was not entirely satisfactory. He subsequently discovered the error in this assumption, and saw that work arose not from the fall, but from the consumption of heat. From this he calculated the mechanical equivalent of heat, but he died prematurely in 1832 of cholera, at the age of thirty-six, and his calculations were not published until 1878.

A clear understanding of the relation between heat and work was not gained until 150 years after the invention of the steam engine in 1712. This was due to the very low efficiency of the early engines. So little of the heat put into them was used that observers thought that heat was the medium through which the work was done, and not its source. The exact measurement of the consumption of heat in a steam engine is difficult, and was not satisfactorily accomplished until the 1860s, twenty years after the equivalence of heat and work had been proved by other methods.

The introduction of the steam locomotive gave a further impulse to the study of heat. Osborne Reynolds has remarked that the Newcomen and Watt condensing engine 'contributed to the discovery of the mechanical origin of heat, in that it led to the recognition of work as the measure of mechanical action; and to the locomotive must be attributed the birth of that philosophical interest respecting heat and work which immediately followed its general introduction. The condensing engine had not been obtrusive—it was not generally seen unless looked for. The locomotive is obtrusive; it will be seen: and by 1842 locomotives had obtruded themselves pretty well all over Europe. They immediately took their places as objects of as much wonder and interest to the grown people who saw them for the first time as they are still to the young; demanding the attention even of philosophers who had previously studied nothing lower than the planets'.

The introduction into physics of the engineer's method of measuring work was made by J. P. Joule, the son of a Manchester brewer. Joule's father had had his son instructed in chemistry by John Dalton, to prepare him for the family business. Joule acquired a knowledge of pumps and engines while playing as a youth among the machinery of the brewery. His precise investigations into the relation between heat and work did not, however, arise directly out of an interest in the steam engine. A new motive power had been discovered. This was the electric current. Volta had discovered in 1800 how to produce an electric current. In 1821 Faraday showed how mutual rotation could be obtained from a magnet and a conductor. Sturgeon invented the electro-magnet in 1825, and the commutator in 1836. In the latter year, when he was eighteen years old, Joule began to investigate the possibility of making electric motors to supersede the steam engine. He started with the erroneous belief that the strength of an electro-magnet might be increased indefinitely, and he was unaware of the electrical effect of induced resistance which prevents the electric motor from becoming a perpetual motion machine.

Joule could not make a balance-sheet of the performance of his improved motors without accurate measurements of the heat produced in them while running. The analysis of his results suggested that heat, work, electricity and chemical affinity were equivalent; and he derived the figure of 838 for the mechanical equivalent of heat. He deduced from his results that the Watt engine, in spite of its low absolute efficiency, would never be superseded by the 'electro-magnetic engine, worked by the voltaic batteries at present used', because the work obtained from one pound of coal in a Watt engine was about equal to the work obtained from one pound of zinc consumed in batteries supplying an electric motor, and zinc was much more expensive than coal.

According to Reynolds, Joule's use of the engineer's method of measuring the work done by his electric motors, by measuring how much weight they would lift in a given time, was the first example in physics of measurement in absolute units. His intro-duction of the engineer's method led to the conclusive proof of the conservation of energy, the chief result of physical research in the nineteenth century. Maxwell subsequently used the ideas of the market to describe this discovery, and compared the material universe with 'a system of credit'. The growth of the ideas of commercial exchange accustomed the mind to the modes of thought which enabled it later to recognize the existence of the conservation of energy.

The discovery of the conservation of energy is connected with the notion of exchange value. Capitalism cannot be operated without an exact knowledge of the equivalence of different forms of energy. This is needed for accurate fixing of the price of coal, electricity, gas and labour. When these are to be sold in exchange, they must be measured, and a common currency found for them. This currency is energy.

When Joule found that heat was equivalent to mechanical work, he perceived that the heat in a gas was probably due to the motion of its constituent particles. He published a calculation in 1844, showing that if this assumption was correct, there must be an absolute zero of temperature, at about −480° Fahrenheit. He confirmed the assumption experimentally, by showing that to a high degree of accuracy 'no change of temperature occurs when air is allowed to expand in such a manner as not to develop mechanical power'.

Mayer in Germany independently developed the mechanical theory of heat. He started from medical observations on the human body, which at first sight have nothing to do with steam engines. But in fact, Mayer made his discoveries through the adoption of Lavoisier's conception of the human body as a heat engine, which had clearly been inspired by the development of the steam engine.

Owing to the erroneous assumption in Carnot's published paper, that no heat is consumed during the working cycle of an engine, theoretical physicists were led to believe that Carnot's cycle and the mechanical equivalence of heat were inconsistent. Clausius was the first to show, in 1850, that this was not so. Kelvin made the same discovery independently, one year later.

The science of heat as a mode of motion, or thermodynamics, was based on two laws: that energy can neither be created nor destroyed, and that on balance of exchange, heat never flows from a cold to a hot body. The new science opened up vast fields of research in two main directions. One was towards a more particular analysis of the properties of gases, and the other was towards the application of the theory of the conservation of energy to general aspects of material nature. Kelvin pointed out that the material universe was moving towards a uniform temperature, and 'within a finite period of time to come the earth must again be unfit for the habitation of man as at present constituted, unless operations have been or are to be performed which are impossible under the laws to which the known operations going on at present in the material world are subject'. According to Lovering, these conclusions led the *Spectator* to call 'heat the communist of the universe', which levels all things. Joule pointed out in 1843 that 'we shall be able to represent the whole phenomena of chemistry by exact numerical expressions, so as to be enabled to predict the existence and properties of new compounds'.

J. Willard Gibbs made an advance towards this aim. His predecessors, following the guidance of the steam engine, which had actually drawn its own indicator diagram and presented it to physicists for their consideration, so that the machine directly led the mind, had investigated the relations between pressure, volume and temperature in a single fluid, which was an idealized steam. Their results were of use to engineers, but not to chemists, for they work with mixtures of fluids rather than single fluids. Gibbs extended the new science of thermodynamics to mixtures, and thus made it of use to chemists. He started by generalizing the engineer's indicator diagram, and showed that more convenient diagrams describing the thermodynamic properties of systems might be made by using properties other than pressure, volume and temperature. For instance, entropy and volume could be used for describing the thermodynamical condition of mixtures, such as one containing ice, water and water-vapour. He advanced towards Joule's aim, and showed how the formation of new bodies may be forecast in such phenomena as superheating and supercooling. He deduced his celebrated phase rule, which governs the separation of components in mixtures. Roozeboom used it to predict the existence of new substances and interpret the constitution of steel, which is a system of iron and carbon. Freeth provided England with adequate supplies of ammonium salts by its aid in 1914. Without this application of the phase rule, England would have lost the war.

The other line of application of thermodynamics, to the motion of particles, continued an ancient development. Democritus and the Ionian Greeks had invented the atomic theory, but the collection of experimental evidence in its favour began only in modern times. Bacon strongly supported the theory, with his pregnant comments on heat as the motion of particles. Boyle acquired belief in the atomic theory from Bacon, and Newton showed that Boyle's celebrated law connecting pressure and volume of a gas could be deduced mathematically if the gas consisted of particles. Daniel Bernouilli showed in 1738 that the pressure of a gas should be proportional to the square of their velocity. The invention of the steam engine stimulated these researches into the properties of gases, and the effects of temperature were also considered. In 1816 Herapath obtained a formula suggesting that the product of the pressure and volume of a gas should be equal to one-third of the square of the velocity of its molecules. He erroneously assumed the temperature of the gas was proportional to the velocity of its molecules. Waterston pointed out in 1846 that the velocities of the molecules of a gas are not all equal, owing to their collisions. He correctly assumed that their temperature was proportional to the square of their velocity, and calculated the energy absorbed in their spin. He even discovered that 'in mixed media the mean square molecular velocity is inversely proportional to the specific weights of the molecules'. The Royal Society rejected his great paper, and placed it in its archives, where it was discovered by Rayleigh in 1892.

Joule calculated in 1848 from Herapath's formula that a molecule of hydrogen at atmospheric pressure and at the freezing point of water would have a velocity of 6,055 feet per second. It was known, however, that molecules did not all travel at the same speed.

When a bottle of ammonia is opened in a room, several seconds elapse before the smell is noticed. The molecules, in spite of their speed, are delayed by collisions with other molecules. Thus the rate of diffusion depends on the distance between molecules, besides their speed. Clausius described this factor as the mean free path. But he assumed the speed of all the molecules was uniform. This could not be true, and the dynamical theory of gases could not progress farther until the actual velocity of any molecule selected at random could be estimated. Clerk Maxwell proposed a method of doing this with the assistance of the mathematical theory of probability. His solution was not entirely sound, but he had incidentally founded the science of statistical mechanics. Since then, the theory of probability has entered ever more deeply into the interpretation of nature. Intimation of the quantum theory of action appeared in the researches of Boltzmann in 1877, and in 1900 Planck proposed the theory in order to explain the observed mode of radiation of heat and energy from black bodies.

Maxwell had assumed that with a lapse of time a collection of molecules would pass through all possible velocities. This has never been proved, and as C. G. Darwin has explained, some new assumption was necessary for a satisfactory discussion of the problem. This was supplied by Willard Gibbs through his invention of the 'canonical ensemble'. Instead of trying to deal with the whole variety of molecular motions over a period of time, Gibbs took a series of mental snapshots of the gas. Each configuration of molecules, with their velocities, was independent of the rest, but he chose the snapshots so that there was some convenient relation between them. He then assumed that the properties of the gas would be the same as that of a collection or ensemble of the independent snapshots or configurations. The canonical ensemble is the one which corresponds to all possible motions of the gas which would have the same temperature. This idea is employed in modern quantum theory for the description of properties of systems of electrons and nuclei.

The study of gases, inspired by the pump and the steam engine, has led the imagination beyond the present frontiers of knowledge. The myriads of flying particles in the cylinders of engines are the modern slaves who have replaced the crowds of Alexandrian and Roman slaves who performed the hard labour of antiquity, and the study of their behaviour has produced a large part of modern science.

65

Lunacy

THE rapid increase in the production of coal and raw materials in the seventeenth century was followed by a development of refining and finishing processes. Acids are needed for the treatment of ores and the processes of dyeing, and the demand for them had become urgent early in the eighteenth century. But the price of acids was still very high. Their first preparation had been inspired by the demands of gold refiners and druggists. Expense is not of the first importance to these users, because they are dealing with small quantities of products that may be sold at a high price. Sulphuric acid, which has the widest use in industry, was distilled from vitriol according to the ancient Arabian process, or by condensing the fumes of burning sulphur under an open bell-shaped glass vessel. Lemery at the end of the seventeenth century improved the latter process by arranging that it should occur in a closed space. Joshua Ward introduced large glass reaction vessels of sixty-six gallons capacity, and began the manufacture of the acid on an industrial scale in 1736. He brought its price down from half a crown an ounce to one shilling and sixpence a pound, a reduction to nearly one thirtieth of its former cost. John Roebuck of Birmingham introduced large leaden reaction chambers in 1746, and reduced the price to sixpence per pound. The British chemical manufacturers created an export trade in the acid, and met most of the world demand, besides supplying the needs of home industry. Roebuck sought the aid of the chemist, Joseph Black, in the invention of a process for making alkalies by decomposing lime with sea-salt. This ultimately proved unsuccessful, but Black asked James Watt, who had recently invented his separate condenser for the steam engine, to assist him in some of the chemical research connected with it. Roebuck became acquainted with Watt through his work on the alkali process. He had begun to develop coal mines in Scotland, and was in trouble with water, so when he heard of Watt's engine he was immediately interested in it. Watt was indebted to Black for scientific advice and financial assistance, but he needed more financial backing than the professor could provide. Watt's financial debts to Black were taken over by Roebuck, and in return Roebuck shared in Watt's first steam engine patent. Roebuck was embarrassed in the economic depression of the 1770s, and was unable to give Watt as much aid as he needed. He became bankrupt in 1773, and his share in the patent was secured by Boulton, who had still greater industrial talent.

James Watt was not satisfied with the construction of a practicable machine by empirical methods. He attempted to analyse the principles of his engine, and the properties of the material used in it. This led him to study the physics and chemistry of steam. Through his chemical interests he introduced the chlorine bleaching process, proposed by Berthollet, into the Glasgow industry. The difficulty of obtaining solutions of chlorine hindered the adoption of the process, but in 1799 the Glasgow manufacturer Charles Tennant overcame this by his successful development of bleaching powder.

The growth of engineering and chemistry in Birmingham attracted scientists to the city, and gave scope to their gifts. The leading personality among them was Matthew Boulton. He provided the intelligent hospitality in which they became friends, and formed a group whose intellectual power was far greater than the sum of their individual abilities. After Boulton, the most important founders of this group were the physicians Erasmus Darwin and William Small. The eminence of the former, who invented a theory of evolution and was the grandfather of Charles Darwin, is well known. William Small is equally eminent, but is less well known. He was a Glasgow doctor who had been professor of natural philosophy for some years in the college of Williamsburg in Virginia. Thomas Jefferson was one of his pupils and has written in his autobiography that Small 'probably fixed the destinies of my life'. Small found the climate of Virginia uncongenial, and returned to England. Benjamin Franklin gave him a very earnest introduction to Boulton, and he settled in Birmingham about 1765, with the aim of succeeding to the practice of the chief doctor in the town. Small was a Glasgow man and an old friend of James Watt. When he found that Boulton was concerned with engines, he recommended Watt to his notice. He worked incessantly for six years to form a partnership between them, and accomplished this in 1774. Watt then settled in Birmingham. His patent for the separate condenser was drawn up with the advice of Boulton and Small.

Boulton, Darwin, Small and their friends dined at intervals in each other's houses. They arranged to meet about the date of the full moon, so that the moonlight would help them home. They accordingly named themselves the Lunar Society. One of the members of this society, which was so much concerned with illumination, was William Murdock, the inventor of coal-gas lighting. The other members were James Watt; James Keir, the chemical manufacturer; Dr. William Withering, who established the value of the foxglove, or digitalis, treatment for dropsy used by peasant women; John Baskerville, the famous type-founder; Thomas Day, the author of *Sandford and Merton* and through this book one of the chief creators of the nineteenth century ethic of the relationship between the upper and lower classes; R. L. Edgworth; R. A. Johnson; Samuel Galton, the rich Quaker, and his son; and Dr. Stokes.

Joseph Priestley settled in Birmingham in 1780. His wife was a sister of John Wilkinson, the son of the inventor of the steam-driven blast for iron smelting. John Wilkinson commissioned the first steam engine built by the Boulton and Watt firm, and was the inventor of the machine by which iron cylinders and big guns could be accurately bored. Through this invention, expensive brass cylinders in steam engines could be replaced by much cheaper iron cylinders.

John Wilkinson and his sister, Mrs. Priestley, were Nonconformists. Mrs. Schimmelpenninck, the daughter of Samuel Galton, records that Mrs. Priestley was her mother's closest friend. She had 'unswerving integrity of purpose, such inflexible truth, and such a deep, though stern sense of duty'. She found Priestley's integrity as great, but he was more charming. He had a serene countenance, and was simple, gentle and kind. Mrs. Schimmelpenninck reported that 'he, indeed, seemed present with God by recollection, and with man by cheerfulness'. She could remember meetings of the Lunar Society in her father's house when she was a child. Boulton 'was tall and of a noble appearance; his temperament was sanguine, with that light mixture of phlegmatic which gives calmness and dignity; his manners were eminently open and cordial; he took the lead in conversations, and with a social heart had a grandiose manner like that arising from position, wealth, and habitual command . . .' He 'was a man to rule society with dignity'. Watt was suited to 'the contemplative life of a deeply introverted and patiently observant philosopher. He was one of the most complete specimens of the melancholic temperament. His head was generally bent forward or leaning on his hand in meditation; his shoulders stooping, and his chest fallen in; his limbs lank and unmuscular, and his complexion sallow. His intellectual development was magnificent'. When Watt entered a room, adults and children thronged round him. He advised everyone on practical problems. He instructed Parisian ladies of fashion on how to cure smoky chimneys and dye clothes, he taught Mrs. Schimmelpenninck 'how to make a dulcimer and improve a Jew's harp', and she could remember 'a celebrated Swedish artist having been instructed by him that rats' whiskers make the most pliant and elastic painting brush'.

She wrote that 'on one occasion, when the Lunar Meeting, or "Lunatics" as our butler called them, were seated at dinner, a blazing fire being in the room, we were astonished by hearing a sudden *hissing* noise, and seeing a large and beautiful, yellow and black snake rushing about the room. My dear mother, who saw it was not venomous, said to me, "Mary Anne, go and catch that snake." She succeeded, after some trouble, and the company wondered where it might have come from. Dr. Stokes then remembered that, as he was riding to the house, he had seen it frozen on a bank, and had put it in his pocket, with the intention of dissecting it later. He had forgotten its presence, and it had thawed in the heat of the room, and had then escaped.'

Joseph Priestley was the son of a cloth dresser, and was born near Leeds in 1733. He studied for the Nonconformist ministry, and read science in 1758. Benjamin Franklin encouraged him in 1766 to write a history of electricity. Priestley repeated the experiments described in the literature to see whether he had understood them, and without design found himself making new observations and experiments. He was appointed to a ministry at Leeds in 1767, and his scientific researches flagged, but were revived by a visit from Franklin in 1772. He lived next to a brewery, and investigated the gas evolved by fermentation. He showed that it could be dissolved in water under pressure, and immediately, in 1772, applied his knowledge to the invention of soda water. This attracted much attention. He improved the pneumatic trough for collecting gases over water, and introduced collection over mercury, which enabled him to deal with gases soluble in water. He discovered nitrous oxide, hydrogen chloride, ammonia, and sulphur dioxide. He handled oxygen and carbon monoxide, though he did not immediately recognize their difference from other gases. He discovered that air vitiated by breathing or combustion may be restored by growing sprigs of mint in it. He deduced from this the grand explanation of why all the fires and animals and putrefaction on the earth did not vitiate the atmosphere. The covering of vegetation continually restored the quality of the air.

Priestley accepted an engagement in 1773 as literary companion to Lord Shelburne, the Whig statesman who signed the peace treaty which recognized the foundation of the United States of America. He had comfortable quarters and resources in Shelburne's mansion in Wiltshire. He continued his experimental researches, and while working in Wiltshire discovered oxygen. This was in 1774. Scheele had already made the same discovery, but had not published it.

Priestley breathed the new gas, and recommended its use in medicine. His results stimulated much research on gases and their medicinal effects, which gave Humphry Davy his opportunity, and led to the discovery of anaesthetics.

Priestley grew tired of the Shelburne appointment, and was attracted to Birmingham by offer of a ministry, and the presence of the Lunar Society. Boulton, Darwin and Wedgwood privately paid the expenses of his experimental researches. Priestley subsequently wrote that his 'settlement at Birmingham was the happiest event in my life, being highly favourable to every object I had in view, philosophical or theological. In the former respect, I had the convenience of good workmen of every kind and the society of persons eminent for their knowledge of chemistry, particularly Mr. Watt, Mr. Keir, and Dr. Withering'.

He showed in 1781 that if a mixture of oxygen and hydrogen was exploded with electric sparks, dew was deposited. James Watt communicated this result to Cavendish, who continued the research with Priestley's permission, and clearly elucidated the composition of water.

Conversation in the Lunar Society was very free. Candidates were not admitted unless they could discuss the newest and unorthodox ideas calmly. The members corresponded with Berthollet and other French leaders of the new science, and when the social changes of the Revolution began, they followed them with sympathy and excitement. Priestley dropped experimental research, defended the revolution, and answered Burke's attack. He criticized the Church of England, and described it as a fungus, and a parasitic plant. He was elected a member for Orne in the French National Convention. James Watt's son, James Watt junior, was sent to the National Convention as a delegate from the Constitutional Society of Manchester, and is said to have prevented a duel between Danton and Robespierre, while acting as second to Danton.

In 1791, eighty gentlemen of Birmingham celebrated the second anniversary of the fall of the Bastille at a private dinner. A mob was urged to attack them, and the property of everyone known to be sympathetic to the revolution, under the slogan: 'No Philosophers—Church and King forever!' They particularly sought the 'Lunatics', and some persons wrote 'No Philosophers' on the front of their houses as a protection. Boulton and Watt armed their workmen for defence. The mob wrecked and looted more than one hundred thousand pounds worth of property, including Priestley's house, with his large collection of historic apparatus and valuable library. Priestley had to flee from Birmingham in disguise, and sailed to America in 1794. There he was subjected to ferocious invective by Cobbett, who had not yet lost hope of advancement by the Tories. Cobbett remarks in his American pamphlet, published in Philadelphia in 1799, that 'a desire to defend you, the People of Birmingham, against the malignant aspersions of Doctor Priestley, was, in some degree, the cause of my first attempting to write.'

Priestley had extraordinary energy. He wrote until the pen dropped from his hand, and he spoke and experimented indefatigably. He said of himself that he had 'a tolerably good habit of circumspection with regard to *facts*; but as to conclusions from them, I am not apt to be very confident'. He and his Lunar Society friends were strong supporters of the phlogiston theory. Partington has commented that though Priestley was heterodox in religion, he was orthodox in science.

The English chemistry of the eighteenth century was largely created by leaders of industry who were nonconformist in religion and radical in politics. It was cultivated in the industrial cities away from Oxford and Cambridge, by a new governing class of industrialists, which created its own academies and learned societies. When Priestley left Birmingham, he wrote to Watt of 'the pleasing intercourse I have had with you and all my friends of the Lunar Society. Such another I can never expect to see. Indeed, London cannot furnish it'. Birmingham provided the most powerful group of minds in contemporary England.

The philosophy of the nonconformist and radical industrialists was expressed by Priestley in his Lecture on History. He said that 'nothing is so favourable to the rise and progress of learning and the arts, as a number of neighbouring independent states, connected by commerce and policy. This was the condition of ancient Greece, and it is that of Europe at present'. He said that the connection between technique and science hardly needed to be pointed out. 'It is the same that holds universally between theory and practice.' The recent great improvement in technique had 'certainly arisen from the late improvements in science'. He was of opinion that 'speculation is only of use as it leads to practice; that the immediate use of natural science is the power it gives us over nature, by means of the knowledge we acquire of its laws, whereby human life is, in its present state, made more comfortable and happy, but that the greatest and noblest use of philosophical speculation is the discipline of the heart, and the opportunity it affords of inculcating benevolent and pious sentiments upon the mind'.

The violence of the opposition of the Church of England and the Tories to Priestley was due to his unconscious application of the mode of thought of industrialists and scientists to the hierarchical ideas of churchmen and hereditary landlords. His unitarianism was a result of the application of the scientific notion of a uniform substance to the conception of the Trinity. As Veblen has explained, the increasing concern with matter through the development of industry strengthened the feeling of the importance of uniformity.

The concentration of the leading nonconformists, industrialists and scientists in the same centres was not accidental. They formed groups more influential than a collection of individuals. They were bound together by ties even stronger than friendship, as they were largely interrelated by marriage. They were part of one organic social movement, whose progressive energy was drawn from the growing industrialism of the eighteenth century.

66

Enlightenment

EARTH, air, water and fire are the commonest objects of nature, so the Greek philosophers concluded they were the primary elements of which matter is compounded. While belief in this theory was strengthened by two thousand years of tradition, metallurgists, pharmacists and other technicians gradually added new facts to knowledge. The ancient theory was periodically restated to assimilate the new facts. The last of these restatements was made at the end of the seventeenth century by the medicinal chemist Stahl, in the form of the phlogiston theory. The word phlogiston is derived from the Greek word for burning, and Stahl used it to describe what he conceived to be the essence of fire. Inflammability was due to a large content of phlogiston. Oil and charcoal were therefore very rich in it. Hydrogen was almost pure phlogiston. Besides explaining the inflammability of this gas, the theory would also explain the very different phenomena of its evolution from mixtures of zinc and acids. The acid drove the phlogiston out of the zinc, and left the remains of the metal in the form of white vitriol, which could be obtained subsequently by evaporation. The theory predicted that if the phlogiston were first removed from the zinc, the residue should dissolve in the acid without the evolution of phlogiston in the form of hydrogen. Experiment confirmed this prediction, for zinc, when heated in air, is converted into a powder that dissolves in acid without effervescence.

The theory gives a satisfactory account of qualitative change. It was indeed invented by a pharmacist whose primary interest in matter was qualitative. The effects of drugs seem to be due much more to intrinsic properties than to the quantity administered, so the pharmacist is primarily interested in intrinsic properties and qualitative differences. The development of pharmacy in the sixteenth and seventeenth centuries, which provided such stimulus to chemical theory, was connected with the new knowledge of drugs and processes brought to Europe through the expansion of world trade. The culmination of the influence of the pharmaceutical tradition is seen in the work of Scheele. His discoveries included oxygen, chlorine, hydrofluoric acid, the preparation of phosphorus from bone ash, arsenic acid, tungstic acid, copper arsenite; the organic acids: tartaric, lactic, uric, prussic, oxalic, malic and gallic; glycerol, aldehyde and casein; and the action of light on silver salts, which is the basis of photography. Scheele combined his unequalled achievement in qualitative chemistry with a firm belief in the phlogiston theory. Priestley followed the qualitative tradition of the pharmacists and retained their belief in phlogiston, but under the influence of the industrial developments with which he was in contact, he turned their qualitative methods more to materials of inorganic or industrial interest.

The growth of industry in the eighteenth century caused the results of the primarily pharmaceutical researches of the previous two centuries to be examined in the perspective of industrial ideas. Much more attention was given to their quantitative aspects. The chemists working under the new industrial inspiration tended to believe that all real things could be measured and weighed. Joseph Black, in the new industrial city of Glasgow, was the first to use this attitude with complete success. He elucidated the chemical relations between lime, quicklime and carbon dioxide by means of the balance, the chief instrument of industry. He used the balance to trace the movement of a definite quantity of carbon dioxide through a cycle of reactions that could be repeated indefinitely. The preservation of the carbon dioxide through an endless series of reactions, and its entrance into chemical combinations in definite quantities, suggested that it was a definite chemical substance. Black therefore asserted that carbon dioxide was not merely a variety of air, as had previously been believed, but was a gas chemically distinct from air. He was the first to prove that gases chemically distinct from air exist, and he had done this by quantitative, not qualitative analysis. The application of Black's method presently revealed facts inconsistent with the phlogiston theory, but for long he remained a phlogistonist, though he reflected the new industrial tendency towards materialism in another part of scientific theory. He developed the caloric theory, in which heat is conceived as a form of matter, and subject to quantitative laws. His measurements led to the conceptions of specific and latent heat.

Black, Watt, Priestley, Cavendish and their British followers failed to expose the contradictions between the phlogiston theory and the results of the new quantitative analysis and find a solution to them. This was first done by Lavoisier, who brought to the problem not only great ability, but a habit of ruthless and logical thought not possessed by the British chemists. He had acquired this habit of thought from the French intellectual environment. This was a product of French social conditions, so that it follows that these have had a special influence on the foundation of modern chemical theory. Clarity became a characteristic of French thought in the seventeenth century. It evolved during the social and religious conflicts of the previous century, and was a reaction against them. In the sixteenth century the conflicts between feudalism and the new urban civilization broke out in France, as elsewhere, in the form of religious wars. The ideals of the French urban civilization were expressed by Calvin, who had to flee from Paris in 1533, which was still the centre of feudal Catholic theology. The reaction of the Catholic feudalists against Calvin and reformed theology was led by Loyola, and the Jesuit order founded by him. He enrolled his first recruits in Paris in

11*

1534. France became a field of battle between Reformation and Counter-Reformation, and the social disorder caused by this struggle culminated in the massacre of the Protestants in 1572. The resolution of the chaos was achieved by Henry IV. He started as a Huguenot, but became a Catholic in order to make a truce with the Church. He appointed Sully, who was a Huguenot and devoted to order and work, his chief minister, to improve the nation's social and economic organization. Among other innovations, Sully founded the French canal system. As Hauser says, Henry's lucid and balanced intellect was absolutely free from prejudice and guided by reason only. When he was murdered in 1610, the French state was definitely evolving towards *bourgeois*, and away from feudal, forms.

The tendency continued, and was expressed in sustained effort towards national unity and organization. When Henry died, his son Louis XIII was a minor, and the management of the state passed into the hands of Richelieu. He aimed at the organization of all classes in the state into a unit that could withstand the power of the Hapsburgs and their American gold. As superintendent of navigation and commerce he urged the development of sea-power, and deplored the *bourgeoisie's* hankering after classical education and public office, and escape from commerce. Richelieu's unification of the state was continued by his successor Mazarin, who conducted the government of the country from 1643 to 1661, during the youth of Louis XIV. Louis subsequently disapproved of the subjection of kings to ministers, and said that 'nothing is more disgraceful than to see the functions and the mere title of a king in different hands'. He was determined to rule himself. But he appointed Colbert, who had managed Mazarin's estates, as his chief minister, and though he made all decisions himself, he acted on the information of men who had been educated in the mercantile tradition of Richelieu and Mazarin.

The reaction against the chaos and enthusiasm of the sixteenth century seen in this political development was accompanied by a corresponding movement in thought. Malherbe insisted on clear, precise and pure language, based on the usage of polite society. The nobility began to change its manners. It turned its castles into country houses, and regulated its boisterous conversation. The Marquise de Rambouillet and other ladies acquired more influence in this environment. They were able to divert conversation to subjects of interest to women. As they were ignorant of Latin and technical affairs, they eliminated from conversation all technical terms used in the schools and work-shops. The simplification of the French language was advanced by their influence, and adapted to psychological observation and subtle wit, and an easy flow of conversation.

This movement inspired two great events in 1637. The French Academy was officially established in that year, and proceeded to compile a dictionary of the French language consciously based on the speech of the people of Paris, and intelligible to women and the mass of the people. The language was clarified, and became independent of Latin, and was given the quality which made it the future international diplomatic language.

Descartes' *Discourse on Method* was published in 1637, and produced a parallel clarification of philosophy. As Tilley says, his glorification of reason, and re-establishment of order and unity in the world of thought was inspired by the same motives as the work of his contemporaries in other fields. In his treatise on the passions, published twelve years later, he insisted that they may be controlled by the will, and contended that the will could receive guidance from the reason, which, he believed, could certainly distinguish good from evil. In this, 'he was merely reducing to a system ideas which the drama of Corneille had already made familiar'.

The movement for national organization continued while clarification of thought progressed. Louis XIV changed the court from a military into a civil society. He carried a stick instead of wearing a sword, and, as Seignobos remarks, he behaved like a rich *bourgeois*. Colbert strove to follow the political unification of the country by unifying its economic system. He created police regulations and taxation to accomplish this, and thereby destroyed the medieval economic system. He believed that the amount of trade in the world was constant, and the prosperity of a nation depended on its securing as large a part of this as it could. He noted that the Dutch possessed 15,000 of the 20,000 ships in Europe, while most of the remainder belonged to England. He encouraged French navigation in order to secure a larger share of sea-borne trade.

When he came into power, nearly all finished goods were im-ported from Italy and the Low Countries. He stimulated home industries to replace these imports, especially the manufacture of textiles. He made remarkably detailed regulations concerning the type and design of goods, and large factories were created. The Van Robais factory at Abbeville had 1,500 workers in 1715.

These industrial and commercial developments were not accompanied by improvements in agriculture. The *bourgeois* king and his ministers were not interested in it. In 1700, four-fifths of the peasants could not live on their agricultural wages, and eked out their living by handicraft. Fénelon said that France had become 'a great desolate hospital, without food'. Nevertheless, France was able to support a population of twenty millions, as she possessed a large part of the most fertile soil in Europe. The population of France at the end of the eighteenth century was about twenty-five millions. It was larger than that of the Russian Empire, and nearly three times as large as that of England, which was nine millions in 1801.

The population provided a large market for the manufactures encouraged by Colbert. The demand for dyed textiles was especially good, and gave a big stimulus to the dyeing industry. The best chemists in the country were placed at the head of the state dye works. Berthollet was made director in the eighteenth century, and drew from the dyeing industry the means and inspiration which enabled him to advance the theory of chemistry. In return, he worked out the industrial application of Scheele's discovery of the bleaching action of chlorine, and revolutionized the bleaching industry.

The systematization pursued by Louis XIV and Colbert failed to achieve their aims. They had tried to create a social organization which was as efficient as those of Holland and England, without introducing their more advanced political and industrial technique. When their regulation of the national life began to break down, a demand for economic and political liberty arose. The men who were impelled to make these demands had inherited the results of the previous two centuries of the parallel organization of thought and language. The great social movement started in the time of Henry IV split into two parts, and the product of the intellectual side criticized the product of the economic and political side. Voltaire was the foremost of these new critics. He visited England and surveyed its institutions, not unlike an Ionian Greek surveying Babylon. He possessed a sharper and clearer intellect than his hosts, though he belonged to a technically less advanced nation. He returned to France, and helped to inspire achievements that surpassed the models he had

seen abroad. His *Letters Concerning the English Nation* explained
the merits of English culture more simply and clearly than the
English could do themselves. His exposition of English religious
tolerance, political liberty, and science had a profound effect.
Younger followers determined to encourage these qualities in
France, and under the leadership of Diderot and Alembert compiled the French Encyclopedia, which was a universal dictionary
of arts, sciences, trades and manufactures. The first volume was
published in 1751.

Diderot and Alembert explain the source of their inspiration
in their famous preface to the *Encyclopédie*. They ascribe it to
Bacon, Descartes, Newton and Locke, and write: 'At the Head
of these illustrious Heroes we deservedly place the immortal
Francis Bacon, Lord High Chancellor of England; whose
works, though justly esteemed, are too little known, and deserve
Perusal more than Praise. To consider the just and extensive
Views of this prodigious Man; the Multiplicity of his Objects;
the Strength of his Style; his sublime Imagery; and extreme
Exactness; we are tempted to esteem him the greatest, the most
universal, and most eloquent of all Philosophers . . . It is to
this great Author we are chiefly indebted for our Encyclopaediac
Plan.'

Descartes succeeded Bacon in the construction of their intellectual perspective. He invented algebraical geometry, proposed
laws of motion, and submitted scholasticism to sceptical criticism.
Nevertheless, thanks were due to the schoolmen who had preserved knowledge and the Greek notion that ideas are not innate,
but the product of reflection on sensation.

Newton completed the invention of the scientific method,
which consists either 'in the application of mathematical calculation to experiments; or in simple observation, conducted by
method, and sometimes assisted by conjectures for further
inquiry; scrupulously avoiding all arbitrary hypotheses'.

The reform of writing and language, intended to make reading
easy for the gentry, had provided them with an admirable ex-
pository prose whose accuracy, purity, and happy choice of terms
had been improved by Pascal and the Society of Port Royal.

They ascribed the greatest recent advances in philosophy to
Locke. 'He may be said to have invented Metaphysics, as Newton
invented Physics . . .' and 'He reduced Metaphysics to what, in
Reality, they ought to be, an Experimental Philosophy of the

Soul.' The study of nature, which leads to the development of science, is due partly to necessity and partly to amusement. Many pleasing discoveries are due to curiosity and 'an unhappy impotence of acquiring such as would prove infinitely more useful.' Pretence of utility is another motive to the exercise of curiosity. 'To have sometimes found a real advantage from inquiries, where at first we did not suspect it, is sufficient to make us regard all curious inquiries as capable of proving useful.' Science is the product of this belief, and agriculture and medicine, which 'principally gave it birth', are now no more than branches on a great tree that sprang from themselves.

The editors understood the essential part of manual practice in the creation of science, and gave adequate expression to it for the first time. 'Should not the inventors of the spring, the, chain and repeating parts of a watch, be equally esteemed with those who have successfully studied to perfect algebra?'

Accordingly, they devoted a new degree of attention to technique. Chambers in his encyclopaedia had given only thirty plates illustrating technical processes. They had had six hundred plates carefully made, and published in two volumes. Chambers had read books, but had rarely visited workshops and seen processes in operation. As these often cannot be understood except from experience, they 'were obliged to have recourse to workmen themselves: and accordingly applied to the best in Paris, and in the kingdom of France'. They worked machines themselves as a preparation to writing articles on them. In many instances, no written accounts of processes existed.

Lavoisier was born in 1743, and reared in the atmosphere created by the previous century of national and linguistic organization. The *Encyclopédie*, which was the first great example of organized knowledge, was published during his youth. He acquired from this environment an understanding of the possibilities of organization, which he applied in civil administration, in scientific thought and experiment, and in exposition.

Lavoisier was born in a prosperous family. His father was attorney to the Parliament of Paris. He was educated at the Collège Mazarin by the distinguished scientists Lacaille, de Jussieu, Guettard and Rouelle. Guettard was the inventor of geological maps and was employed by the Government to make an atlas of the nation's mineralogical resources. He invited Lavoisier to collaborate with him, and for three years Lavoisier travelled through France collecting and examining minerals. His first chemical researches arose from his analyses of specimens of gypsum, or plaster of Paris.

He made detailed notes of the features of the land and soil, of mines, iron-works, bleaching-works, and stone and plaster deposits; and he kept a careful meteorological diary. Reports of the national industries based on these notes were sent to the Academy. He was elected a member at the age of twenty-five. Thereafter, he reported to the Academy on such matters as the water supply of Paris, prisons, the adulteration of cider, the site of slaughter-houses, bleaching, lamps, smokeless grates, paper, the cultivation of cabbages, the working of coal-mines, the manufacture of starch and white soap, dyeing, inks, glass, alkalies, gunpowder, cesspools, metal refining, and scores of other technical problems.

The Government referred inventions to the Academy for expert opinion, and Lavoisier performed the functions of a government chemist and patent examiner.

Shortly after he had become an academician, and still at the age of twenty-five, he purchased a position in the Ferme, the company that farmed the French taxes. These farmers paid the Government fixed sums in return for the right to collect taxes. Some of them made profits of one million livres per annum, or about fifty thousand pounds in modern money. The magnitude of these profits was due to a combination of efficient organization and extortion, and drew public opprobrium on the farmers. Lavoisier received 1,200,000 livres, or sixty thousand pounds, from the Ferme in eighteen years, and was appointed Farmer-General in 1779. He had in addition been appointed to the State Powder Company in 1775, and in that year received quarters in the Arsenal.

Lavoisier improved the manufacture of saltpetre and gunpowder, and made the French product superior to the English. The excellence of the powder was one of the causes of the subsequent successes of the revolutionary armies. He also accumulated large stores of musket powder. This was of particular value for police action in cities, and as there was public unrest at the time, his enemies said that he had accumulated the powder for use against the populace.

Lavoisier made his most famous researches in the laboratory at the Arsenal. He received much assistance from his wife, but he was able to spare only one day a week for experiments. The rest of his working time was devoted to the administration of tax-collecting, powder manufacture, and the conduct of the Academy, of which he became director in 1785.

He spent much of his large income on research, and he did not exceed the rights of exploitation granted him by law. But his acceptance of financial laws widely held to be unjust presently caused him to be condemned by the National Convention.

Lavoisier's association with industry and the Academy gave him a very wide knowledge of the facts of chemistry. He began to compare and organize these facts with the administrative skill that he exercised in tax-collecting and powder manufacture. Instead of concentrating, like Scheele and Priestley, on the discovery of surprising substances by experimental ingenuity, he reflected rather on what was already known. He viewed it as an intellectual administrator, and began a critical examination of the current administration of chemical knowledge, or, in more usual language, of chemical theory. Early in his career, his critical administrative eye was dissatisfied with the current theory of the elements.

Following the Aristotelian tradition, water and earth were supposed to contain a common quality, and were capable of being transmuted into each other. This was apparently proved by the powdery substance that appeared in water after prolonged boiling in glass flasks.

Lavoisier had made many experiments on water in his work on the Paris water supply, and he drew on his experience to test the truth of this apparent transformation. He proved by critical experiments that the powdery substance was dissolved by the water out of the glass. This demonstration of the stability of water assisted him to adopt Boyle's definition of a chemical element as a substance not decomposable by any known method. He subsequently made the first list of chemical elements on the basis of this definition.

Lavoisier obtained his proof that water could not be transmuted into earth with the help of the balance. He had noticed that Black had used the balance to trace the movements of a quantity of carbon dioxide through a cycle of chemical changes, so he carefully weighed the flask before and after the boiling, and found that its loss of weight was equal to the weight of the powder that appeared in the water. He saw that Black's results and his own proved that matter is indestructible. He was therefore able to announce the law of the conservation of mass. Further, he saw that if this law were true, weighing provided a general method of analysis which would elucidate all the chemical changes of matter. Chemistry was thenceforth to be based on the study of masses, and mass became the most fundamental property of chemistry. According to this view, substances without mass could not exist, and mass became the first qualification for legitimacy in chemistry. Lavoisier now considered phlogiston from this view. If it existed, it must have mass, and this must be traceable through chemical changes, and in particular through the processes of combustion. He had a vision of this argument in 1773, when he was thirty years old, and he wrote a memorandum on a plan of research to establish it. He says that he felt impelled to set down in writing an outline of researches on the gaseous substances released in every sort of chemical change, and of the absorption of the air by many substances. Some thought that these gaseous substances were forms of air, others thought they were Black's 'fixed air', a third group believed they were emanations of the ultimate parts of innumerable different sorts of substances. The whole range of facts concerning gases was to be carefully re-examined by Black's methods.

'The importance of the end in view prompted me to undertake all this work, which seemed to me destined to bring about a revolution in physics and in chemistry. I have felt bound to look upon all that has been done before me merely as suggestive: I have proposed to repeat it all with new safeguards, in order to link our knowledge of the air that goes into combination or that is liberated from substances, with other acquired knowledge, and to form a theory.'

Lavoisier elucidated the process of combustion by following very carefully with a balance the changes of weight that occur when metals are heated in air. He obtained conclusive results in 1778, after researches spread over five years. He showed that if mercury is heated in a sealed flask containing air, it absorbs a constituent of the air, and increases in weight by a definite amount, which is equal to the weight lost by the enclosed air. The gas left in the flask does not support combustion and respiration. The mercury meanwhile has been transformed into a red powder. If this is removed from the flask and heated, it supplies a volume of gas whose weight is equal to that lost by the enclosed air in the first combustion. When this gas is added to the gas left in the flask after the first combustion, it produces a gas which is indistinguishable in quantity and quality from the original volume of enclosed air. Thus the combustion of mercury in air is reversible, and can be explained entirely in terms of interaction with a constituent of air which has a definite mass and distinct properties. Combustion in general is therefore completely explicable, in terms of this constituent, without the hypothetical phlogiston. He discarded phlogiston as an unnecessary multiplication of hypotheses.

He now recast the theory of chemistry in the perspective of this principle. He writes in his *Elementary Treatise*, published in 1789, that he has imposed on himself 'the law of never advancing but from the known to the unknown, of deducing no consequence that does not immediately derive from experiments and observations'. Einstein followed the same principle when he discarded the ether from physics, and Heisenberg created the new quantum mechanics by making a theory of what is observable, and excluding the interpolation of hypothetical entities in the explanation of physical processes.

Lavoisier and a small group led by him were able to introduce a rational nomenclature into chemistry after phlogiston had been discarded. He gave oxygen its name, and invented the terminations still used to describe classes of substances. The reform of the language of chemistry was elegantly accomplished by the heirs of the reformation of the French language in the previous century.

Chemistry has been expanded enormously since Lavoisier's time, but it still has his mark. His *Treatise* still reads like an early edition of a modern book. Many fertile ideas have since been introduced into chemistry, but as yet none is as important as the theoretical revolution accomplished by Lavoisier.

Why was this revolution accomplished by Lavoisier, rather than by Black and Priestley, and the English chemists? Because Lavoisier inherited the habit of clear and systematic thought that was the product of the circumstances of French history, while the Englishmen inherited a habit of ingenuity and compromise from the circumstances of English history, which assisted them in brilliant individual experiments, but inhibited the impulse to explore general theory with ruthless logic, and thus discover its limitations.

Lavoisier's success was due not only to his great abilities, but also to acquisition from his social environment of a mode of thought that was particularly well adapted to assist in the solution of the problem with which he was concerned.

67

The Raw Material of Everything

THE Greeks and Romans were acquainted with manifestations of electricity and magnetism at least two thousand years ago. The Greeks knew that when amber is rubbed it is able to attract small objects. The Romans were familiar with the attractive power of certain iron ores. These lodestones were found in the province of Magnesia, and their property was accordingly named magnetism. These forms of electricity and magnetism were known for more than one thousand years before they were put to any effective use. They were exploited as agents for curing physical and mental diseases. Roman doctors treated gout with electric shocks from the torpedo fish, and jilted persons were advised to increase their attractive power by touching electrified objects and magnets.

Virtually no progress in magnetism and electricity was made until knowledge of the magnetic compass reached Europe from China about the eleventh century, and was utilized for steering ships. The vigorous development of trade and navigation at that time, especially where the skies are cloudy, and the altitude of the sun varies greatly with the seasons, stimulated the search for improved methods of steering.

This circumstance caused magnetism to be considered in a new perspective. Hard-headed ocean traders, and men who served them, brought an attitude to the study of magnetism that was different from that of the doctors and magicians. They investigated it with practical realism.

The monk Peregrinus, who had taken part in the Crusades, and had probably sailed to Palestine, wrote the first known experimental work on magnetism in 1269. The next big advance in magnetism was due to Christopher Columbus, who noticed two centuries later, on his voyage of discovery, that the direction of the compass varies with longitude.

The great navigations focussed intense attention on magnetism, especially in the new maritime countries of the north, such as England. Owing to the esteem in which it was held by the important members of the community who organized colonial expeditions, the attention of men of ability was drawn to it. Queen Elizabeth's personal physician, William Gilbert, studied it from the new practical point of view. He dismissed the alleged magical properties of magnetism as 'idle tales and trumpery'. He made a series of experiment which proved that magnets have two poles, and that these are different; one seeking the north and the other the south. He showed that like poles repel each other, and that if a magnet is cut into two, each part is a little magnet with its own pair of poles.

He then sought to explore the laws governing the influence of the earth on a compass. He accomplished this by making a globe out of a lodestone, so that it served as a model of the earth. He found that it had two poles. He explored the direction of the magnetic force at various points on the surface with the aid of a small compass, and found that they agreed with those reported by mariners at corresponding points on the earth's surface. He concluded that the earth was a magnetized globe. He found from his model that a magnetic needle points vertically downwards over the poles, and forecast that the needle would point downwards in the northern regions of the earth. His forecast was confirmed by Hudson, the discoverer of Hudson's Bay, in 1608.

While Gilbert was deepening the English knowledge of the chief aid to navigation, his countrymen were founding their first important joint stock company. This was the East India Company, which was incorporated in 1600. Gilbert was the first great scientist of modern England, and he published the first great book on magnetism and electricity in the same year, 1600.

Dryden noted the association between Gilbert's researches on magnetism and England's maritime supremacy when he wrote:

> Gilbert shall live till loadstones cease to draw
> Or British fleets the boundless oceans awe.

Gilbert extended his study to the power of attraction produced in amber when it is rubbed. He described any substance that had this property as an 'electric', after electron, the Greek word for amber. He discovered that many other substances besides amber could be electrified. These included glass, resin, sulphur, diamonds, sapphires, and other substances. His list reminds one of the contents of a shop, and suggests how the variety of materials assembled by an expanding trade assists the progress of research. Discovery is virtually impossible without a variety of materials for comparison.

Gilbert proved that electric and magnetic attractions are different, and he found that electrified objects were discharged by the presence of flames. He noted that electrical experiments were more difficult in wet than in dry weather. Gilbert obtained all his electrical effects by simple manual operations. Otto von Guericke, the redoubtable burgomaster of Magdeburg, who was born one year before Gilbert died, extended his researches by pursuing them on a mechanical and engineering scale.

The early fellows of the Royal Society continued electrical research. Isaac Newton found that electrical attractions penetrated glass, and Hawkesbee showed that if an exhausted glass globe was electrified, a coloured glow appeared in the empty space.

Progress quickened in the eighteenth century. Gray and Wheeler recognized the difference between insulators and conductors, and transmitted currents along a hempen thread several hundred feet long. Improved forms of Guericke's machine were invented, which would maintain continuous sparks in glass tubes containing air at reduced pressure. This advance was made by scientists living in a mining district in Germany, and proposals to use these discharge tubes as miners' lamps were made in 1744. In the same year Winkler bent a discharge tube to spell the name of a neighbouring duke at night. The discharge tube, which is used today so much for advertisement, is the oldest type of electric lamp, and was invented nearly two centuries ago. It was not successfully utilized in the eighteenth century because it had not yet been made reliable and efficient, and a practicable system for generating and distributing electricity had not yet been invented. But the possibility of electricity as an illuminant which possessed certain advantages had been demonstrated.

Much of the curiosity focussed by the strengthening interest in material phenomena in the eighteenth century was devoted to electrical experiments. They were clean and entertaining, and apparently simple. Benjamin Franklin embarked on them in the dry winter atmosphere of Philadelphia. The powerful and clear-cut effects obtained under these conditions assisted him to clarify the theory of electricity, and invent the lightning conductor. This was the first contribution to electrical engineering, and it had great psychological besides practical value. It brought lightning, which since prehistoric times had been widely regarded as supernatural, under a degree of human control. This was a splendid contribution towards man's mastery of nature, and it brought Franklin great fame. He used his fame to increase his diplomatic influence and secure support from France for the United States in their struggle for independence. Subsequently, the example of the United States was a powerful stimulant to the revolutionary movement in France.

The curiosity of the students of electricity varied from the superficial to the profound. Some were interested merely in bigger and better sparks. Others enjoyed giving shocks to their friends. This side of electrical research raised hopes of cures for paralysis and other diseases, and presently received serious study. But the best minds were attracted to electricity by an insight into its philosophical importance. This was very well expressed by Joseph Priestley. He pointed out that it appeared to be a universal property of matter. It was the first universal discovery since that of gravitation. He foresaw its implications and wrote in the preface to his *History of Electricity*: 'Hitherto philosophy has been chiefly conversant about the more sensible properties of bodies. Electricity together with chemistry and the doctrine of light and colours, seems to be giving us an inlet into their internal structure, on which all their sensible properties depend. By pursuing this new light, therefore, the bounds of natural science may possibly be extended beyond what we can now form an idea of. New worlds may open to our view, and the glory of the great Sir Isaac Newton himself, and all his contemporaries, be eclipsed by a new set of philosophers, in quite a new field of speculation. Could that great man revisit the earth, and view the experiments of the present race of electricians, he would be no less amazed than Roger Bacon or Sir Francis would have been at his. The electric shock itself, if it be considered attentively, will appear almost as surprising as any discovery that he made.'

The next great advances in electrical knowledge came from an attentive consideration of electric shocks. Luigi Galvani, the professor of anatomy and obstetrics at Bologna, like other able medical research workers of the day, investigated the effects of electric shocks on the body. One day somebody in his laboratory was working an electrical machine while dissected frogs were lying on a bench nearby. Another person touched an exposed nerve of one of the frogs very lightly with a knife. Such a light touch would not normally have produced any contraction, but in this case the frog's legs gave a big kick. The phenomenon was noticed by those present, and it was found that it could be repeated only when the electrical machine was running.

Galvani recognized the importance of the phenomenon, and investigated it for eleven years. He showed that kicks could be obtained if the muscle and the attached nerve were connected respectively to two different metals in contact. He ascribed the effects to 'animal electricity' generated in the frogs.

Galvani's remarkable observations were carefully analysed by the Italian physicist Alessandro Volta, who thought very clearly and had great experimental skill. Volta placed a piece of tin foil on the tip of his tongue and a silver coin on the back. He noted a sour taste when they were connected by a copper wire. If a metal coin was placed on his forehead, and another metal object on his palate, he experienced a strong sensation of a flash of light when they were connected. He concluded that the electricity did not come from the tissues of his body, as Galvani would have supposed, but from the contact of the metals. He wrote that 'they are in a real sense the exciters of electricity, while the nerves themselves are passive'.

He proceeded to see whether electricity could be drawn from two metals in other ways. He replaced the frog's tissues in Galvani's experiments by various liquids, and discovered that electricity still went round the circuit even when all living material had been removed. He was then led to make the greatest electrical discovery since the discovery of electricity itself. He found that the electrical effect in this experiment, though slight, was continuous. He had discovered the electric current. He did not rest with this. He discovered how to multiply the strength of the current by connecting together a series of metal plates separated by moistened cloth. He sent an account of his Voltaic battery to the Royal Society of London, which published it in 1800.

The discovery of the electric current aroused enormous interest. Napoleon invited Volta to give demonstrations in Paris, and the Emperor of Austria rewarded him with appointments. Within a few weeks, the electric current had been used to decompose water. The youthful Humphry Davy, then twenty-two years old, explored the new phenomenon with zest. He presently decomposed the caustic alkalies, and discovered sodium and potassium. He sent a current through two carbons held in contact, and discovered the electric arc when he drew the two carbons apart. He also employed the arc as an electric furnace to decompose substances. He suggested that mineral deposits should be located by the electric currents which they must produce in the earth, and he invented the process of ionic medication, by suggesting that electric currents should be used to transport irritating substances out of the body.

In spite of all these advances, no definite connection between electricity and magnetism was as yet discovered. The magnetization of steel objects struck by lightning had been noticed, but the phenomenon could not be controlled, and its significance was uncertain. Many experimenters searched for a connection, and at last, in 1819, Ørsted of Copenhagen found that an electric current tended to twist a magnetic pole around it. The complete theory of the interaction between currents and magnets was given almost immediately by Ampère, who was the first to point out that the deflection of magnets by currents could be used as a telegraph. Faraday showed in 1821 that a wire bearing a current could be made to rotate round the pole of a magnet, and thus invented the first electric motor. Sturgeon invented the electromagnet in 1825. He received an award of twenty-five pounds for this. He also invented the commutator. He drew no more benefits from his achievements, and died in destitution.

Ørsted's experiment showed that magnetism could be obtained from electricity. Numerous investigators now tried to obtain electricity from magnetism. This proved unexpectedly difficult, and was not solved until 1831, when Faraday discovered electromagnetic induction. The effect was so elusive because no one suspected that relative motion between the wire and the magnet was necessary. No relative motion seemed to be involved in Ørsted's experiment, when a magnetic needle lay still under a constant deflection by a steady current. The relative motion was in fact there, but was supplied by the moving current, which was invisible. It is fundamental in electromagnetic phenomena, and a century later, from a consideration of the electromagnetic field, Einstein derived his theory of relativity.

Faraday's success depended on his utilization of the improved electromagnet designed by Joseph Henry. This young American physicist had applied the engineering methods of James Watt to the improvement of electromagnets. He systematically tested various designs until he had found the most powerful, and he converted the electromagnet from a toy into a machine. Faraday would not have obtained a detectable effect unless he had adopted this. Thus engineering methods inspired by industrialism made an essential contribution to his success.

It was now known how to produce light, heat, communication and motion by electricity. The prospect aroused industrial and social hopes, expressed enthusiastically by Davy, Shelley, Joule and many others. Far-sighted men saw that electrical appliances would become a source of profit, and inventors strove to develop them. The social pressure on electrical development was greatest in the richly endowed virgin continent of America, where swift communications were urgently needed both for political unification and material development. The newly invented railway systems in Europe also created a powerful demand for swift communications, as express trains cannot be safely operated without an almost instantaneous signalling system.

The American portrait-painter Morse, and the English physicist Wheatstone, invented the first practicable electric telegraphs almost simultaneously. The development of the electric telegraph in the United States assisted stock market operations, and was pursued with intense energy. The victory of the North in the civil war implied that business, in opposition to planting, had definitely secured the control of American society. Edison has described the events that directed his inventive energies into telegraphy. When he was a boy of fourteen, selling newspapers on a Detroit train, he heard of the result of the battle of Shiloh, the decisive battle of the civil war. He telegraphed along the line to the stations that he was bringing news of the battle in his papers. Crowds assembled to buy his papers, and he said that then he 'realized that the telegraph was a great invention'. He began to learn telegraphy assiduously, and after some years' service in the unsettled post-war Middle-West, he was engaged in 1869 on the ticker system of the Gold Indicator Company of New York. This company telegraphed the price of gold to brokers and speculators. Shortly after Edison's arrival, Fisk and Gould attempted to corner all the gold in America, and produced the most notorious speculative crisis in the nineteenth century. C. F. Adams, a great-grandson of John Adams, gave a classical account of this event, and Edison has dictated a not less remarkable account of it. He observed the mob of frantic speculators from the top of the Western Union Telegraph booth in the gold exchange office. He saw men too excited to write, and five men were required to hold the banker Speyer, who had gone crazy. 'The Western Union operator came to me and said: "Shake, Edison, we are all right. We haven't got a cent." I felt very happy because we were poor. These occasions are very enjoyable to a poor man, but they occur rarely.'

The clearing house was overwhelmed with an inextricable confusion of transactions totalling $500,000,000.

Edison saw that there was money in tickers, and six days later founded a firm for manufacturing telegraphic equipment and pursuing inventions to order. He thereby created two new professions, for he invented the term 'electrical engineer' in the description of the firm, and he was the first man who attempted to professionalize invention. Before him, technicians had invented improvements in the course of their work, but he was the first man who undertook to attempt to invent anything to order. This was a social innovation, as it was an advance towards the transformation of inventing from an erratic art into a science.

Edison's invention of the gramophone arose out of his work on instruments for rapid telegraphy which registered messages on a revolving disc with a pointer. When the machine was run backwards with the disc and its indentations jarring the pointer, it produced a humming noise. This suggested to Edison that such an arrangement might reproduce the human voice, and a successful model was made immediately.

The wonderful invention of the telephone was made almost simultaneously by Bell and Asa Gray in the midst of the strenuous development of telegraphy. Their designs were registered on the same day, but Bell's was registered some hours earlier than Gray's.

The economic and political need to connect America and Europe had stimulated research on Atlantic cables some years earlier. The great physicist William Thomson was drawn into this work, and through it he invented the mirror galvanometer, which established a new degree of sensitivity in electrical instruments. The need for testing the resistance of the copper wire used in the cable led to the improvement of electrical measuring instruments, and the formation of the British Association's famous Committee on electrical measurements, which presently inspired the formation of the National Physical Laboratory. Electrical telegraphy brought into existence a new type of scientist, the technical physicist. No scientific society existed in England for the discussion of his problems, and the Physical Society of London was founded in 1874 to meet his needs. J. A. Fleming, who subsequently became electrical adviser to Edison and to Marconi, and invented the radio valve, delivered the first paper to the new society in 1874. Sixty-five years later, at the age of eighty-nine, he again addressed the society, and spoke on the conditions of technical physics when the society was founded. He said that the academic scientists, such as Clerk Maxwell, were opposed to the new society and its journal, on the ground that no scientific research was worth publishing if it was unsuitable for acceptance by the Royal Society. This left no medium for the publication of the increasing body of men engaged in the scientific problems of telegraphy. The General Post Office had bought the telegraph companies for ten million pounds. This sum indicated the size of the new industry and the relatively large number of scientists employed by it. The introduction of the telephone in 1876 and the electric lamp in 1878 provided the possibility for still larger expansion.

British Government interest in the Atlantic cable was first aroused in 1858, through the Indian Mutiny. A British regiment in Canada had received orders by ship to sail for India. Meanwhile, the Mutiny ended while the ship was on its voyage, and the sailing was unnecessary. But cancellation sent by the next mail boat would not have arrived in time. The authorities were then persuaded to send the cancellation by cable. This succeeded, though the cable was faulty, and a needless expenditure of £50,000 on transport was saved.

Though Clerk Maxwell had not sympathized with the founders of the Physical Society, he had fostered one of the most important aids to the development of industrial science. The universities had in the past gradually adjusted their teaching of science to the needs of mercantile society. They appointed many professors of mathematics and astronomy in the seventeenth and eighteenth centuries, who taught the science that is most useful to navigators. Isaac Newton was the greatest of these professors, and for nearly two centuries after his day, when ocean trade was the foundation of world economy, his chief study, mathematical astronomy, was the science that had the highest prestige in university teaching. This prestige still survived at the beginning of the nineteenth century, for it was preserved by the conservative tradition of the universities. The centre of importance in science had, however, moved elsewhere.

Mercantilism had surrendered the initiative to industrialism, and navigation gave place to the steam engine and the telegraph. In parallel with this social movement, mathematical astronomy gave place to heat and electricity. Physics took precedence of astronomy as the senior science. But at Cambridge in the middle of the nineteenth century, astronomy was still the senior science, and the study of heat and electricity had no official place in the university teaching. Maxwell had the leading part in introducing the official teaching of heat and electricity, and of experimental physics. The Cavendish Laboratory was opened in 1874, with him as the first Cavendish professor of experimental physics. Maxwell made the teaching at Cambridge more suitable for men who were to operate the science of an industrial age. Similar reforms occurred at other universities in Europe and America.

Maxwell was an intellectual instrument of a development determined by the main social forces of his time, while his choice of studies appeared to himself to be determined by the logic of their own development.

Maxwell's most famous achievement arose out of his study of Faraday's experimental researches on electromagnetism. He succeeded in expressing Faraday's results in a coherent mathematical theory. Faraday had suggested that electrical influences were transmitted by a wave-motion. Maxwell showed that such a wave-motion would be mathematically consistent with the known facts about electricity, and deduced that the speed of propagation should be equal to that of light. The existence of these electric waves was proved twenty-seven years later by Hertz, in 1887; and radio-communication had been achieved. The explanation of certain strange observations now became clear. Joseph Henry had noticed in 1842 that the magnetism of a needle in a coil attached to a lightning conductor was affected by flashes that occurred twenty miles away. He had unwittingly observed radio waves. D. E. Hughes noticed in 1872 that an induction coil would produce clicks in a distant microphone. He presently showed the experiment to G. G. Stokes, who was then the president of the Royal Society, and other eminent scientists, but they were not impressed, and he did not persevere with an investigation of the phenomenon. That also was due to radio waves. There is little doubt that radio waves would have been discovered empirically, even if Maxwell had never lived. Great men are not absolutely essential to the progress of science, but they increase its speed.

The first considerable demand for electric power was created by the use of arc lamps. This could not be met economically by Voltaic batteries, so the dynamo was developed to replace them. Arc lights were used in lighthouses, railway goods yards, and big buildings. As they were too powerful for domestic lighting, many inventors attempted to make small incandescent lamps that would serve the domestic user, and supply the demand of a vast potential market. The solution of this problem was due mainly to Edison. Besides working out practicable methods of manufacturing incandescent lamps, he designed and constructed complete electrical power supply systems. He sold electricity as a commodity for the first time, and had to devise meters for measuring the quantity consumed. He had to invent new methods of insulation, systems of wiring for distribution, and a hitherto unparalleled number of new details. The incandescent lamp systems required a current supply different from those serving arc lamps, which had to be met by the construction of new types of dynamos.

In addition to these technical developments, Edison made a thorough investigation of the economics of the gas industry, to discover under what conditions competition with it might be successful. This new type of research on all aspects of electrical engineering stimulated the growth of a new type of institution: the industrial research laboratory. Edison's laboratory at Menlo Park, where he directed most of the work on the incandescent lamp and its utilization, was the most striking early example.

One pure scientific observation of first-rate importance was made by Edison in 1883 through his studies of incandescent lamps. As carbon filament lamps age, some of the carbon is deposited as a film on the inside of the bulb. Shadows sometimes appeared in this film, as if particles that had been ejected by one part of the hot filament had been intercepted by other parts of the filament, and prevented from falling on the bulb. Investigation showed that electricity was indeed leaking from the hot filament. Fleming showed in 1904 that this leak could be used for obtaining direct from alternating currents, and thus invented the radio valve. In 1907 Lee de Forrest introduced the grid, which gives the value its amplifying effect.

While Edison and others were creating the new electrical industry, scientists in the reformed departments of the universities were pursuing researches in the new physics. The incandescent lamps gave the study of high vacua and the electrical phenomena associated with it a new importance. When J. J. Thomson was appointed professor at Cambridge in 1884, ten years after the Cavendish Laboratory had been opened, he chose the conduction of electricity through gases as the most promising line of research. He did not make that choice because this subject seemed of any practical importance at the time. He was prompted by motives that appeared to him as purely philosophical. But as Maxwell adapted university teaching to the higher scientific needs of industry, so J. J. Thomson adapted experimental research to the same needs. His investigations led to the discovery of the electron in 1897. The implications of this discovery were explored during the first decades of the twentieth century. They led to the science of electronics and the creation of the electronics industry. It became evident that electrons were a constituent of all matter. Einstein presently identified mass with energy. The transmutation of material particles into electrical radiation was observed in the laboratory. Thus the matter in the universe could be considered as an electrical manifestation. Industrial civilization had at length succeeded in interpreting the universe in terms of its own concepts. The cosmos was conceived as made of one universal raw material, electrical in nature.

68

The Working Conditions in which Discoveries are Made

THE working conditions in which scientific discoveries have been made may be classified into four types, associated with the exercise of a craft, with teaching, with the pursuit of intellectual amusement, and with professional research. In the first condition, discoveries are made incidentally by technicians in the course of their daily work. Experience suggests how improvements might be made. An immense body of knowledge has been accumulated in this way, and in some techniques, such as agriculture, a large part of the present practice is still based on this sort of knowledge.

In the second, discoveries are made by teachers of technique through reflection on what they are teaching. This condition is characteristic of academic research.

In the third, discoveries are made by wealthy amateurs, who seek pleasure in the satisfaction of their curiosity, or in the pursuit of intellectual prestige. In many instances, they have combined this motive with a desire for profit. The Marquis of Worcester in the seventeenth, and the Hon. Sir Charles Parsons in the nineteenth century, are notable examples.

In the fourth, discoveries are made by professional research workers as the source of their livelihood.

The relative amounts of discovery in these four conditions have varied according to the period. Discovery in prehistoric times was made chiefly by men in the first condition; and in Greek times, in the second and third conditions. In the first two centuries after the Renaissance, the proportion of discovery by men in the third condition increased. During the last hundred years, discovery in the first and third conditions has much decreased; in the second it has increased, while in the fourth, that of professional research, it has virtually begun. Today, scientific discovery is confined almost entirely to men working in the second and fourth conditions: in academic research, and in professional research.

Even discovery made in the second, or academic, condition is acquiring more of the characteristics of research done in the fourth condition, owing to the foundation of chairs and appointments in the universities in which research takes precedence of teaching.

The virtual disappearance of research among both craftsmen and wealthy amateurs is due in part to change in the scale of experiments. The apparatus needed in many modern researches is expensive, and difficult to work and understand. A wealthy amateur might require five years' strenuous scientific education before he could enjoy his apparatus. He is more inclined nowadays to make endowments for research, rather than do research himself.

The craftsman can do little individual research today because he cannot afford the equipment, and in his daily work is no longer the master of a complete machine. Before the sub-division of labour and the development of big power-driven machinery, the craftsman made most of his own simple machines, and knew all their points as a whole. Now he makes part of a machine designed by another man. He frequently does not understand the complete machine that he operates, and does not know it with the completeness that gives the possibility to suggest effective improvements.

Individual discovery grows more difficult as individual is supplanted by factory production. The scientist who works in his personal workshop is increasingly supplanted by a team of scientists working in a large laboratory that resembles a factory. The major part of discovery nowadays is made by scientists organized in teams, and following a programme of research, in industrial, medical and university research laboratories.

Industrial research laboratories may be divided into two groups, those belonging to private firms, and those belonging to the government. Both groups have evolved from the activities of craftsmen in private and in government employ, and they retain marks of these origins.

The transition of craftsmen's individual research into modern organized industrial research is seen in the activities of the Boulton and Watt firm in the eighteenth century. Watt, Murdock, Southern and other members of the firm made improvements in the course of their daily work. They also pursued a number of systematic researches on particular problems, such as the accurate measurement of power, and they discussed their problems with Small, Priestley and others, who were forerunners of a type of consulting research scientist. But their various systematic researches did not follow a clearly-expressed programme, and such men as Small and Priestley were not formal research consultants, and did not regard this work as their profession.

The interest of governments in armaments has had a great influence on the development of science. The first big factories in medieval and modern times were arsenals. As this word is derived from the Arabic, it reveals the influence of Muslim practice on the creation of the forerunners of modern industry. The Italians adopted the institution and the term, and, as has already been mentioned, their arsenals were famous in the time of

Dante, and provided inspiration to Galileo. Lavoisier used the resources of the French Arsenal in making the researches that laid the foundation for modern chemistry. The experiments of Rumford on the nature of heat owed their convincing features to the large scale on which they were performed, and this was due to his command of the resources of the Bavarian Arsenal. He showed that when a cannon was rubbed with a blunt borer, an indefinite amount of heat could be produced during the removal of a negligible quantity of turnings. If the experiment had been made on a small scale, the contrast between the size of the cannon and the quantity of the turnings would have been much less striking.

By 1936, a large part of scientific research in countries such as Great Britain was done in industrial research laboratories. In a society based on private enterprise, it was not the duty of the owners of a private research laboratory to publish any particulars of their laboratory, and its researches, staff and equipment; or even of its existence. This conviction, characteristic of nineteenth century industrialists, was gradually replaced by the belief that complete information on research laboratories, and all other institutions, should be collected and published. This work was begun, and was gradually extended. It was inspired by several motives. These included the publication of research activities as a form of advertisement, and the general social movement towards collective organization.

In 1936 a list of 120 industrial research laboratories in Britain was published, of which 19 belonged to the government.

The British universities and university colleges contained at least four hundred science departments. These were furnished with laboratories which varied much in size and equipment, and some research was done in most of them. Many were old, and even less suited to research than teaching. A good new laboratory cost at that time about £50,000, and the best in universities such as Oxford, Cambridge, Bristol, Glasgow and Edinburgh cost from £100,000 to £250,000.

Research on the problems of agriculture, horticulture and fisheries was conducted in at least sixty laboratories in Britain. Many of these were part of, or associated with, departments in universities.

Medical knowledge was advanced by doctors working mainly under two conditions: as individual practitioners, and as teachers

12

in hospital schools. It was not advanced much by the personal researches of wealthy amateurs, as the subject is not an attractive medium of intellectual entertainment. Medical research as a profession is even newer than industrial research as a profession.

Teachers have contributed relatively more to medicine than to technology. This is owing to the superior status of medical doctors in ancient society. In Britain in 1938, some important hospital medical schools and laboratories were still virtually autonomous and independent of universities. The number of medical research institutes whose staffs were primarily engaged in research and not in teaching and treatment was only about thirteen.

This retarded development of professional medical as compared with professional industrial research was mainly due to lack of endowment. Doctors in medical practice were generally able to earn much more than in research.

The organization of research in modern times began in the seventeenth century. In England it was conducted informally by the members of the Royal Society, who drew their incomes from other sources. As the members were under no economic obligation to continue research, they were inclined to make grand schemes for investigating all the universe, but dropped most of them disappointingly soon.

The French Academy, like the French Government, had a more formal organization. Voltaire contended that this was an advantage, because the Royal Society was lacking in two things most essential to man: rewards and laws. A seat in the French Academy conferred a salary on a chemist or a geometrician, and gave him the opportunity for sustained research.

The French Academy and its members acted as state advisers on science, technology and patents, and contributed much to the great power of the French state at the end of the eighteenth century. If dominance had been due entirely to science, the French would have entered the nineteenth century with a decisive advantage. But the economic situation and possibilities of England were superior, and these provided the basis on which English science was able to overhaul French science, in spite of its inferior organization. Owing to the accessibility of coalfields, and the convenience of water transport, the British industrialists prospered without receiving organized scientific assistance from the state, and they sought scientific advice only when they needed it urgently. They depended on consultants, and did not prosecute systematic researches through their permanent staff.

American industrialists followed the same line at the beginning of the nineteenth century, but their circumstances were considerably different. The country and its economic potentialities were greater, and almost undeveloped. The scarcity of workmen and the promise of quick profits stimulated the invention of labour-saving devices. The introduction of the American sewing-machine in 1846 was a characteristic example of this tendency.

The absence of small workshop industry with a long tradition reduced the opposition to the creation of large and well-organized new industries. Better communications were urgently needed by the scattered population, and by financiers who desired to follow the new possibilities for investment, which altered and multiplied continually, as quickly as possible. Systems of communication themselves became profitable investments, and possession of them conferred much power on their owners, for communications are the nerves through which society is organized.

69

Two Industrial Research Laboratories

THE telephone was invented at Boston in 1875 by A. Graham Bell, while attempting to apply electrical vibrating systems to multiple telegraphy. He was the son of A. M. Bell, who experimented on the analysis of speech, vocal physiology and phonetics, and lectured on elocution in London. He learned the technique of teaching deaf mutes from his father, and had emigrated to Boston, where he practised such teaching, besides engaging in telegraphic research. He was appropriately equipped to attack the technical problem he solved so successfully. Financiers and engineers assisted him in the utilization of the invention, and created the telephone industry.

Research was the midwife that presented society with its telephonic offspring, and as these have grown up, they have continually extended the sphere of research with which they were originally surrounded. The telephone started in the laboratory and the laboratory has grown with it.

The company that operates the telephone system in the United States still bears the inventor's name. By 1937, it controlled 17,500,000 telephones, and employed more than 300,000 persons. It was organized in three subsidiary companies, which respectively maintained and operated the telephones, manufactured the equipment, and conducted research. This latter company was named the Bell Telephone Laboratories, and was nominally independent, but did not in fact undertake research for companies that did not belong to the Bell System.

This was situated in a block of buildings in New York City. They contained thirteen floors, with an area of twenty acres. They had a staff of about 4,200 persons, of whom 2,000 were qualified engineers and scientists. The majority were engaged in the solution of routine problems, but about 500 had contributed to the 1,100 papers on original research that had been issued from the laboratories between 1920 and 1937.

The technical problems of a telephone system involve many sciences. Good transmitting and receiving instruments must be made of materials which possess suitable magnetic and electrical properties. Their design entails the skilful use of electric currents and circuits, and the production of the right acoustic properties. The transmission of currents over thousands of miles of wire presents another series of problems. In addition to securing strong and undistorted messages over great distances, there is the problem of making the service durable. Wires are exposed to weather. The scientist must discover metals that will resist corrosion and wear, and circuits that will suffer the least interference from stray currents produced by lightning and other disturbances. He must discover how wooden poles for supporting wires may be protected from rot, or from boring insects. He must find the explanation and remedy for unexpected break-downs.

The manufacture of the instruments, exchange equipment, switch boards, cables, etc., presents another series of testing and routine research problems. Difficulties that arise in factory processes must be overcome. The research activities mentioned so far refer chiefly to the perfection of standard equipment.

Another division of research was concerned with the development of new operations such as picture telegraphy and television, and the exploration of ideas, to foresee and provide future methods of communication, possibly of entirely new types.

A large part of the researches made by the staff was published in the Company's own journal, whose volumes contained more than one thousand papers. These were classified under the following subjects: acoustics, chemistry, reviews of contemporary physics, crystallography, electron diffraction, inspection, instruments and measurements, insulation, magnetics, mathematical physics, metallurgy, optics, photoelectricity, thermionics, communication systems with the sub-divisions: picture transmission, powerline telephony, public address, sound pictures, television, train dispatching and miscellaneous, radio, telegraphy, telephone equipment, telephony, and vacuum tubes as circuit elements.

The efficiency of a telephone depends on its adaptation to the peculiarities of human speech and hearing. Callers often receive wrong numbers because their speech is not correctly understood by the operator in the exchange. Harvey Fletcher and his colleagues analysed these problems in the Bell laboratories, and have much improved the exactitude of acoustic research by the development of better quantitative methods, depending largely on the possibilities of amplification presented by the radio valve. They constructed an experimental microphone and telephone apparatus which would reproduce speech without distortion. They proved that the human ear varies in sensitivity for different tones, and that different ears have different sensitivities. If several people listen to the same speech, each of them hears a slightly different series of sounds, and interpretation of what they hear starts in each case from the consideration of slightly different physiological data, quite apart from the different psychological perspective in which notice of these data is received in the brain.

The chemist R. R. Williams studied the effect of moisture on textiles and rubber used in insulation, and published papers on chemical methods of preserving wood in poles, etc. He applied biochemical technique to the study of vitamins, and established the formula of, and synthesized, vitamin B_1, known as thiamin. Its absence from a diet produces the disease of beri-beri. This research had great significance for biology and medicine, and also for the future of scientific research. It was an example, which was to be repeated with increasing frequency, of how a scientist engaged in an industrial research laboratory has been given opportunities for research in directions not closely connected with the laboratory's original industrial aims. The advancement of pure science will in the future depend more and more on the support of the industrial research laboratory.

Radio telephony, sound films, television and many other recent innovations depend on the emission of electrons from metal surfaces in vacuum tubes. The reverse phenomenon, in which metals are bombarded by electrons, produces X-rays. It is evident that the structure of metallic surfaces, which may be of interest for the design of improved instruments, might be explored by shooting electrons at the surfaces and seeing how they bounce off.

C. J. Davisson and his colleagues started a research of this sort, and in 1920 noticed that the electrons rebounded from a nickel surface in an anomalous manner. The nickel consisted of the usual conglomerate of small crystals. Davisson reinvestigated the phenomenon in 1927 with a single crystal of nickel, and owing to the perfect uniformity of its structure, the anomalies were much more pronounced. The reflected beam was not uniform, but split into a bundle of rays, analogous to a beam of light diffracted by rows of parallel scratches.

De Broglie had suggested in 1924 that electrons possessed wave-properties, and he gave a formula for calculating the size of the waves. Davisson calculated how his beam of electrons ought to behave according to this formula, and found that the result agreed completely with the experimental observations he had already obtained. He had given the first experimental proof of the wave theory of matter. An independent proof was obtained somewhat later by G. P. Thomson. Davisson and Thomson shared a Nobel prize for these achievements.

Many papers on the theory and application of statistics were published in connection with inspection. Probability theory was used in telephone transmission, in the sampling of manufactured parts for telephones, in the analysis of wearing properties, etc. This gave an impetus to the development of quality control.

Another fundamental discovery of major importance was K. G. Jansky's detection in 1932 of radio waves from outer space, in course of researches on the ionosphere for the improvement of long-distance radio transmission. Thus the new science of radio-astronomy was founded by the Bell Laboratories, but its importance was not fully recognized until after the Second World War.

The Bell Laboratory scientists worked intensively on the

development of carrier currents and coaxial cables for long-distance and multiple messages.

Finally, there was the long series of papers on Contemporary Physics by K. K. Darrow. These were expositions of recent advances in such subjects as wave-mechanics, radioactivity, and cosmic rays. They were written primarily for the information of technical physicists and engineers, to assist them to follow the general direction of physical discovery.

In 1939, the research laboratory of the Philips Lamp Factory at Eindhoven in Holland was possibly the finest industrial research laboratory in the world. It had beautiful buildings designed in the excellent style of modern Dutch architecture. The rooms and corridors were spacious, clean and quiet, and free from the rush, constriction and dirt often seen in industrial laboratories. It had the calm of a college rather than the bustle of a factory.

The development which led to the erection of this laboratory in 1923 was an outcome of the war of 1914. The Philips firm was making at that time a small number of electric lamps, with glass imported from Germany. When the war started, their supply of glass was cut, and they had either to close the factory or discover how to make the glass. This stimulation to solve its own problems established the tradition of research.

The firm had four scientific research workers in 1914. This group increased to 55 in 1924, 165 in 1931, and 415 in 1936. Of the latter number, 40 were physicists, 12 chemists, 53 engineers, 71 assistants, 24 instrument makers, 81 mechanics, 27 glass blowers, and 10 electricians. The laboratory was created by the physicist G. Holst, the collaborator of Kamerlingh Onnes in the discovery of superconductivity. Its most remarkable feature was its reflective intellectual atmosphere, unusual in a large industrial organization, and due in part to the virtual absence of administrative staff. The scientific heads of departments had much initiative in discussions with persons outside the laboratory, so that scientific business was conducted directly by scientists, rather than by administrators on behalf of scientists.

An important achievement of the laboratory was the invention of glass and metal seals. Platinum was formerly used for conducting electricity through glass, in X-ray tubes, etc., because it makes a good joint. But it cannot be used in large quantities because of expense. This was a bar to the use of big tubes needing thick wires for transmitting heavy currents. Bouwers and Bol searched for metals that would make a good joint with glass, and found certain alloys of iron and chromium were effective. The joints between these alloys and glass are strong enough to resist blows from a hammer, and heavy glass and metal objects made with them do not break when dropped on the floor. Through this invention it became possible to manufacture large radio transmission valves consuming several hundred horse-power. Van der Pol introduced the use of such valves for short-wave transmission.

The laboratory developed the sodium vapour lamp, and small high-pressure mercury lamps. These operated at pressures up to one ton per square inch, and gave an illumination of 180,000 candles per square centimetre, more brilliant than the surface of the sun, which gives only 165,000. These sources of intense light were used for the illumination of aerodromes, cinema projection and other purposes.

The most outstanding theoretical research up to this period was carried out by van der Pol on non-linear oscillations, which are important in radio circuits. He applied his knowledge to the interpretation of the oscillatory diagrams produced by electro-cardiographs, and deduced from them the existence of hitherto unrecognized rhythms in heart-beats. With van der Mark he constructed an electrical model heart, governed by the oscillations of a neon tube, that gave exact imitations of both normal and abnormal rhythms in the human heart.

Since Cockcroft and Walton accomplished the first artificial disintegration of atoms by machinery at Cambridge in 1932, the Philips engineers became the first to manufacture such machinery as a commercial product.

70

Research in Universities

THE growth of scientific teaching and research in universities may be illustrated by some features of the development at Cambridge in England. The University had ten chairs of science and medicine in 1816. These were in medicine, mathematics, experimental philosophy, paleontological mineralogy, chemistry, botany, anatomy, petrographical mineralogy, astronomy, natural and experimental philosophy, and domestic medicine. These chairs were founded between 1540 and 1800, and carried salaries of £40 to £300 per annum.

The Jacksonian professor of natural and experimental philosophy in 1816 was W. Farish. His lectures are described as embracing a great variety of subjects. 'In the original arrangement of them, the Professor conceived that the application of the principle of Natural Philosophy, Natural History, Chemistry . . . to the arts, manufactures and agriculture of Britain, presented a new and useful field of instruction. After having taken an *actual survey* of everything curious in the kingdom on such subjects, he contrived a mode of exhibiting the operations and processes that are in use in nearly all of them. Having provided himself with a number of brass wheels of all forms and sizes, such that any two of them can work with each other; and also with a variety of axles, bars, screws, clamps . . . he constructs at pleasure, with the addition of the peculiar parts, working models of almost every kind of machine. These he puts in motion by a water-wheel or a steam engine in such a way as to make them in general do the actual work of the real machines, on a small scale; and he explains at the same time the chemical and philosophical principles, on which the various processes of the art exhibited, depend.'

Farish's lectures were of the type delivered by Davy at the Royal Institution. Though their aim and content were admirable and intended to prepare men for a part in the development of the rising industrialism, they do not appear to have had much influence at Cambridge. The university was still mainly engaged in training men for the Church.

The number of scientists paid by the university rose from 26 in 1816 to 29 in 1840.

The adaptation of the university to contemporary needs was advanced by the Prince Consort, who was elected Chancellor in 1847. There was no degree examination in science, and one of the first effects of the Commission of 1851, formed under the Prince's influence, was to establish such an examination in 1851.

The syllabus of the mathematical examination included mechanics, optics, spherical astronomy, lunar and planetary theories,

12*

hydrodynamics, sound, waves and tides, and elasticity. Heat, electricity and magnetism were added under the influence of Clerk Maxwell, who was the first examiner to be appointed for these subjects.

This wide range could be covered only by intensive reading and coaching. A large number of new textbooks were written between 1865 and 1875 to assist the increasing number of students to assimilate these subjects.

While all this reading and writing was in progress, there was still no official laboratory for experimental work on the subjects taught. Like Newton, the professors still conducted their experimental researches in their living rooms, or set up apparatus temporarily in a lecture hall. The contrast between the reading and the absence of practical work could not be overlooked, and the movement for the foundation of a chair and laboratory for experimental physics began. The funds were provided by the Duke of Devonshire, who was himself a capable mathematician and a relative of the famous Henry Cavendish. The new laboratory cost £8,450. It was the occasion for another important innovation; the university appointed its first science demonstrator. This was W. Garnett. Hitherto, the university's official science teachers had been professors only.

In 1874, the university had sixteen professors of science, and one demonstrator. The sixteen Sadlerian lecturerships on algebra had been merged into a professorship of pure mathematics, and in 1866, a chair of zoology and comparative anatomy had been founded, seven years after the publication of the *Origin of Species*. Chairs of physiology and pathology were founded in 1883, and agriculture in 1899.

The need for teaching in organic chemistry became acute. Dewar asked Hofmann in Berlin to recommend an organic chemist. He sent S. Ruhemann, who arrived in Cambridge in 1885, at the age of twenty-six. Ruhemann found that the university did not possess a laboratory for organic chemistry. He presently found a small dark room where he could lecture and demonstrate to a few students. There were no stores of apparatus, and the available reagents were impure. He drew attention to this situation, and the authorities said that he could have £25 to go to Berlin and secure all the necessary material.

In 1900, Cambridge had twenty professors of science, and the number of junior staff had increased from one to twenty-eight.

These consisted of four readers, twenty-one demonstrators, and three assistants to professors. The total of forty-eight science teachers in 1900 had increased to 212 in 1938. There were then 34 professors of science, 16 readers, 107 lecturers, 46 demonstrators and 9 assistants to professors. This does not include science fellows of colleges without university appointments, laboratory assistants and mechanics.

This growth of personnel was accompanied by corresponding increases in endowments for laboratories. The university staff of the Cavendish Laboratory increased from two in 1874 to fourteen in 1938, and the number of research students had increased to more than thirty.

The Laboratory buildings were extended at a cost of £4,000 in 1896, and again, in 1908, at a cost of £7,135, including £5,000 donated by Rayleigh from his Nobel Prize money. This series of relatively small buildings formed an odd conglomeration of research and lecture rooms, workshops and corridors.

So far, when expenditure had been made, it was spread over the whole teaching and research activities of the laboratory, and was not devoted to special researches. Much of the apparatus used for research in 1874 and the early days was also used for teaching. Galvanometers were temporarily disconnected from the apparatus set up in the research rooms, for use by students during their practical classes. The equipment in apparatus and workshops slowly increased, but was still quite small in 1914, though in the previous thirty years, fifty professors of physics had been trained, including Rutherford, the Braggs, C. T. R. Wilson, O. W. Richardson, Callendar, and Langevin; the electron had been discovered, and the first advances towards the elucidation of atomic structure had been started.

The scale of experiments still remained small for the first few years after Rutherford's appointment as Cavendish Professor in 1919. Expenditure on apparatus was conceived in units of £50, and there was intense competition for the use of these small sums by research workers who were then well known, and have since become famous.

A new scale of experimentation and expenditure arose out of the work of P. Kapitza. He began research in 1922 on a method of producing intense magnetic fields by short-circuiting a battery of accumulators through a coil. It was successful, so he suggested that still more intense fields might be made by short-circuiting a dynamo through a coil. The design and construction of this machinery was far more expensive than that of any previous single piece of apparatus used in the Cavendish Laboratory. It cost many thousands of pounds, and could not have been done without large grants, which came especially from the Department of Scientific and Industrial Research. The late Lord Balfour was then the Minister to whom the Department was responsible, and he was active in promoting support for these large-scale experiments. The new scale of expenditure arising out of Kapitza's work was confirmed in 1930, when the Royal Society granted £15,000 for the construction of a laboratory for research with strong magnetic fields at low temperatures. This was an innovation in the Cavendish tradition, as formerly no equipment of this size and cost had been built purely for research, unconnected with teaching.

Research on radioactivity was still confined to the utilization of natural radioactive substances. These existed in very small quantities, and the apparatus designed to investigate them remained for a long time on the small scale. But in the thirty years of research that had passed since the discovery of radioactivity in 1896, most of the experiments practicable with existing small apparatus had been performed. Progress depended on the submission of radioactive substances to more powerful modifying forces. Research had passed to the study of the structure of the nucleus of the atom, and forces of a new degree of strength were needed to elucidate its inaccessible features. The disintegrating radioactive nucleus emits particles in groups with definite speeds. The accurate determination of these speeds was necessary for the advance of the theory of the nucleus, and it is most conveniently obtained by deflecting the emitted particles in a powerful magnetic field. A suitable big magnet did not exist at Cambridge for the analysis of rays of emitted helium nuclei, and the experiment was first performed successfully with the great electro-magnet at Paris.

In this general situation, new types of knowledge and ability were required in the Cavendish Laboratory. Kapitza was an electrical engineer by training, and his success with the short-circuiting dynamo was due to his command of engineering design. J. D. Cockcroft assisted him in this work.

Cockcroft was an electrical engineer who had graduated at the Manchester College of Technology under Miles Walker, and had entered Metropolitan Vickers Ltd., which subsequently became part of A.E.I. Ltd. After the war of 1914–18, he returned to the firm, and in his spare time he and another engineer made researches in electrical engineering under Walker's direction. The Institution of Electrical Engineers had collected a sum of money to celebrate the end of the war, and decided to found a scholarship to assist electrical engineers to continue research. The other engineer was asked whether he would like it, but said that he did not wish to interrupt his career by resigning a paid appointment and returning to further years of study. The scholarship was then offered to Cockcroft, who accepted. He went to Cambridge, took a course of applied mathematics, and continued research. In 1928–30 he had a table in a corner of the shed where Kapitza's dynamo was erected, and quietly and obscurely worked there. The dynamo was manufactured by Metropolitan Vickers, where he was formerly an engineer, and he did invaluable work in interpreting the needs of the scientists to the manufacturing engineers, besides joining in the research. He assisted C. D. Ellis and H. Kershaw to design a large permanent magnet for the separation of the electrons emitted from disintegrating atoms into groups. It was possible to adopt a permanent magnet for this purpose by utilizing the properties of the new cobalt steels. The magnetic field in these steels may be fixed by a temporary current, and later destroyed and fixed at a different strength by another temporary current. The permanence of the field at a suitable strength for any interval of time obviates the consumption of a continuous current that would be necessary in an electro-magnet, and it also removes the trouble of keeping such a current constant. This magnet was made by Metropolitan Vickers.

Cockcroft also assisted Kapitza in the design of the equipment and building of the new laboratory for research on strong magnetic fields at low temperatures. They constructed a hydrogen liquefier in which part of the cooling was done with commercial hydrogen. This made the cost of liquefaction less than if purified hydrogen had been used throughout.

While Cockcroft was assisting in these various works, he was building a small high tension apparatus in a corner of a room which was subsequently taken over by the department of physical chemistry. He had a few big insulators and transformers, of the type used in the transmission of high-tension electric currents, and large glass tubes of the kind used in petrol pumps. He was attempting to construct an apparatus for producing streams of protons accelerated to a high speed by a strong electric field. He was aided in this work by T. E. Allibone of Metropolitan Vickers. The firm also presented much of the material, which consisted of standard electrical engineering products.

The apparatus was perfected, and in 1932 Cockcroft, with E. T. S. Walton, successfully disintegrated atoms with it. This was one of the supreme experiments in science, because it had reduced the transmutation of the elements to a process that could be conducted with machinery of an industrial type, and so had brought it within sight of exploitation for the benefit of man.

The experiment was the trigger which released the full pressure of American industrialism on the development of science. America led in electrical engineering, and now that physical research depended so directly on electrical engineering, America would assume the lead in experimental physics. This happened through E. O. Lawrence's invention of the cyclotron. The construction of such a machine, which produces swift particles by whirling them round while contained by a magnetic field, like stones on the ends of bits of string, and then letting them go, had been considered by others, but was believed to be impracticable. Even seven years later, Lawrence was far the most successful in making cyclotrons work.

When Kapitza did not return from the Soviet Union in 1934, Cockcroft became the virtual director of the Mond Laboratory, and mastered the subject of low-temperature physics, which is quite different from electrical engineering.

The Metropolitan Vickers Company made an essential contribution to the achievements of the atomic physicists. Many branches of physical research in universities could no longer be undertaken without the collaboration of the industrial research laboratories of such firms, and the intermediation of engineering physicists, of whom Cockcroft was already a distinguished example.

The Metropolitan Vickers firm made cyclotrons for J. Chadwick at Liverpool and also for the Cavendish Laboratory. It constructed the improved Bush calculating machine used by D. R. Hartree at Manchester University. This machine cost more than £4,000. It also constructed the special air-cooled magnet used by P. M. S. Blackett in the same university. This cost more than £1,000. With it, after the Second World War, the first V or 'strange' particle was discovered.

The success of the researches on atomic disintegration by electrical machinery depended on a technical invention made in the Metropolitan Vickers Laboratory by C. R. Burch. In 1930 he showed how to manufacture oils of very low vapour pressure by the molecular distillation of lubricating oils. Hitherto, high vacua had been made by removing residual gas from a vessel with a blast of mercury vapour, and then condensing the mercury vapour with liquid air cooling. The new oils were up to ten thousand times less volatile than mercury, and when they were used in vacuum pumps instead of mercury, they left a high vacuum when condensed only with water cooling. Thus they eliminated the need for liquid air in producing high vacua. Vessels could be evacuated continuously, and the application of drastic heat treatment to remove the remnants of gases sticking to the inside surfaces became unnecessary. It became possible to obtain good vacua very quickly in vessels connected to pumps merely through ground glass joints, without sealing the glass by flame. Burch prepared greases from the residues of his distilled oils, which had an extremely low vapour pressure, and could be used for plastering the ground-glass joints, and swiftly making them gas-tight.

The discovery of these oils and greases has proved of great economic importance, for besides facilitating the manufacture of small valves and X-ray tubes, it has made the use of big demountable valves and tubes practicable. Big valves are needed for transatlantic telephony, and big X-ray tubes for cancer treatment. The use of such big apparatuses would not be practicable unless they could be taken to pieces, repaired, and re-evacuated quickly and inexpensively. That would have been impossible with mercury pumps.

Similarly, it would have been very difficult to accomplish the disintegration of atoms with the assistance of big vacuum tubes, unless these tubes could be opened, the experimental targets inside rearranged, and the tubes re-evacuated expeditiously.

The introduction of Burch's oil so facilitated evacuation that the time of one experiment with the atomic disintegrating apparatus was reduced from about a fortnight to one hour. This enormously increased the possibilities for trying various experimental arrangements, and finding the successful one. Burch introduced the oils in 1930; and atoms were disintegrated with the aid of big high-tension vacuum tubes for the first time in 1932.

Research on atoms, cosmic rays, and other subjects of modern physics has been greatly assisted by amplifying devices which utilize electrical instruments and circuits developed by the radio industry. With these devices it is possible to count automatically over any interval of time, from a ten-thousandth of a second up to a year or more, the number of particles emitted during atomic disintegrations. This established a new order of accuracy and scope in investigating disintegrative processes. The development of the use of these devices in atomic researches at the Cavendish Laboratory was due especially to C. E. Wynn-Williams.

The conduct of physical experiments on an engineering scale created the need for a new scale of endowment. The cost of units of apparatus had risen from the order of £50 in 1925 to £500 in 1935. In 1936, Lord Austin presented £250,000 to the Cavendish Laboratory to enable it to meet the new need. A two-million volt high-tension laboratory was constructed, a fifty-ton cyclotron installed, and a large block of research rooms added.

The researches in the Cavendish Laboratory belong to the most advanced and purest part of experimental physics. Rutherford's successor, W. L. Bragg, specialized in the structure of solids. His pupils have had the leading part in the creation of the revolutionary new subject of molecular biology.

The Cavendish Laboratory is devoted entirely to pure science, but its researches show how an ancient university has adapted itself to modern interests. These interests, or social needs, have also secured more direct attention by the creation of special universities to serve them. These are technical universities. The Massachusetts Institute of Technology is one of the most striking examples. It was founded at Boston in 1861 during the American Civil War, and was intended to serve the whole of the United States. Its aim was to educate men for the industrial civilization whose domination was assured by the victory of the North. Its foundation occurred at about the same time as Clerk Maxwell's movement for the reform of science teaching at Cambridge in England. After the Cavendish Laboratory was opened in 1874, the methods of teaching practical physics evolved by Pickering at the M.I.T. were adopted.

By 1938, the institution had an endowment and plant worth

£10,000,000. George Eastman, who invented the Kodak camera and photographic film, and created a new industry, gave £4,000,000 of this. It had a core of buildings erected in 1916 on a site of eighty acres beside the Charles River Basin. The city of Boston, and the neighbouring town of Cambridge, which contains Harvard University, are on the banks of the Charles River, and formerly suffered from flooding. This trouble was removed by a splendid piece of municipal engineering. A barrage was built across the mouth of the river, which created a basin or river-lake several miles long. The new buildings of the M.I.T. and Harvard are on different parts of the banks of the basin, those of the M.I.T. being nearer the centre of Boston. The students from both institutions have excellent sailing and boating facilities, and on hot summer days can read in dinghies while drifting in the cool air over the water.

By this time, the M.I.T. had about 2,600 students, of whom 500 were graduates, and a teaching staff of five hundred. The latter included thirty-one professors of chemistry, twenty-eight of engineering, and twenty-five in physics. They were divided into three grades, professor, associate professor and assistant professor, in about equal numbers. The senior grade did not contain all of the eminent scientists. For instance, in 1938, the junior grade included such physicists as Van de Graaff, M. S. Vallarta and F. W. Sears.

The work on calculating machines by Vannevar Bush at M.I.T. was of outstanding importance. He created a fund of experience, which prepared the way for the introduction of electronic techniques in computer design. Bush was a lean, keen man of evident genius and humour, who must have been stimulating to good students and disconcerting to lazy ones. His work on the invention of numerous types of calculating machine was not a form of gadgeteering, but the pursuit of a philosophical idea. He considered that the greatest mathematical discoveries have arisen in the past out of the use of mechanical aids to calculation, and similar discoveries inspired by calculating machines may be expected in the future. The invention of the Arabic system of numerals and a symbol for zero arose out of the form of the abacus. He contended that the mechanical fact that it is convenient to mount wires parallel to a frame inspired the invention of positional numeration and zero. The formal mathematicians of classical times declined to use the plebeian abacus.

They stuck to their cumbersome notation, while men of trade, with a mechanical aid, produced the most far-reaching of mathematical inventions. The formalist's insistence that ruler and compass were the only tools worthy of the gentleman scholar directed the attention of the learned for centuries to insoluble problems, such as the trisection of an angle with these instruments. As the decimal system arose out of the abacus, so a new mathematics may arise out of the development of calculating machines for the assistance of engineers and business men.

Such were the views held by Bush in 1938. During the Second World War he became the head of the American scientific war effort, in which his genius and insight were applied with great effect.

The work of Van de Graaff on high-voltage generators became very well known. He had already built a machine with two aluminium discharge spheres fifteen feet in diameter, mounted on insulating cylinders thirty feet high. One sphere was charged positively and the other negatively, and sparks jumped between them at 10,000,000 volts.

Aerodynamical research was already another strong department at the M.I.T. Several wind-tunnels were used, and aerological observations, including a daily flight to 20,000 feet for data, were made in collaboration with the United States Air Corps.

71

Research as an Independent Social Activity

RESEARCH arose incidentally out of the work of the craftsman and teacher. It has begun only recently to attempt to emancipate itself, and pursue its own life as an autonomous social organism, with its own factories, or laboratories. An impressive manifestation of this development, both in achievement and fate, was the Kaiser Wilhelm Gesellschaft for the Promotion of Science. It possessed some thirty institutes designed entirely for research.

This society was founded in 1911 by Wilhelm II, under the inspiration of German scholars and scientists. Its aim was derived from the project of Wilhelm von Humboldt, the minister of education in Prussia at the beginning of the nineteenth century, who moulded the features of the German system of education. Humboldt combined Prussian ideas of organization with French Enlightenment, and through the latter drew inspiration from Francis Bacon. The institutes of the Kaiser Wilhelm Gesellschaft were a partial realization of Bacon's aims.

Humboldt said that the German universities and academies should be helped by a third type of institute, independently engaged in discovery.

The Kaiser Wilhelm Gesellschaft started with two hundred members, most of whom were industrialists, bankers, business men, etc. These subscribed funds which provided the society with a private endowment, and gave it the means to pursue its own research policy, free from direct control by the state.

The new institutes were devoted to three purposes: the promotion of new fields of inquiry which could not be conveniently started in universities, the provision of temporary or permanent opportunities for research to academic scientists overburdened with teaching, and the training of graduates in research before they have entered an academic career.

The society adopted the principle of an evolving, and not a settled, research programme to achieve these purposes. Its first president, von Harnack, said that the society 'must not build institutes and then seek for the right man, but must first find an eminent scholar and then build an institute for him'. It consciously watched for innovations in learning, and sought to aid those that seemed most promising. It offered to build for the scientist who had created a new branch of research an institute designed to suit his needs, and provide him permanently with the best conditions for work. When the scientist died or retired, the institute was to be closed, or adapted to the needs of a scientist working in another field, but no successor in the same field was to be appointed unless there was a clearly outstanding candidate.

The realization of this scheme was hindered by the war of 1914, but after the war, it was prosecuted with energy, in spite of poverty. The number of the society's financial supporters had increased by 1930 to seven hundred, and included the government of Germany, and local governments. The state donations were given without conditions, so that the initiative of the society remained legally free. Contributions were received from all the Prussian provinces, the greater towns and districts, and the principal trade unions, besides industrialists and others.

Motions in the Reichstag for the support of the society were invariably supported by all parties, from the National Socialists to the Communists. The statement by Harnack in 1910 that 'armed defence and science are the two strong pillars to support the greatness of Germany, the care of which must never cease or stand still', was widely approved. After the war, when Germany's military forces were limited by treaty, there was an extra effort to strengthen the other pillar, 'to hinder the undoing of Germany'.

The policy of the society was guided by a senate, one half of which was elected by the members, and the other half originally nominated by Wilhelm II, and then, during the period of the Republic, by the German and local governments. The senate elected the presidents and executive committee. Harnack remained president until his death in 1930. Krupp von Bohlen was then first vice-president, and the board included Planck and Duisberg.

The Ministers for Internal Affairs, and for Science, Art and Education in Prussia, were entitled to send representatives to all meetings. The latter position in 1930 was held by Becker, the Republican statesman and Islamic scholar. After Harnack's death, Becker and Planck became candidates for the presidency. They received support respectively from various scientific groups, but there was also a political alignment. The Republicans supported Becker, and the Nationalists Planck, and Planck was elected.

In addition to the senate there was a scientific advisory council, containing all the senior scientists working for the society. It was organized in three sections, for biology and medicine, chemistry and physics, and the humanities. The presidents of these sections helped to choose scientists and subjects to be aided.

The work of the society was arranged under the divisions of theoretical and applied science, which were to be pursued in two series of institutes. The first institutes in the series for theoretical science were devoted to chemistry, physics, zoology, botany and medicine. An institute for biology was built at Berlin–Dahlem.

This contained six lesser institutes, or departments, as it was found that biology might be advanced more easily by a collaboration of a group of independent workers, than by the work of a big institute devoted to a single branch of biology. The independent departments in this institute were directed at various times by Correns, Goldschmidt, Hartmann, Mangold, Warburg, Meyerhof, Herbst, Spemann and A. Fischer. Separate institutes were built for Neuberg for biochemical investigations, and for Eugen Fischer, for inquiries on human heredity and genetics, and an institute for Abderhalden for physiological chemistry was established at Halle.

Two institutes for chemistry were built at Dahlem; one, for physical chemistry, was directed by Haber, and the other, for general chemistry, was directed at various times by Willstätter and Hahn.

An institute for physics, directed by Einstein and von Laue, was established in Berlin, and one for aerodynamics at Göttingen.

In medical research, an institute for Wassermann for work on experimental therapeutics was established at Dahlem. One for Oskar and Cécile Vogt on brain research was built at Berlin–Buch. The society undertook the support of Kraepelin's institute for psychiatry in Munich. It built an institute at Heidelberg for the application of physics, chemistry and physiology to clinical research. In 1939 it was directed by R. Kuhn, who was awarded the Nobel Prize for chemistry for 1938.

The institutes in the second division were devoted to applied science. These included the institute for coal research at Mühlheim, directed by Franz Fischer. A second was built at Breslau, to deal with the problems of Silesian coal. This was directed by F. Hofmann, who also made important contributions towards the chemistry of the synthesis of rubber.

A great institute for research on iron was built at Düsseldorf, and another for the study of light alloys at Berlin–Lichterfelde. Institutes for the study of silicates and textile fibres were built at Dahlem. The first papers of Bergmann, Mark and Polanyi were issued from the latter. An institute for leather research was established under Bergmann at Dresden, and another for hydraulics at Munich.

The applications of biology were pursued in a great institute for industrial physiology built at Dortmund, and in an institute for animal breeding established near Berlin, and directed by Baur.

The society assisted various smaller laboratories for hydro-biology at Plön and Lunz and Rovigno; meteorological stations in the Austrian mountains, and a bird observatory in the Kurische Nehrung, where the study of the flight of birds by the ring-system was begun.

The society jointly founded the laboratory on the Jungfrau-joch, now so much used by students of cosmic rays. It also founded institutes for history and law, and possessed a library of art history in the Palazzo Zuccari, in Rome.

The group of a dozen institutes at Dahlem produced an extraordinary concentration of research ability. A hostel, named the Harnack House, was built for foreign scientists visiting and working in the institutes, and rest rooms, libraries and refectories were attached for the comfort of the permanent staffs. About two hundred research scientists from the various institutes met in the Harnack House, and exchanged ideas. Anything new that happened anywhere in the scientific world was known almost immediately by this varied body of workers, and its possibilities were eagerly discussed. This was one of the causes of the rapidity of the advance of science in Germany at that period. A similar effect was seen in the colloquium on physics at Berlin University. Many of the research workers at Dahlem delivered occasional lectures at the University, and attended its colloquia. The concentration of talent produced an accumulation of knowledge, and the assembly of wits an intellectual competition. Einstein, Laue, and others fired the flame of discussion, and it darted swiftly to new regions of thought.

Haber led an equally brilliant colloquium at Dahlem on chemistry. He was the most characteristic figure in the development of science in Germany during the last generation. He was a hard, generous and lively man, whose achievements had been accomplished through untiring pursuit of detail, and a driving capacity in organization. He was nearly always animated, and either smiling or severe. He had a sense of the dignity of his position, and a child-like vanity. He had the strongest personality among German scientists, and had something of the manner and authority of a Rutherford. One could often hear German scientists say: 'Haber is our greatest man.' He raised the standard of scientific discussions by vigorous criticism, and he hated humbug and superficiality from any quarter.

In spite of his love of German ways, he believed his countrymen were apt to be rude. He therefore cultivated the most courtly manners. Visitors to his house at Dahlem, which was not large, but decorated with elegant Chinese and Japanese works of art, were most graciously received. He sometimes invited Englishmen to tea from an exquisite silver service on a rare lace table cover, while he drank coffee and glasses of Fachinger mineral water. He started conversation in a very quiet and polished style, and considerately excused points of view contrary to his own, but after some time, as his enthusiasm arose, he could not restrain the natural vigour of his expression of opinion, and perhaps after an hour, if he was deeply interested in his subject, he had forgotten his theories of style, and was speaking and gesticulating vehemently. A stranger entering the room at that moment might have been surprised to learn that he was engaged in nothing more than an academic discussion.

Haber solved the problem of the synthesis of ammonia from nitrogen and hydrogen or intermediary substances. He began to investigate this problem in 1904. Nernst and others made important contributions to the solution, but success was not obtained until Haber experimented with mixtures of the gases at temperatures of 550° C. and pressures of 200 atmospheres, working conditions that were far more severe than had ever been used before in large-scale operations.

This research was done at the Technical University at Karlsruhe. It was not encouraged by the German chemical industrialists, as they were interested in synthesis by the electric arc, which had been started in Norway. Nevertheless, in 1909 Haber demonstrated the production of ammonia by his process to Carl Bosch, an engineer of the Bavarian Dye Company. Bosch immediately started the construction of a synthetic ammonia factory, and after three years, in 1912, the factory was in regular operation. Haber continually advised Bosch, but he had little part in the solution of the new engineering problems presented by operations on an industrial scale. This feat has been described as the most difficult ever achieved up to that time in chemical engineering, and its social effects were immense.

When the German Army invaded France in 1914, its leaders had given little consideration to questions of supply. They had not expected a long war. They knew that they could obtain sufficient nitrates for explosives from the coke oven plants of the coal industry, but they had not foreseen that there would be an additional demand for nitrogen fertilizers. But the march on Paris was halted, and the nitrates for fertilizers, which had formerly been imported from Chile, were cut off. If the German Army had not unexpectedly captured 50,000 tons of nitrates in Antwerp, Germany would have been in a very difficult position as early as 1915. When the significance of the situation was perceived, the raw materials department of the War Ministry was placed in Haber's charge. He increased the production of ammonia by the cyanamide process ten-fold, and synthetic ammonia from 6,500 tons in 1913 to 200,000 tons in 1918.

The battle of the Marne convinced the German Command that new weapons would be required to wage successful trench warfare. They consulted Nernst on the possibilities of gas, and afterwards, Haber. The Command presently requested Haber to prepare material for an attack by a cloud of chlorine gas. He did this, and in six months also devised an ingenious gas mask. He was made chief of the Chemical Warfare Service in 1916. Thenceforth he directed the research, supply, and training of personnel. His department introduced mustard gas in 1917, and tried hundreds of other substances. He managed all this organization, and the large number of scientists and soldiers, with great executive ability.

In 1911, the Kasier Wilhelm Gesellschaft had invited Haber to direct an institute for physical chemistry, after his triumph with the synthesis of ammonia at Karlsruhe. The institute was opened by Wilhelm II in 1912. When the war started, Haber immediately placed it at the disposal of the War Ministry, and many of the researches on chemical warfare directed by him were done there.

He had intense confidence in the certainty of victory, and was profoundly shaken by the defeat. In addition to this, he was subjected to widespread and ill-informed abuse as the inventor of gas warfare. This accusation was as stupid as it was ill-founded. Haber subsequently made interesting comments on the psychology of the critics of gas warfare. He remarked that gas, submarine, and air warfare were the three chief innovations in military technique in the war of 1914–18. The introduction of new military weapons has always been condemned as barbarous. Gunpowder and artillery were condemned as fiercely in the fourteenth century as gas in the twentieth. The submarine has been condemned less than gas because it operates out of the sight of large numbers of people, while the air weapon has earned the greatest honour, because it has renewed 'the heroic age of single combat, that had almost died in modern war'.

Haber received the most severe blows in his personal relationships through his work in gas warfare. Then his enormous effort and personal suffering was followed by the defeat in war, which struck at his pride in Germany. But he did not despair. He at once began to rally German science, saying that without an army and without colonies, and bearing the burden of reparations, Germany would need science more than ever. He was one of the most active founders of the Society for Protecting German Science, which held research institutions and scientists together through the period of inflation and reconstruction.

He even investigated the possibility of recovering gold from the sea, as a means of meeting the reparations. His love of the Fatherland persisted as strongly as ever. He began a speech to the German Club in Buenos Aires in 1923 with the words: 'Nothing is more precious, when far away in a strange part of the earth, than to find once more the mother tongue and the mode of thought of the homeland.' He told his hearers that they, who, after the downfall of Germany had stood up for her in a strange land, were permitted to adopt as a motto the great saying of Fichte: 'To be German, is to have character'; and he thanked them for their gifts to 'German youth and German science, which together make the German future'.

Haber was the greatest authority of his time on the relations between chemistry and industry, and he was fond of the theme. He liked to discourse on the explanations of the difference between the history of chemical industry in Germany and in other countries. He remarked that chemical industry began in England, and arose out of the industrial revolution. This created a new demand for chemicals. Where formerly they had been required in small quantities for dyeing and other small-scale industries conducted in the home, they were now required by the ton for treating the products of the recently developed factories. The early English industrialists discovered how to produce the required quantities of chemicals by empirical methods. Their profits were so great that they had not much stimulus to discover economical, that is, scientific, methods of working. They became rich and accumulated large reserves. They dominated the markets for years, and their wealth hindered competition from new firms.

As the years passed, they did not fail to discover many tricks of chemical manufacture through chance events in the factory. So by 1860, English chemical manufacturers had become wealthy and experienced. As their position seemed so commanding, they saw no reason for modifying their methods. Certainly many of their chemical processes were rather obscure, but they were very profitable, so why improve them?

About this time, German academic chemists began to go to England to work as operatives in the chemical factories. They carefully learned the practical English methods and then returned to Germany, where they started firms of their own. But as they were trained chemists, they succeeded in making small improvements in the English technique. The new German firms soon became famous for quality, and their business rapidly expanded. As the directors of the firms were chemists, they appreciated their clients' difficulties, and tried to solve them and obtain their custom. The English directors were businessmen. They knew how to drive hard bargains but had not the scientist's mental suppleness in approaching new requirements and solving the problems created by new demands. After enjoying a position of extraordinary strength, they saw their business slip away to German firms. They could not counter it. Not being scientists, they did not know how to handle scientists. They thought that the scientific chemist could be kept entirely subordinate to the business management. The tradition died very hard. But in Germany, where chemical industry had been created by men who were chemists first and businessmen afterwards, the division never existed in a comparable degree.

The development was characteristic for German industry. Germany was not an industrial nation until the middle of the nineteenth century. Her industries were created by scientists and leaders, and were not the outcome of an unconscious evolution, as in England. Liebig was a chemist, and he inspired the manufacture of chemical fertilizers; von Welsbach exploited the chemical properties of the rare earths, and created the gas mantle industry, and built a large private laboratory for himself in an old castle; Siemens was a physicist and an electrical engineer, and was the founder of a firm that employed at one time 130,000 operatives.

Haber was of the opinion that the English social system hindered the growth of a fertile relation between industrialist and scientist. The social aim of both of them was to be leisured gentlemen. Consequently, whenever they met on social occasions, or in their club, the last subjects they discussed were business and chemistry. 'Shop' was taboo. This was not the tradition in Germany. There the businessman was expected to talk about business, and the scientist about science. He believed that a similar situation existed in America, and this helped to explain why scientists often received such large endowments from American businessmen.

H. Levinstein suggested in his Perkin Memorial Lecture of 1938, that the decline of the English chemical industry in the latter half of the nineteenth century might be due to social causes. He held that it was not due to the chemists or technologists, nor even perhaps to the salesmen or the direction. 'Perhaps it was more our social system. Certainly chemists had very little standing, but in general, business was looked down on and was not encouraged or rewarded as it was in Germany. The Kaiser would call in quite informally in passing to see one of the great works. Here in England a man would retire when he had made enough money to live in the country, to be a sportsman, to shoot birds with skill, or to hunt foxes with resolution. It was a quicker route to social success.'

The superior development of chemistry in Germany was due, in Haber's opinion, to two sources: the better management of research, and the superior inner structure of industry, in which businessman, technologist and chemist collaborated on a more equal footing than elsewhere. The first source arose from the tradition of training in the universities. Chemists of genius were not more common in Germany than elsewhere, but when they appeared, they became professors, and spent far more energy than the French and English chemists of genius in training a body of men who, though without genius, were capable of learning. These acted as able assistants to them in their own researches, and provided a large reserve from which industry could draw competent technical recruits. The existence of this large reserve of competent men was a decisive factor in the supersession of French and English by German chemistry, for while men of genius could always find a track, the conversion of the track into a smooth highway of progress could be accomplished only by the tramping of a large body of followers.

Haber found the origins of the German system of training research workers in the circumstances of German history. The

Germans had learned to think in the school of Kant, and to observe nature through the example of Humboldt. Decades of conscription had taught them how to fit into large organizations, and life on an infertile soil had taught them how to work. The energy with which they adopted modern technology was released through the success of the struggle for national unification, typified by the formation of the Empire in 1871.

Haber continued his guidance of German science after the war in his great institute at Dahlem. It was a fine light building, cleanly designed and magnificently equipped. It was the best of its kind, and research students went to work there from all parts of the world. They enjoyed not only Haber's inspiration and the resources of his institute, but also the body of intellectual life centred in the group of institutes at Dahlem.

Then, in 1933, when the Nazis seized power, Jewish members of his institute were immediately persecuted. As he was of Jewish descent himself, he felt he must resign in protest. The man who had done more than any other to enable his country, nearly with success, to resist almost the whole of the world, was virtually dismissed and expatriated. It was not the first humiliation that he had received as a Jew. In spite of his great work as chief of the department of Chemical Warfare, the Imperial Army never gave him higher rank than captain.

He found refuge in the country he had struggled to defeat, and was invited to work in the laboratory of W. J. Pope, the Cambridge professor who had been one of the leaders in the English reply to his chemical warfare. Haber said that Rutherford's laboratory was now the world's chief centre of research, and its presence made Cambridge more attractive to him than any other place of research.

Haber was ill when he arrived in England. He suffered from a weak heart. Shortly after his arrival he was entertained by friends in a restaurant in London, and no doubt he expressed his opinion on affairs in Germany in his customary outspoken manner. He presently received a letter from Planck, as head of the Kaiser Wilhelm Gesellschaft, saying that the German Government had learned that he had expressed disloyal sentiments, and asking him to furnish an explanation. This gave him a great shock.

He left England to rest in January, 1934, and died on the journey, at Basle, after a severe heart attack.

Haber's life is a microcosm of German history. The energy, the discipline, the achievement and the collapse, and the combination of great virtues and weaknesses, which were illustrated in his career by the grand synthesis of ammonia, and the endearing but comic attempt to pay reparations by extracting gold from the sea.

The destruction of Haber's scientific organization in the institute of physical chemistry at Dahlem, and the general shrinkage and decline of the Kaiser Wilhelm Gesellschaft, also showed the dependence of science on social conditions, and the illusory nature of the principle that research may be pursued in independence of them. Science does become an organism with a degree of autonomy, whose growth is stimulated in part through its own internal mechanism of development, but it cannot pursue a life independent of social conditions. It is like a powerful limb on the body of society, which to some extent possesses its own life and growth, and can accomplish many things, but is not an independent organism, and dies when the social body that supports it is diseased.

72

The Social Background of German Science

THORSTEIN VEBLEN gave an illuminating analysis of the rise of German science and technology. He argued that the composition of the populations in Germany, England, Holland, Northern France and Scandinavia is biologically uniform, so no explanation of its features is due to peculiar biological characters. All of these peoples sprang from the populations who lived on the shores of the Baltic and the North Sea in neolithic times. The prehistoric evidence, he thought, seems to show that these peoples lived in small peaceable agricultural communities, whose social acts were governed by assemblies of a majority of their members. Kings and leaders had only a loose control over the communities to which they belonged, and the members were relatively free and anarchistic. They borrowed techniques very freely from southern and eastern sources, but were able to improve on them, as has been shown by the tools that have survived. Veblen believed that the neolithic activities of the Baltic

peoples were the most natural expression of their biological aptitudes, as the neolithic was the only period through which they
had lived that was long enough for biological selection to have had
some effect in giving them definite biological characters. He
thought that the descendants of these peoples, i.e. the Germans,
English, Northern French, etc., would always tend, if circumstances permitted, to an anarchistic, or democratic society
resembling the neolithic.

The present English and German peoples were founded by
marauders from the Baltic and North Sea coasts. These consisted
of groups who were unable to find a comfortable living in the
expanding communities at home. The neolithic tradition of freedom within the community was still too strong to allow such
dissatisfied chiefs to become hereditary kings, so they sought
power abroad. Those who sailed overseas came to England and
conquered peoples who had long been governed by Romans and
Churchmen, and they soon acquired some elements of their
civilization and peaceableness. Those who wandered away from
the coasts came to Germany, where they conquered a barbarian
population from whom they had nothing to learn, and they
established themselves there as predatory chiefs.

These chiefs adopted Christianity some six centuries later,
when their predatory tradition was already ancient and firmly
established. After the adoption of their new creed they invaded
Prussia. Thus Prussia became the newest part of Germany, with
a fresh and strong predatory tradition. This tradition was still in
Prussia when it was declining in countries with older social
systems, such as England and France.

The contrast between the descendants of the Germanic
peoples in England and in Prussia had become marked by the
beginning of the sixteenth century. Those in England were
beginning to enjoy the safety of her island isolation, and were
already reverting to the habits of freedom and technological
borrowing of their Baltic neolithic ancestors. Those on the
defenceless plains of Prussia were still as predatory and dynastic
as ever, through their continual fighting with Slav neighbours.

The English technical borrowings in the Elizabethan period
diverted interest to technology, during a time when the nation
could not engage in big offensive wars. As technology involves
the study of impersonal forces, it tends to undermine respect
for personal domination, so the Elizabethan imperialism that

imported the technology was itself undermined by it. In the next century, the triumph of the new spirit was signified by the execution of Charles I and the deposition of James II, and the establishment of government for the service of trade, and not of personal domination.

During the next two centuries, the English, with their partial reversion to the initiative of neolithic anarchism through continuous national safety, and their establishment of a business society, were able to carry out the industrial revolution, creating modern technology and science as a by-product.

Prussia and the German principalities were still substantially feudal at the beginning of the nineteenth century. Their productive system was still based on handicraft, and they were now beginning to feel the pressure of English economic supremacy severely. It was evident that Germany must unite, or she would be economically exploited by the more progressive society.

The threat of economic subjection made the German principalities unite. This was carried out under the leadership of Prussia. As she still had a feudal social structure, she accomplished this unification by feudal methods. She dominated the whole of Germany, and confirmed her leadership by successful wars, culminating in 1871.

Germany, with her feudal unity, now decided to acquire the technique laboriously worked out in England during two centuries. Technically, she had a fairly clean sheet. She could choose the methods that time had revealed as the best. Owing to the principle of domination, the population could be ordered to adopt these at once.

The adoption presented few difficulties. The fundamental ideas had been worked out. Feudal Germany was not short of trained scholars. Veblen was of the opinion that this was due to the poverty of German feudal society. In England, men proved their social status by racing and sport. In Germany they could not afford this, so they acquired learning, which is the cheapest way of acquiring social prestige. They naturally applied their trained minds to meditation on the notions of feudal society, and the ideas of personal relationship. They evolved the typical German philosophical systems from this set of ideas.

Veblen believed that German philosophy has no fundamental connection with science or with an industrial society, and has value only to those who accept the values of feudalism. He was careful to add that he did not suggest that industrialism was necessarily better than feudalism, or that modern science is better than classical German philosophy, but he contended that they must be assessed by different scales of value.

The new German industrialists had a large reserve of former philosophers accustomed to a very thrifty life. They made excellent managers, and ran industry more efficiently than the English, whose system was already old and hampered with obsolescence.

The German workmen were literate and quickly learned machine methods, which were simpler than the handicrafts they had formerly practised. As members of a feudal state they understood how to obey orders, for they had not, like English workmen, become troublesome by reverting to the free and lazy habits of their Baltic ancestors.

The industrialization of Germany advanced with tremendous success. The power of her society, with its feudal traditions, was correspondingly increased, and sought expansion. It came into collision with that of England, with her older industrial society. America and France, whose social forms are closer to England's, sided with her, and the expansion of Germany was temporarily halted. The feudal tradition did not die, and the rationalization of industry was continued, with a corresponding development of science of unparalleled magnitude. In 1933, four years after Veblen's death, the feudal German state recovered its normal mode of leadership, and, in 1939, again attacked England and France.

Veblen forecast in 1915 that Germany must remain unstable as long as she attempted to combine a feudal social tradition with scientific industrialism. These are essentially antagonistic, and though feudalistic authoritarianism can learn technique quickly through its command of force, it is improbable that it will discover anything fundamentally new in science. Germany has not created modern science. She has only extended it, and it is not probable that she will invent the fundamentally new science of the future, because this will not be conceivable in terms of the sort of thought fostered in a society organized by personal domination.

He thought that Germany might subside into a second-rate power or might liquidate her feudalism, but she also might conquer the world, and that then society might decline to a lower level of civilization 'by recourse to so drastic a reaction in their civil and political institutions as will offset, presently neutralize, and eventually dispel the effects wrought by habituation to the ways and means of modern industry and the exact sciences'.

Veblen pointed out that the spread of pacifism in the interest of trade, and the decline of the prestige of social status in industrial society through attention to matter instead of persons, did not form a certain foundation for peace and democracy. 'Temperamentally erratic individuals, however, and such as are schooled by special class traditions or predisposed by special class interest, will readily see the merits of warlike enterprise and keep alive the tradition of national animosity. Patriotism, piracy and prerogative converge to a common issue. Where it happens that an individual gifted with an extravagant congenital bias of this character is at the same time exposed to circumstances favouring the development of a truculent megalomania and is placed in such a position of irresponsible authority and authentic prerogative as will lend countenance to his idiosyncrasies, his bent may easily gather vogue, become fashionable, and with due persistence and shrewd management come so ubiquitously into habitual acceptance as in effect to throw the population at large into an enthusiastically bellicose frame of mind. Such is particularly apt to be the consequence in the case of a people whose historical traditions run in terms of dynastic strategy and whose workaday scheme of institutions is drawn on lines of coercion, prerogative and loyalty.' So Veblen forecast the emergence, and delineated the characteristics of a Hitler.

The incidents of Haber's career confirmed his view of the uneasy combination of feudalistic modes of thought with modern scientific ideas which exists in German civilization, and how, after tremendous achievements, it is liable to sudden breakdown.

73

Personal Motives for Research

THE personal motives that direct scientists to engage in research are of at least five sorts. The one which is best known, and most frequently announced by scientists themselves,

13

is curiosity, or the desire for understanding for its own sake. Another very powerful and general motive is the desire for reputation. A third is the need to earn a living. A fourth is the desire to enjoy oneself. A fifth is the desire to serve humanity. Very little psychological research has been done to discover the relative weight of these motives in practice.

The classical view that discovery is primarily due to the motivation of pure curiosity has been admirably restated by Polanyi in his review of J. D. Bernal's book on the *Social Function of Science*. He believes that science is in the first place a body of valid ideas. It consists of autonomous branches, such as mathematics, physics, chemistry and biology. Each new addition to them is produced by methods characteristic for each branch and is incorporated only after it has been accepted by recognized experts. The various branches of science are thus independent organisms of ideas, which grow with a life of their own. Polanyi contends that these systems of ideas are the most permanent human creations. The science of Mesopotamia, Egypt and Europe has survived, while creeds and laws, and even crafts, have been forgotten. 'It seems that an ordered framework of ideas in which each single part is borne out by the cohesion of the whole is of supreme attraction to the human mind. Struggling for a foothold in a shifting world, the mind clings persistently to these rare structures of sound and consistent ideas. It is in these structures, accordingly, that all scientific interest resides.' Polanyi follows Bernal in quoting T. H. Huxley's statement that that which stirs the pulses of scientists 'is the love of knowledge and the joy of discovery of the causes of things sung by the old poet—the supreme delight of extending the realms of law and order ever farther towards the unattainable goals of the infinitely great and the infinitely small, between which our little race of life is run'. Sometimes, the scientist lights on something of practical value. Those who are benefited rejoice, but 'even while the cries of jubilation resound and this flotsam and jetsam of the tide of investigation is being turned into the wages of workmen and the wealth of capitalists, the crest of the wave of scientific investigation is far away on its course over the illimitable oceans of the unknown'.

In view of these statements it will be useful to see what motives for research are implied by the behaviour and accounts of some other scientists. Those in whom the motive to understand, and to construct a coherent system of ideas that will explain phenomena, is very strong, often publish their results reluctantly or not at all. Newton, Cavendish and Darwin were striking examples. Before Newton published his first paper he wrote in a letter to Collins, which contained the solution of a problem in annuities: 'You have my leave to insert it into the Philosophical Transactions, so it be without my name to it. For I see not what there is desirable in public esteem, were I able to acquire and maintain it. It would perhaps increase my acquaintance, the thing which I chiefly study to decline.'

He 'designed to suppress' the third book of the *Principia*, because 'philosophy is such an impertinently litigious Lady, that a man had as good be engaged in lawsuits, as have to do with her'.

Cavendish invented electrical condensers, and discovered and measured specific inductive capacity with them. This work remained unpublished and its results were rediscovered by Faraday. Cavendish 'studied to decline increasing his acquaintance' by having his meals placed through a hole in the wall of his room, so that he need not speak to anyone, and interruptions be reduced to a minimum. Darwin worked on the material of the *Origin of Species* for more than twenty years, and might never have prepared it for publication without pressure from Lyell. This sort of behaviour is best explained by the existence of the desire to understand as a motive for research.

Scientists have generally not been so explicit in acknowledging the motive of desire for reputation. But it is implicit in the behaviour of many, and especially in some of those who deny it. Newton himself, whose behaviour showed such strong marks of the motive of the desire to understand, dropped scientific research as soon as he had acquired social position through his scientific reputation. He had been elected member of Parliament for Cambridge University, which brought him in contact with men of affairs. He then conceived an intense desire for a higher social position. He assiduously pressed Locke to use his influence with statesmen to find him a place, and when at first Locke did not succeed, he lamented that the philosopher, as L. T. More says, 'would not care to visit such an unsuccessful place-hunter as himself, and if the Monmouths now forsook him, there would be no hope left; and he must reconcile himself to end his days in the obscurity of an academic life. Lest he may have hurt this last chance, he apologized with almost abject humility for what may have seemed to be an intrusion upon the nobleman's society'.

Disputes over priority are one of the strongest proofs of desire for reputation. Newton was engaged in several, and Charles Darwin wrote that though he 'hated the idea of writing for priority', he would be 'vexed if anyone were to publish my doctrines before me'.

One of the rare accounts by a scientist of his mode of work is Blackett's essay on the *Craft of Experimental Physics*. He says that the experimental physicist has 'changed the technique of living by his intense curiosity to find out about obscure things'. He is a 'Jack-of-All-Trades, a versatile but amateur craftsman'. He must be able to blow glass, turn metal, carpenter, photograph, wire electric circuits, and be a master of gadgets, though he would not be sufficiently expert in any one of these things to earn his living by it. He has to do these things for three-quarters of his working day. He must 'be enough of a theorist to know what experiments are worth doing and enough of a craftsman to be able to do them'. His 'choice of subject will often be mainly determined by his special aptitudes', as to whether he is a glass-blower or engineer. In English laboratories he tends to depend on his own resources in making apparatus, and there is perhaps a relation between this tradition and the vogue of practical hobbies. 'So perhaps English experimental physics has derived strength from the social tradition and moral principles which led the growing middle class to spend the leisure of its prosperity in the home rather than the café.'

Experimental discovery depends on the utilization to their limit of the properties of available materials. Much of an experimenter's time is devoted to 'overcoming these limitations'. The progress of technique 'is continually opening up the possibility of new fields of research', and 'the development of theoretical physics both suggests new fields of inquiry and brings new relevance to old ones'. But 'the experimenter is always a specialist and does not often change his technique to follow the latest theoretical fashion. Often he cannot usefully do so, for there are few experiments which do not need a considerable apprenticeship'.

The experimenter gains knowledge of machinery and moving objects in 'this mechanical and ball-playing age'. The experimenter acquires an intuitive knowledge that assists him to guess how processes work. It is 'a very complicated process involving a combination of abstract thinking with the use of visual and motor imagery.'

'With such varied manual and mental skills as have been described does the experimenter go about his work in the laboratory, an amateur in each alone, but unique in commanding them all.

'It is the intimate relation between these activities of hand and mind, which gives to the craft of the experimenter its peculiar charm. It is difficult to find in other professions such a happy mixture of both activities. Few people are content with an occupation whose only manual element is the handling of a pen or a typewriter. Yet many, who embark on the career of an engineer from love of using tools, find later on that their main activity is as sedentary as that of a bank clerk. A common reaction to the fact that the office worker is, with some notable exceptions, paid more than the skilled mechanic, is to embrace, when possible, the career of the former while adopting some practical hobby to offset the loss of the satisfaction to be derived from the latter. The experimental scientist is luckier; his legitimate field of activity ranges from carpentering to mechanics; it is his job both to make and to think, and he can divide his time as he thinks fit between both these pleasurable occupations.'

This account of the experimental physicist's activities gives a strong impression of one of his chief motives. It is a desire for a legitimate excuse to engage in enjoyable tinkering. The exalted search for certainties in a world of flux, mentioned by Polanyi and T. H. Huxley, is not very prominent.

In Newton, Cavendish and Darwin, the pleasure they found in the exercise of their special aptitudes was probably a stronger motive. This helps to explain their reluctance to publish. They all possessed intense curiosity, but the pyramids of fact and theory that they built were the result of an acquisitive motive, rather than a desire to assist mankind to resolve the problems of its destiny.

The view that has been expressed so eloquently by T. H. Huxley and Polanyi is in fact more characteristic of the propagandist scientist than the research worker. Some light on Huxley's mind and motives may be gained by comparing his diary of the voyage on the *Rattlesnake* with Darwin's diary of the voyage on the *Beagle*. Both were written when their authors were twenty-five, under similar conditions in the most formative years. They present an illuminating contrast of the differences in mind between men who were to become the greatest propagandist and the greatest research worker of their generation. There is little concern with scientific matters in Huxley's book. He was involved primarily with personal psychological problems, and resistance to fits of depression. Darwin's book, in spite of his bad health, was primarily devoted, from the beginning, to the collection of facts and the development of scientific ideas.

It is evident that Darwin started at once to exercise his tremendous aptitude for collecting and resuming facts. This went forward like a great force of nature, overshadowing his earnest reflections on the value of his activities. The stirring reflections of Huxley on man's place in nature have their root in his personal psychological problems, and they deal with the implications of the results of research, rather than the motives that prompted it.

Curiosity is not in itself, or in its processes, particularly noble. Various animals possess it, and it is apt to lead to trivial activities. It is often associated with acquisitiveness, and in this combination, has led especially to the accumulation of a large part of biological science. As a psychological process, it is a sublimation of the desire for power. The curious person wishes to discover the knowledge that will place a phenomenon under his control, either in fact or in understanding. His feeling of triumph when he has made a discovery is a feeling of triumph over something; he has brought some aspect of nature under his power.

The psychology of discovery is in all circumstances substantially the same. The scientist working in his own home, or in a university research laboratory, is in virtually the same psychological condition in all of these institutions during the moment or period of discovery. In his own home, or if he is a senior professor, he may tell himself to attempt to elucidate some as yet unexplained phenomenon; if he is working in an industrial research laboratory particular problems will be chosen for him. In the first instances, he appears to choose his problem of his own volition, while in the second he is definitely aware that it has been suggested to him by persons who form part of his environment. These circumstances help to explain the difference between pure and applied science. A scientist feels he is engaged in pure science when he is not conscious of motives other than his own volition and the internal logic of development of the problem with which he is concerned. The latter is in his own mind, and appears to him to be independent of the environment and the external world.

When a scientist engages in applied science he is more generally aware of the external influences that have directed his choice of investigation.

The scientist who makes important discoveries usually does it at the expense of severe concentration. Difficult problems are solved only by the most intense mental focussing, and as a result the research scientist is apt to become unconscious of all the objective conditions that have influenced his research. This circumstance provides the basis for N. I. Vavilov's view that 'all scientists are anarchists at heart'. If objective conditions that have influenced his research are subtle and obscure, he may forget, or never be conscious of, their existence. This is the condition of the majority of scientists engaged in academic research laboratories. The intense concentration that frequently inhibits the awareness of scientists of social relations is also the cause of the traditional absent-mindedness of professors.

But those who work in industrial research laboratories cannot forget the objective conditions for long, though even they forget them in the periods of mental concentration during actual discovery. If the industrial research scientist could be asked during his moment of concentration how he has solved his problem, he will say that he has done it by following its internal logic. This is true, but it is also quite clear that he would never have solved it unless his attention had been directed to it by external influences.

The view that science is an independent system of ideas is a product of subjectivism. It springs from the same motives as Plato's philosophy. Plato advocated the dictatorship of the intellectual, and sketched a social philosophy resembling fascism. His representation of science as an organism of ideas independent of the material world appears to be disinterested, but in fact it concealed political ambition. He identified these ideas with truth, and concluded that as only intellectuals could deal with ideas, they only were acquainted with truth, and therefore they only deserved political power.

The desire to follow the internal logic of systems of ideas is more philosophical than scientific. It is seen very strongly in German philosophy. When a German student was asked: 'What is the point of Fichte's philosophy?' he was quite nonplussed. He could not understand what was meant. He was then asked why he studied Fichte. After some thought he answered:

'Because it is interesting to see how he deduces one thing from another.' This is not the essence of scientific activity. Clerk Maxwell described it when he said that it consisted in 'wrenching the mind away from the symbols to the objects and from the objects back to the symbols'. It is an interaction between the internal and external worlds. Of these, the priority of the external world is a historical fact.

The motive of desire for reputation is much stronger than is generally admitted. The output of research by many scientists declines after they have secured election to distinguished societies, or after they have been appointed senior professors or directors of institutions. Scientists primarily interested in research can nearly always use the power given by senior positions to extend the scope of their researches. They can organize their staff as a team. But many do not do this, under the excuse that their administrative duties are too exacting. It is hardly necessary to mention the aspiration for titles sometimes seen in scientists whose work is world famous.

C. P. Snow has given interesting sketches of the influence on scientists of the motive of reputation in his novel, *The Search*.

The simple motive of earning a living is also underrated. The need for bread and lodging is the motive of far more research than is commonly realized. A man with aptitude for research can often earn his living more easily through that aptitude than in any other way. It is said that he could easily earn more in other professions if he cared to enter them. The number of cases in which this is true is probably exaggerated. The absence of the best conditions for research does not necessarily repel a gifted man into another profession where he can do good work; it often means that he can do no creative work at all. He may become a garage mechanic or a library assistant. The National Union of Scientific Workers (later the A.Sc.W.) expressed the opinion that the provision of 'such material comfort as is necessary for a well-developed life, and for such luxuries as are usual in the society which the worker frequents' would be a strong stimulus to research, and that this could be made most satisfactorily by paying scientists salaries at rates and in conditions similar to those of the civil service.

The fifth of the motives under consideration is the desire to serve humanity. Bernal has stated that 'men require that what they do has social importance' besides satisfying their own curiosity and enjoyment. Polanyi complains that he rejects 'any claim of science to be pursued merely for the sake of discovering truth'. No analysis has been made of the size of the contributions to science due respectively to the personal motives of discovering truth, acquiring reputation and power, seeking enjoyment, gaining a living, or serving humanity. One might as well guess that each has contributed equally.

At any rate, it is certain that the last motive has made a large contribution, and historical research may subsequently prove that it is the largest of all. The progress of humanity, which is always positive when the periods considered are sufficiently long, is a proof that mankind in the long run encourages those things of benefit to itself. It is sufficient to recall the tremendous inspiration of Bacon, and how it contributed through Boyle, Sprat and their colleagues to the formation of the Royal Society, and all that that implied for the advancement of science.

Benjamin Franklin owed much of his inspiration to that desire. When he founded the American Philosophical Society he proposed a long list of subjects for research, which were to include 'all philosophical experiments that let light into the nature of things, tend to increase the power of man over matter and multiply the conveniences or pleasures of life'.

Franklin refused to seek patents for his inventions, so that they should freely benefit all men. Davy refused to patent the safety lamp because his 'sole object was to serve the cause of humanity'.

The Royal Institution, where Davy worked, and which has contributed so much to scientific research, was founded 'for diffusing the knowledge and facilitating the general and speedy introduction of new and useful mechanical inventions and improvements; and also for teaching, by regular courses of philosophical lectures and experiments, the applications of the new discoveries in science to the improvement of arts and manufactures, and in facilitating the means of procuring the comforts and conveniences of life.

'A good cook was engaged for the improvement of culinary advancement—one object, and not the least important—for the Royal Institution.'

Researches on improved recipes for soup, which were to give the maximum nutriment at the minimum price; more economical fire-grates, etc., were conducted for the benefit of the poor.

13*

Some years later, in Paris, Pasteur was making researches which owed much to the inspiration of the social motive. He passionately desired to save diseased men, animals and plants, and he helped to demonstrate that the cultivation of science was one of the best ways of achieving this. He wrote that 'in our century science is the soul of the prosperity of nations and the living source of all progress. Undoubtedly the tiring discussions of politics seem to be our guide—empty appearances. What really leads us forward is a few scientific discoveries and their application'. One can recognize the social motive in this.

A large part of medical research has been done chiefly from the social motive. Numbers of medical research workers have died while submitting themselves to experiments.

Those who have furnished the means that have enabled scientists to make discoveries have assisted science through their personal desire to serve humanity. The founder of the Rockefeller Foundation, with its aim of promoting 'the Well-being of Mankind throughout the World', was no doubt moved by several motives, but one of these was the desire to help humanity.

The justification of the cultivation of science because it adds to a fascinating organism of ideas, or to the discovery of pure truth, seems a little cold, mean and selfish when compared with the motives that inspired Bacon and his successors. The progress of science has owed much to the desire to serve humanity, and it is probable that in the future, through better organization of the expression of this motive, science will owe more to it than to any other personal motive.

74

External Motives of Research: The Expansion of Business

THE reasons why industrial firms are creating research laboratories have been explained particularly clearly by F. B. Jewett, the president of the Bell Telephone Laboratories.

He said that the research workers in any industrial concern are motivated by the same considerations and are governed by the same rules as those that apply to other groups in the organization. The primary difference between them and those engaged in operation, finance, purchasing and selling is in training. They are skilled in the facts and methods of science rather than in the techniques required in the other branches.

The successful industrial research organization must operate as an integral part of the industry.

The systematic creation of industrial research laboratories began about 1900. It arose from the exhaustion of the method of improvement used by the engineers who had invented the steam engine and founded the industrial revolution. The great achievements of these men rested on their rough grasp of scientific methods, which had gradually been discovered since the Renaissance, and indicated that there was a positive best way of dealing with new things, and that this led to improvements more quickly than innumerable and uncorrelated experiments. But the pioneers had relatively little understanding of the finer points of the fundamental sciences that underlay their practice. When their accumulation of knowledge had been pretty well worked over by the cruder methods, 'the recovery of the hidden values' required the introduction into industry of men who understood the basic facts of science and the methods by which they are obtained.

Different industries begin to establish research laboratories at different dates, because this situation concerning technical knowledge arises in different industries at different dates.

Jewett compared the introduction of industrial researches with the introduction of finer techniques in the mining of gold, as lodes become poorer and less accessible. At first, the gold is gained by two or three men with the washing pan. Then it is ground out of the rock by hydraulic mills, which required engineering supervision. Finally, good returns from the remaining poorer lodes are possible only by the cyanide and other refined processes. Through these, skilled men with a training of a type entirely different from that of their predecessors are drawn into the industry.

This situation arose in the electrical communications industry about 1900. It became evident that 'the recovery of further values from science, which we knew to exist', could not be obtained by men whose knowledge was restricted to what they had learned at college and had since acquired by experience. Such men, who knew little of 'the fundamentals of science itself', found themselves impotent to produce in the electrical field the advances that were obviously potentially at hand. 'In our particular industry it became evident quite rapidly that we had to introduce men of a different type of training, if we were going to continue to progress'.

The investigators in the universities were advancing physical and chemical knowledge at an enormous rate, and provided a 'great array of new and as yet unapplied material'.

These could be utilized in industry only by men who 'knew as much about the new things and the methods of their production and manipulation as the scientists who were their discoverers'. Consequently, the juxtaposition of 'the obstacles to further progress along old lines and the assemblage of new facts on which progress could be made', was the cause of the foundation of the first great research laboratory in the electrical industry.

The research laboratory in industrial organization has become not only the source of continued progress, but a bulwark against the vicissitudes of hard times. Experience has shown that progress may be made most rapidly, cheaply, and with the less number of missteps in the laboratory. They have found this to be the case, not only in times of expanding business, when there were urgent demands for new things and production on a larger and more economical scale, but also in periods of depression, when further economy in standard processes, and the 'development of new things for which a demand can be created', became more pressing.

Jewett said that in 1931, when American trade was very bad, his organization was doing everything it could to keep its trained research personnel, and transfer them from 'problems of an expanding business period to the type of problems which will most directly benefit our situation in these depressed times or most surely benefit us in the years ahead when, as we all hope, the sun of prosperity will again be shining'.

The preliminary training of industrial research staff is long and arduous, and the period of time required 'to mould wholly efficient men into an efficient team is long'. It is therefore impossible to contemplate the sort of ups and downs in the research part that may be regarded with equanimity in other parts of a business.

The industrial research laboratory has a relation to the rest of an industrial organization which resembles that of a gland to the body. The size and expenditure is less than in many other departments, but without it, vigorous life would soon cease. The importance of research had been recognized in the electrical communications industry by the appointment of its directors as members of the controlling executive management.

Jewett complained that there had been much foolish talk from persons who should know better that research laboratories are places provided by industry in which trained scientists 'are free to do whatever they please on any kind of a problem that happens to strike their fancy'. This picture had done great harm. As the research laboratory is part of an industrial organization, it 'must of necessity be guided by the conditions governing the particular industry of which it is a part'. Except for a little transient advertising value, there is 'little real worth in any industrial group which does not concern itself primarily and practically exclusively with the problem of its own industry or with the fields into which that industry may legitimately and logically expand its operations'.

In times of flush and lavish prosperity, a management might delude itself into believing that expenditure on research uncoordinated with their business might enhance its prestige as a great, progressive, far-seeing group of men. But when the cold wind of adversity begins to blow, this exotic flower would shrivel up with extreme rapidity.

And yet, in his own research organization they have men who investigate problems that have no practical relations to the business. One reason why these researches are tolerated is that they are regarded as avocations, similar to those of men in other departments. 'We do not hire scientific men to do these extraneous things, nor do we ask them to do them after they are hired.' If, however, they are inclined to investigate problems foreign to the business, no obstacles are placed in their way as long as they 'continue to be of value as cultivators of our field'. In fact, within limits, they further their avocational desires, because this allows fuller exercise of creative ability, which is the chief source of happiness to the scientist, and it is recognized that the best work is obtained from the men who are most happy in their environment. They do not put rigid iron clamps on men and say 'You must do this kind of research work to the total exclusion of all other kinds of research work'. This would defeat its own ends by killing creative ability, or causing the man to leave the organization.

They had in their laboratories a number of scientists who had made researches that were famous outside the field of telephony. They are, however, amongst the most valuable men in the organization because of their deep knowledge of other problems bearing on the principal concern of the business.

These men have been trained in the business, so though they may spend a considerable part of their time on matters far removed from telephony, they are able to recognize recondite information which may be of assistance to it, and in some instances, owing to their own original researches, they are the sole persons aware of the existence of this information. But if these scientists lose interest in the major problems of telephony and devote themselves exclusively to foreign fields of research, 'there would be no justification for our maintaining them on the pay roll'.

Industrial research is not undertaken primarily to secure patents. It would continue, even if patents as a form of property of limited life were abolished. 'Practically all organized industrial research is undertaken for the purpose of solving problems thought to be of benefit to the industry.'

It is of great assistance in the development of large-scale processes. Large sums have been wasted on attempting to proceed directly from theoretical conceptions to large-scale production. In many cases the attempt failed, and it was concluded that the theoretical conceptions were wrong and unworkable, whereas the failure was due to ignorance of control and operational methods, which could have been removed by preliminary experimental research. Owing to their success in solving problems and creating new demands, research methods have gradually spread to the manufacturing and operating departments of the business, and this has been accompanied by the transfer of men trained in research into these departments, where they have shown that systematic study is more profitable than 'cut-and-dried' methods in eliminating difficulties.

It is certain that industrial research laboratories will extend, and will arise in industries where they do not exist. This is due to the avalanche of new facts coming from the laboratories for fundamental research. Much of this has an obvious bearing on existing industries, and much presages the possibility of new industries. As much of the new knowledge concerns the ultimate structure of matter and the laws that it obeys, it can be utilized only by research men, as they only are the persons who understand it. One can forecast that industrial research workers will need a still more highly specialized training in this knowledge, in order to find how it may be utilized.

Jewett considered that 'modern science in all its forms had birth' in colleges and universities. Its utilization has made much industrial work more interesting, though, 'to be sure, it enlarged things more, possibly, on the material side by opening up hitherto unsuspected regions where the forces of nature were at play than it did on the more directly human side'.

Jewett stated that in 1914 the improvement of telephone equipment had come virtually to an end. They had advanced for forty years by steadily improving the design of instruments, many of whose parts were made of magnetic materials. These were purchased in the market. They were the best available, and their properties were utilized to the best advantage by careful refinements in the design of the instruments in which they were used. The performances of these instruments were definitely limited by the range of properties in their magnetic parts. But it was known on theoretical grounds that instruments giving far higher performance could be made, if materials with a different range of magnetic properties could be produced. The telephone industry had been buying its irons and steels from manufacturers who produced them for other purposes. Was it possible that magnetic materials with the desired properties could be made ? The search was planned and begun. Existing knowledge of magnetic materials was scrutinized, and the properties of metals that might be used in magnetic alloys were investigated. After lengthy researches, a simple alloy of iron and nickel was found, which, when prepared under rigidly controlled conditions, had magnetic properties many times greater than the materials previously used in telephone and telegraph instruments. It was given the name 'permalloy'.

Its first application was unexpected. For nearly sixty years, the speed of transmission of submarine cables had remained virtually constant, though it was known theoretically that the association of magnetic material with the conducting wire might increase it. Many attempts to apply this knowledge were made, but failed. Then, after the discovery of permalloy, research was started to see whether it might be applied to this purpose. It was found that if very thin strips were coiled around the conducting wire, an enormous increase in speed of transmission could be obtained. The amount of permalloy needed, and the cost of the additional process in manufacture, was not great, but six or more times as many messages could be sent on one of the new cables than on an old one of the same size.

Before the discovery of permalloy, the limit of telephonic communication was about one thousand miles. Chiefly through its aid, and that of another consciously sought implement, the vacuum tube amplifier, transcontinental telephony became possible.

The amplifier was required to strengthen the effects of very weak and attenuated voice currents without distorting them, so that the message borne by them would be intelligible after travelling several thousand miles. These amplifiers were produced through intense co-ordinated research on the properties of ions and electrons, by men with the finest training and the best tools that could be obtained. They were first used on a large scale in long-distance telephone cables, but they provided the basis of the modern loudspeaker, which was first used for magnifying the voice of speakers to large audiences, and antedated the radio and the talking films.

The effects of these advances have been described by Jewett: 'A great industry once powerful and prosperous, threatened with decay and dissolution through lack of change and advancement, revivified overnight—its figures on the red side of the ledger changed, as if by magic, to larger and more imposing black figures; organizations which seemed stable as the eternal hills, shaken to their foundations and forced to revamp their entire business structure as well as their outlook on the future; other businesses struggling to eke out a bare livelihood, suddenly raised to the pinnacles of opulence; professions learned through hard and dreary years, thrown into the limbo of the unwanted and new professional requirements established; these and more are the direct results of man's desire to use the by-product results which have come from the work of research men seeking to improve a nation's telephone sytem.'

75

External Motives of Research: National Safety

THE BRITISH GOVERNMENT established in 1915 a committee which was the parent of the former Department of Scientific and Industrial Research. The circumstances in which this occurred were described in the introduction to the committee's first report. Its authors state that certain events which preceded the establishment of the committee 'are worthy of record because they are now seen to have a general significance which was not realized at the time'.

The Imperial Institute had been founded in 1887. Its purpose was to encourage the trades and industries of the British Empire, by the provision of exact information on the raw materials and manufactured products yielded by various parts of the Empire. 'Knowledge of this kind necessitated careful scientific tests and these in turn revealed the need for research directed to the elucidation of obscure qualities in a product in the interests alike of the producer and of the user.'

This movement was extended by the foundation of the National Physical Laboratory in 1902. This had grown out of the work of the British Association's Committee on Standards, which in turn had been formed to assist the new industries of the second half of the nineteenth century, by providing them with accurate methods of measuring and standardizing materials. Until this had been done, the manufacture of very uniform materials, necessary for the industrial technique of mass-production, was not possible.

When King George V, then Prince of Wales, opened the Laboratory, he said that he understood that its object was 'to bring scientific knowledge to bear practically upon our everyday industrial and commercial life, to break down the barrier between theory and practice, to effect a union between science and commerce'.

This movement extended slowly until 1914, when the need for accelerating it suddenly became acute. The outbreak of war cut off the imports from Germany of certain products manufactured by highly scientific processes, and essential for modern armaments and industry. The existing British industry was unable to make even two dozen of the hundred different sorts of optical glass, used in range finders, field glasses and other instruments, hitherto supplied by Germany. It could not supply ten per cent of the dyes needed by the great textile industry, and it was also unable to replace the German exports of drugs, magnetos and tungsten, or even the zinc smelted in Germany from ores mined in parts of the British Empire.

It was evident that the movement for cooperation between science and industry required rapid acceleration. 'Other machinery and additional State assistance were absolutely necessary . . . but it needed the shock of the Great War to make the need manifest.'

The State had recognized the necessity of organizing the national brain power in the interests of the nation during the normal times of peace by creating the education system. 'The necessity for the central control of our machinery for war had been obvious for centuries, but the essential unity of the knowledge which supports both the military and industrial efforts of the country was not generally understood until the First World War revealed it in so many directions as to bring it home to all. War has remained as much an art as ever, but its instruments, originally the work of the craftsman and the artist, are now not only forged by the man of science; they need a scientific training for their effective use. This is equally true of the weapon of industry. The brains, even the very process, that today are necessary to the output of munitions were yesterday needed, and will be needed again tomorrow, for the arts of peace.'

It was evident that if the requisite scientific industries were not established, the nation would fail in the war, and if, further, new industrial processes were not discovered, it would fail in the 'equally difficult period of reconstruction which would follow the war.'

In these circumstances, the Royal Society, and other scientific societies, sent a deputation to the presidents of the Boards of Trade and Education, to ask for assistance for scientific research. This was granted, and the parent committee of the Department of Scientific and Industrial Research was formed to work out the best way of administering it.

The committee started a survey to discover how industrialists might be helped by research. The chemical industries were so divided that the societies of chemists had neither the influence nor the means to promote much research of value to them. The textile trades were even less advanced. They did not care where dyes and machinery came from, as long as profits were satisfactory.

A national register of researches was compiled, but in their first survey they discovered only forty individuals whose work was worthy of assistance.

The research organization of the engineering industry proved to be the most advanced. But in general, 'so long as an industry was prosperous it was apt to take short views and feel little enthusiasm for systematic research, especially if the firms it comprised were small, or if the capital engaged had a speculative value on the Stock Exchange'.

British firms were only just beginning to realize that their most dangerous competitors were not other British firms, but foreign trusts supported by tariffs. Their tradition of individualism made them suspicious of co-operation, and they did not understand that it 'is not the negation of individual effort; it raises initiative to a higher power'.

Their failure to co-operate had prevented them from engaging in thorough research, as many had learned from experience that research on the small scale, which individual firms could afford, was unprofitable.

The creation of a satisfactory system of industrial research required the better employment of the nation's scientific ability. England had produced a fair quota of scientists of the first order, but she did not make the best use of those of moderate ability. The intellectual war could not be won by a corps of officers alone, and 'without the scientific rank and file it will be as impossible to staff the industrial research laboratories which are coming, as to fight a European war with seven divisions'.

The universities were contributing more to science than in 1868, when T. H. Huxley complained that only one in every ten learned books published was written by a professor or academic person, but could still do far more, with better laboratories and grants for research expenses, and the education of a larger number of students in science.

The authors of the report remarked that 'it is not often in our history that the nation has found time to think. Now, by a curious paradox, while the flower of her youth and strength are fighting for her freedom and her life, the others have a chance of thinking out the best use to which that life and freedom can be put when they are safe once more'.

The progress of fundamental research and its utilization in industry 'will inevitably tend to bring industries into intimate relations, which are at present independent of each other, to transform what have hitherto been crafts into scientific industries, and to require co-operation not only between different firms in the same industry, but between groups of industries in a continuously widening series of interrelated trades. The forces which are at work in this direction have elsewhere found their expression in connection with the trust and combine, but we believe, if the real nature of these forces is clearly grasped, that it will be possible to organize them for the benefit not only of the industries but of the nation as a whole'.

Shortly after the Department of Scientific and Industrial Research was established in England, and plans had been made for corresponding departments in Australia, Canada and elsewhere, the National Academy of Sciences in the United States founded its National Research Council, chiefly from the initiative of George Ellery Hale. The National Academy itself had been founded in 1863 during the Civil War, by Lincoln, and it had been charged, whenever called upon by a government department, to investigate, examine, experiment, and report on any subject of science or art. It gave the Government much aid during the Civil War, through its studies of military and industrial problems, and when the engagement of the United States in the war of 1914–18 became imminent, it offered its services again to the Government in 1916. A National Research Council was then formed, but on lines different from those of the British Department of Scientific and Industrial Research. It was not a government department, but an independent body, consisting of a federation of government, university, private foundation and industrial research agencies. It immediately organized research for military and industrial purposes.

The National Research Council was strongly opposed to the central control of research, but was in favour of co-operative organization.

The forces which bring into existence medical research organizations may be illustrated by the origin of the British Medical Research Council. This was established in 1914, in connection with the Government's department for National Health Insurance. The National Insurance Act of 1911 contained a provision that one penny for each person insured in the United Kingdom was to be contributed by the Government for the endowment of research. A committee was formed in 1913 to administer the fund on research which would extend medical knowledge with the view of increasing the power of preserving health and preventing and combating disease. The biochemist, W. M. Fletcher, was appointed secretary of this committee in July, 1914. By that date, the fund had accumulated £55,000 in pennies. It founded a national institute of medical research at Mount Vernon, Hampstead. H. H. Dale was appointed to the department of biochemistry and pharmacology, and later became director of the institute. He shared a Nobel Prize in 1936 for researches on the chemical transmission of nervous impulses.

The activities of the Medical Research Council were much increased through the First World War. In its fifth Report, for 1918–19, it is noted that 'the stimulus and the special occasions of war have led to great progress in many parts of medical science. This has not only given direct aid in the practical conduct of war, but has led also to many permanent gains in scientific knowledge'. In particular, much had been learned of wound 'shock'; the replacing of lost blood; the respiratory system, through the treatment of patients suffering from gas poisoning; and of wound infection and gangrene. 'If these advances made in war time are to be continued and multiplied in peace, it may be well to note what the conditions have been that have allowed so many important contributions to medical science to be made during a time of such disaster and stress.'

They were chiefly three: the availability of able men; immediacy of problems and the opportunity for investigation on a large scale; and that 'men fitted to the work have received— perhaps for the first time in the history of war, or indeed of peace—a large measure of public support'.

The influence of national danger during war on the foundation of the scientific and industrial research councils of both Britain and the United States is notable. On these occasions, the fear of defeat was sufficient to make men and firms co-operate, and governments spend more money, in research. It is evident, too, that at these times the truth about motives and behaviour is often expressed in official publications with unusual candour.

The foundation of the British Medical Research Council arose, however, out of the legislation of the social reformers, who had passed the national laws of health insurance. But its development also owed much to the stimulus of the war of 1914–18. Medicine was advanced then, as hospital services and surgery had been improved during the campaigns of the Roman legions. In England, as elsewhere, the poor physique of the recruits for the armies, and the shortage of food, stimulated much research on nutrition, and systematic attention to problems of industrial fatigue and psychology was encouraged, so that the output of munitions might be raised to a maximum. Lloyd George remarked in a foreword to a book on Welfare Work that 'it is a strange irony, but no small compensation, that the making of weapons of destruction should afford the occasion to humanize industry'.

76

The Finance of Research

THE most striking feature of this subject in 1939 was the absence of exact information. No precise figures of the expenditure on scientific research in Britain were known, and efforts to collect them had only just begun. The total income of the British universities was about £7,000,000 per annum, and their total expenditure on scientific research was probably not more than £700,000 annually.

The Department of Scientific and Industrial Research had a net expenditure of about £637,200 in the year 1937–38. In the previous year it had been £583,230, so the increase for the year was about ten per cent. When the Department had been formed in 1915, it was granted one million pounds for establishing co-operative industrial research. It was believed that after this sum had been expended, the various industries would have been convinced of the profitability of research, and would be prepared in the future to pay the whole cost of the work done for their benefit. The million pounds was exhausted in 1932–33, but co-operative industrial research was still not self-supporting.

The Department also spent £26,391 on grants to students, to provide aid and apparatus for the prosecution of research. This part of the Department's activities has had notable results. P. M. S. Blackett and many others were enabled to become research scientists owing to D.S.I.R. grants.

The British Government's Agricultural Research Council provided for an expenditure of £111,922 in 1937–38. The total had risen to this figure from £15,525 in 1935–36.

The Medical Research Council received a grant of £195,000 in 1936–37 for the encouragement of research.

The three research councils thus had a total budget of about one million pounds per annum. In addition to this, the British Government spent through its other departments, such as the Ministries of Health and Agriculture, an indefinite sum of about one million pounds on a variety of research and scientific advisory work. Further, in times of peace, the Government spent probably about one million pounds annually on scientific research concerned with military problems. Thus the total expenditure of the British Government in peace time on activities that might be classified as scientific research was about three million pounds per annum.

The total expenditure of British firms on private research was quite unknown. Perhaps they spent as much as five million pounds per annum, but a large fraction of this would be devoted to the solution of routine problems arising in the manufacture and use of products. An estimate of two million pounds per annum would probably cover all activities which strictly involved some elements of research.

The total expenditure by government, industry and universities on scientific research was probably not more than £5,700,000 per annum, at a generous estimate, and if the cost of development work and routine research is included, not more than £8,700,000.

The total expenditure on scientific research in industrial, government and university institutions in the United States at this date was estimated at the equivalent of £47,000,000.

As the British national income was about five thousand million pounds per annum, the British people were spending only from one-tenth to two-tenths of one per cent of their income on research. The comparable figures for the American people were two-tenths to five-tenths of one per cent. Thus the rate of expenditure on research in the United States was about twice that in Britain, and the absolute expenditure was about five to ten times as great.

The figures were in fact much less favourable to Britain. Her expenditure at that time had largely to meet the needs of the British Empire. Thus the total British expenditure on research, amounting to perhaps ten million pounds, had to meet the needs of five hundred million people, while the Americans spent forty-seven million pounds per annum on research for the benefit of one hundred and fifty millions. According to this comparison, the Americans spent about sixteen times as much for each person under their rule.

The situation in France was even worse than in Britain. No department of scientific research existed in France until 1933, and the expenditure of French firms on industrial research was very small. The output of research by French universities was also small for the first decade after the war of 1914–18. This situation was due to various factors. A very large number of young Frenchmen were killed. Of the students at the Ecole Normale at the outbreak of the war, eighty per cent were killed, and of those at the École Polytechnique, ninety per cent. These were the flower of French youth. When the war was over, there were few young scientists to succeed the older professors. The scientific interests of these older men had been fixed before the development of the quantum theory and the theory of relativity, so they were exclusively interested in classical physics. There were few men of the middle generation to preserve continuity between the old and the young men, and the situation became worse than disconnected. Many of the old professors definitely attacked the new science, and discouraged its development. Another unsatisfactory feature in France was the concentration of ability in the capital. Scientists regarded provincial universities as mere stepping-stones to Paris.

The effects of these developments were ignored for the first decade after 1918. The French nation was politically and financially powerful, and could obtain what it wanted without intense efforts in science. Its businessmen were not interested in research, because they were prosperous and had no difficulty in buying the rights in any valuable inventions made abroad.

Perspicacious Frenchmen presently became disturbed. They noticed the development of science in the Weimar Republic, accompanied by the production of new processes and the rationalization of industry. Accordingly, in 1933, the Minister of Education founded a Council of Scientific Research, because 'disinterested researches in pure science are the source of all progress in human powers', and 'apart from motives of idealism and prestige it is of practical importance to discover those capable of scientific research'. A national fund for scientific research was formed in 1935. When the Government of the Popular Front was elected, the framework of a state organization of science was already formed. It was immediately strengthened by the appointment of Irène Curie-Joliot as Under Secretary of State for Scientific Research. This was the first occasion on which a scientist, as such, was 'taken into the councils of the French nation'. She was succeeded by Jean Perrin, the eminent physicist.

The expenditure on the new department in 1935–36 was £160,000, compared with £572,000 for the British Department of Scientific and Industrial Research. It rose to £240,000 in 1938.

Their system of grants to aid research workers had an important part in reviving science in France. They gave £100 per annum for trial scholarships in research. If the candidate was successful, he became a recognized research worker, with a salary of £200. After the publication of approved research, he was raised to the status of master, with status equivalent to that of an assistant professor. If very successful, he became a director of research, with the status of a full professor. The highest salary paid to a professor in Paris, in virtue of one appointment, was about £600 per annum. The cost of living was lower than in England, so this figure was not directly comparable with the corresponding figure in England.

In 1936 about 350 research workers in France were assisted in this scheme. Joliot benefited from it during the period when he was making his researches that led to the discovery of artificial radioactivity. The Department of Scientific Research subsequently provided considerable sums for his new laboratory for nuclear chemistry in the Collège de France.

The system of bursaries was of great assistance to Joliot's school. He had twenty research colleagues at the Collège de France and ten in his high tension laboratory at Ivry, and many of these would not have been able to work with him without the bursaries. He was glad to count Italians, Russians, Poles,

Austrians, Palestinians, as well as Frenchmen among his colleagues. Joliot was deeply interested in the internationalizing influence of science. He had noticed that men of all nationalities, when they have worked together in the laboratory, tend to preserve contact when they return to their own countries, whereas the study of literature seemed to encourage nationalism.

The brilliant work of the younger French scientists raised much hope, but the support for scientific research was quite inadequate. The French expenditure on research was probably less than half the small sum spent by the British.

The financing of scientific research in Britain, France and the United States was chaotic. No one knew how much was actually spent, and those who sought financial support had to collect it in driblets from many places. When a young British scientist did good work and was appointed to a chair at an early age, he found that his opportunities had not always increased. He might have succeeded an elderly man whose laboratory was out-of-date. He then had to find the money for improving his laboratory. At best, this was done by preserving good social relations with monied sources; at worst, it degenerated into fantastic cadging.

He might have had to collect grants from several different sources for the support of his research assistants, £200 from one firm, £100 from a second, and £50 from a third, and so on. This involved attendance at a series of committee meetings. If his department was large, he might have had to spend a great deal of time attending university senate meetings, writing testimonials, etc., so that he was not able to do more than supervise a team of research assistants.

In the United States, the lawyers of sick millionaires were sedulously courted by the directors of some scientific institutions, with the hope of receiving new endowments for research.

As research had not originally been brought into existence by a conscious system, it did not proceed according to a plan. It shared the general characteristics of private enterprise in which it had developed.

The financing of research had now become too large a matter to be left to the enterprise of individual and casual adjustment. There was a necessary evolution towards the planning of the finance of research. Some thought that British research could be helped best by the creation of a national research fund. The Association of Scientific Workers estimated that a fund of thirty to forty million pounds was desirable. It might have been raised from customs duties that had been designed to assist British industry in the home market. Such a fund would have relieved men who could do creative work from wasting their time on soliciting and administration, for which they are often unfitted. It would have provided adequate laboratories and equipment, and satisfactory salaries and permanency of appointment to men of proved ability.

Something of the sort happened in a partial and haphazard way. The establishment of the duties on imported motor-cars provided the situation in which certain British manufacturers of motor-cars made very large fortunes. Parts of these fortunes were subsequently devoted to the endowment of medical and scientific research.

Generous provision for research was essential for national security, besides the advancement of civilization. A nation of forty-five million persons in a small island would have increasing difficulty in competing with nations of one hundred millions, settled in compact continental blocks. Superior technique is essential for survival in such a situation, and the largest expenditure and most thorough organization are justified to secure it.

77

Planned Research

UP TO 1939, the only country in which scientific research had been consciously planned on a national scale was Soviet Russia, where society had been reorganized according to the principles of Marxist philosophy. Marx based his philosophy on the properties of the real world, and therefore on natural history. Science was a fundamental part of its structure, and he viewed the evolution of society 'as a process of natural history'. He regarded Darwin's work as doubly important, because it dealt with some of the data of natural history, and also because the meaning of these data was analysed with the assistance of the concept of evolution, and he had already adopted both data and concept as basic to his philosophy before Darwin's work was published.

Further, in the development of his social theory, he attributed a fundamental rôle to science and technology. In his view, socialism would have been a utopian dream if production, through the agency of science, had not been multiplied to such a degree that equal means, which are the basis of social equality, could be supplied to all.

When the government of Russia was undertaken by men with Marxist views, the development of science and technology became a necessary part of the society's life. This was a new feature in government, for in other countries science was not held, in theory, to be necessary in social organizations.

Lenin was aware on philosophical grounds that science should be an integral and not an accessory part of the social system, and he said in 1920, that 'not until the country is electrified, and our industry, agriculture and transport are built up on the foundations of up-to-date large-scale production, shall we be finally victorious'.

Plans were accordingly prepared for the construction of a social system in which science and technology had an essential rôle. The starting point of the planning was an estimate of the requirements for creating a satisfactory standard of life for everyone. It was relatively easy to calculate how much food, clothing, housing, medical service, etc., would be needed to provide comfort and health. From these figures, estimates for the size of the industries for supplying them could be calculated. An output of so much agricultural goods, so much coal, oil, iron, ores, etc., was necessary. The required quantities were far larger than those hitherto produced. The planners therefore considered, for instance, how the output of agriculture might be increased. A system of research institutes was created to assist in the discovery and introduction of better methods.

Very large surveys of the natural resources of the country were made, to find the necessary supplies of minerals, and these yielded much new geological knowledge.

The requisite metallurgical industries called for institutes where the problems of metallurgy, refractories, and operation could be solved.

A very large electrical industry was planned, to supply power for the manufacturing industries, and light to the population.

The number of scientific problems whose solution was made urgent inspired the revival of the Academy of Sciences. This had been founded by Peter the Great, after the model of the French and other Academies. It had been founded as an emblem of power, an ostentatious demonstration of the wealth which gave clever men the leisure to perform impressive feats of intellectual skill, rather than as an organic part of the state. The scientific demands created by the new planning led to a fundamental reorganization. Its first duty under its new statutes was to direct the study and application of science towards the fulfilment of socialist construction, and the growth of socialist culture. The Academy, which formerly had been restricted to pure scientists, was opened to technicians and social scientists, and its number increased to about a hundred.

This reorganization gave the Academy a working rôle in the state, and transformed it into a purposeful institution, directing numerous institutes and expeditions, and several thousand research workers of various qualifications.

The Soviet organizers regarded the human ability in their country as one of their chief natural resources. Special institutes were built for men of notable genius. The application of ability to unsuitable tasks was bad planning because it was an abuse of part of society's most precious resources. Planning was regarded as the aid which would provide able men with better opportunities. The belief that planning was intrinsically inimical to creative work was considered mistaken. This was the explanation of the apparent paradox that while the Soviet planned research, it gave exceptional facilities to outstanding individuals.

The planning of research associated with the electrical industry may be taken as a general example. The required output of electrical units was estimated, and plans were made for the requisite number of electric power stations to supply them. The stations, and the transmission system that they supplied, had to be designed, built, and operated. This presented all the usual problems of electrical engineering, and new ones arising out of special conditions, or which had not previously occurred in practice.

A big electrical industry accompanied by a system of research institutes where its problems may be solved, and the most skilled of its technical staff trained, had to be set up.

Their programmes of research were co-ordinated through a

series of about a dozen committees, each containing ten to fifteen members. They held two or more meetings in the year. Each committee prepared a plan for research in its subject for one year, and laid down the general line of the work for each related laboratory. They apportioned researches among the various institutes, so that overlapping was avoided, and particular problems were studied in the places most suitably staffed and equipped. The work done in the year was reviewed and assessed at the second yearly meeting.

The work of these committees was done mainly by correspondence. The majority of their members were directors of institutes, and this committee work occupied perhaps two full weeks' work spread through the year. These committees also decided the size of the allowances for books and periodicals, and arranged conferences on research and organization.

The scientists of the Soviet Union accumulated unique experience in making the first planned system of scientific research. They were the first to give comprehensive expression to the tendency to organize research which is seen in all countries.

78

American Foresight

THE development of the United States was conducted under the initiative of private enterprise. During the latter half of the nineteenth century, its governments were, on the whole, satisfied with the developments when the leaders of private enterprise were satisfied with them.

This general view had always been contested, but without much effect until after the end of the First World War. This upheaval heightened consciousness of social discontents, and at the same time victory had provided the optimism that inspired hopes of better social construction.

The eminent mining engineer, H. C. Hoover, whose edition of Agricola was of such help for Section 52 of this book, had become famous as a world organizer of relief during the First

World War. He was drawn into politics through his administrative abilities, and in 1921, as a statesman, he began to sponsor
inquiries into American society, to discover whether it could be
improved by action based on accurate knowledge based on some
of its features.

Under his chairmanship, a notable report on *Waste in Industry*
was prepared in 1921. After he had been elected President of the
United States, he appointed in 1929 a group of scientists to make
a survey of American society, to obtain accurate knowledge of its
stresses, as data for the preparation of policies to deal with them
constructively. This committee published its findings under the
title of *Recent Social Trends*, in 1932. It had noted a multitude of
problems, ranging from foreign policy, governmental regulation
of industry, urbanization, shifting moral standards, etc., to the
future of democracy and capitalism. The combination of immigration from many lands, and swift development of natural
resources had hurried the nation at a dizzy pace from the
frontier life into a whirl of modernism.

A marked indifference to the interrelation among the parts of
the huge social system accompanied this amazing mobility and
complexity. 'Powerful individuals and groups have gone their
own way without realizing the meaning of the old phrase, "No
man liveth unto himself".'

Splendid technical proficiency was exhibited in some incredible
skyscraper, while monstrous backwardness was to be found in a
neighbouring, equally incredible slum.

America's outstanding problem was to realize the inter-
dependence of the factors in its complicated social structure, so
that the advancing sections of its forward movement 'in agriculture, labour, industry, government, education, religion and
science may develop a higher degree of co-ordination in the next
phase of national growth'. Their investigations showed that
American life was strained by unequal rates of change in its parts,
as if 'the parts of an automobile were operating at unsynchronized
speeds'. They noted that 'scientific discoveries and inventions
instigate changes first in the economic organization', and the
social habits most closely connected with it, such as urbanization,
and labour organization. These in turn influenced the institutions of the family, government, schools and churches. Industry
and government were gaining regulatory influence over the
population at the expense of the Church and family. Technology

and organization had affected spiritual values. This made moral guidance in the present peculiarly difficult, because moral values had been evolved through long periods when social conditions were very different. The Committee did not believe that the enhanced difficulties of modern times could be solved by a moratorium on research in physical science and invention. It held, on the contrary, that social invention should be stimulated to keep pace with mechanical invention.

The Committee concluded that the people of the United States must make important reorganizations in its social life, especially in the economic and political aspects, and stop drifting. They must recognize the rôle that science and technology would play in such reorganizations. Some recognition of the need for finding the exact facts of American life had been obtained, and the next step would consist in devising a policy based on these facts. A National Advisory Council might be formed, which would include scientists, educationists, statesmen, economists and others, who would consider the basic social problems of the nation, 'always in their interrelation, and in the light of the trends and possibilities of modern science'.

They did not wish 'to exaggerate the rôle of intelligence in social direction'. They admitted the importance of tradition, stupidity, the raw will to power, and other factors, but too much preoccupation with them led to 'hopeless resignation'.

But there were more definite alternatives in dictatorship, in which violence may supplant technical intelligence in the direction of social change. Unless there was a more impressive integration of social skills and purposes than was revealed by recent trends, there could be 'no assurance that these alternatives, with their accompaniments of violent revolution, dark periods of serious repression of libertarian and democratic forms, the proscription and loss of many useful elements in the present productive system, can be averted'.

The administration of his successor, Franklin D. Roosevelt, continued and extended his line of investigation. The National Resources Committee organized a study of technological trends, including the social implications of new inventions, through its science sub-committee, and published a report on Technological Trends and National Policy in 1937. This was transmitted to President Roosevelt as 'the first major attempt to show the kinds of new inventions which may affect living and working conditions in America in the next ten to twenty-five years. It indicates some of the problems which the adoption and use of these inventions will inevitably bring in their train. It emphasizes the importance of national efforts to bring about prompt adjustment to these changing situations, with the least possible social suffering and loss, and sketches some of the lines of national policy directed to this end'.

The report contained a large collection of facts about contemporary American agriculture, transportation, communication, power; mineral, metal, chemical and electrical industries; and constructional engineering. A glance at these revealed some of the chief directions of change in American life.

In 1787, the surplus produced by nineteen farmers was required to support one city dweller. In 1937, nineteen farmers produced on the average sufficient to support fifty-six city dwellers and ten foreigners. Crop production increased by twenty-seven per cent in the interval 1922–26, while the crop acreage remained almost constant, and the number of agricultural workers decreased. Between 1918 and 1932, ten million horses and mules were displaced by automobiles. This released thirty million acres of grazing land for the production of saleable commodities.

The domestic consumption of farm products remained relatively stable during the years 1930 to 1933, in spite of very low prices. It was concluded that it is doubtful if any but the very poor would consume much more as the result of a substantial increase in income.

American farmhouses were still very backward. Only about fifteen per cent had electricity, twenty-seven per cent kitchen sinks and drains, seventeen per cent cold water laid on to the house, eight per cent a constant hot water supply, nine per cent flush toilets, eight per cent furnace heat, and four per cent gas or electricity for cooking. In Holland, one hundred per cent of farms had electricity, and in Germany, ninety per cent.

The elimination of forests had removed the natural sponges for moisture, and had increased desiccation and dust storms. The dust storm of May 1934 shifted three hundred million tons of fertile top soil. The wind erosion increased the destructiveness of water erosion. Four hundred million tons of material were carried into the Gulf of Mexico every year by the Mississippi. Deforestation, which had such a serious influence on erosion, was a result of exploitation.

14

The restoration of an equilibrium in land life is essential to the security and permanence of America. The scientist and technician must find ways whereby restored forests may perpetually supply the products at present obtained from resources that cannot be renewed.

As for the mineral industries, ninety per cent of power was still drawn from minerals, and only ten per cent from water. But mineral technology worked with an increasing handicap, as mines became poorer and deeper. No new fields of mineral deposits had been found in the United States since 1910. The known deposits of coal could supply the present rate of consumption for two thousand years.

The deposits of oil known until recently were sufficient only for some ten years. But fifty new oil and gas pools had been discovered in Texas alone in 1935. This was largely due to geophysical methods of prospecting.

The number of bituminous coal miners had declined by 247,000 between 1923 and 1935. Nevertheless, the long-term effects of mechanization were beneficial to the miners, and in any case, technological progress was essential to meet the growing competition from petroleum and natural gas.

The average American travelled 2,000 miles in 1929, compared with 500 in 1920. This increase was chiefly due to the motor-car. The berths in trains had not been substantially changed for half a century, but the competition of other modes of travel had already brought about a change. Berths in transcontinental planes were already longer and wider.

The growth of aviation was expected to benefit employment, as it required an exceptionally large ground staff. Motor lorries also need much accessory labour; about twenty to thirty times as much as the railways per ton mile. 'Shorter hours, higher wages, greater old-age security and better education will favour increased passenger travel, just as the long hours and poverty attendant upon farming submarginal land virtually root people to the soil.'

Improved electrical communications should provide the possibility of having one's newspaper printed in the home from a central office. News should be seen and heard in the making. The contents of documents should be swiftly transmissible. The ability to see and hear persons at a distance, whether in the aeroplane, motor-car or steamship, will produce an outlook quite different from that limited by vision, horizon and social contact.

The rapid introduction of the dial system in telephony was due in part to its advantages in serving a cosmopolitan population.

The improvement in the steam industry, which is the oldest of the modern forms of power, was among the most striking in recent decades. Steam was still very definitely holding its own. The cost of steam power plants for producing electricity was about $75 to $125 per kilowatt. In 1880 the consumption of coal needed to produce one kilowatt for one hour was 10 lb. In 1900 the figure had been reduced to 5 lb.; in 1918 to $3\frac{1}{3}$ lb., and in 1935 to less than 1 lb. The cost of transporting coal 900 miles was no greater than conducting electricity 200 miles.

There would be a steady increase of automatic working in chemical plant. Its aim was not the reduction of labour costs by eliminating hands, but accuracy in operation, improved uniformity in the product, and hence lower overall costs. Automatic and remote control was simplifying architecture.

The introduction of lead tetraethyl for removing knock in motor engines had created a demand for bromine. A great plant for extracting bromine from the sea had been built to meet it. Progress had already been made towards the replacement of natural by synthetic rubber.

The kingdom of chemical synthesis had been created in addition to the animal, vegetable and mineral kingdoms. It would not be possible to govern this new kingdom without adding a fifth estate of scientists to those of the spirit, the earth, the commons, and the press.

Great developments were anticipated in lighting. More was to be expected from luminescent paints, which will store up sunlight during the day and glow in colours at night. Air-conditioning plants would become universal. Patents for them had been registered in the United States at the rate of 300 a day.

Photo-electric cells were already used for hundreds of automatic operations in metallurgical and chemical industry, counting, sorting, opening doors, etc. At least one million workers could already be replaced by them. Electric timing would be used for roasting beef, turning on lights and heating, etc., when the occupant is away or sleeps.

The scope for housing construction in the United States was immense. Four million American families were without running water, indoor closets and baths. One third to one half of the families in America could not afford modern houses. Houses could be made in parts in the factory and assembled on the site. Through the assistance of modern machinery, men may build nearly two thousand times more quickly than the ancient Egyptians.

What effects have these, and a thousand other developments, had on employment? Formerly a man worked 3,000 hours in a year, latterly he worked 2,000. If production and employment were represented by the index number of 100 in 1920, the figures for 1935 were 114 and 82. The productivity of the worker in 1935 was 39 per cent higher. An increase of 16 per cent in total employment occurred between 1920 and 1929, but towards this, the basic industries of agriculture, mining, manufacture, construction, transportation, communication and public utilities contributed an increase of only 3 per cent. The main contribution came from the service industries of trade, and professional, public, personal and domestic service, in which the increase was 50 per cent.

A large part of the increase in productivity after 1932 was attributable to new processes, which had been known for some time, but had not previously been introduced, owing to lack of confidence by investors of capital.

The total employment in the basic industries fell from an index number of 100 in 1920 to 77·4 in 1935. The biggest fall occurred in railway employment. There was only one big rise. This was in transportation other than steam railways, the percentage rising from 6·3 in 1920 to 9·2 in 1935.

It was found that under 'the prosperous conditions between 1923 and 1929, one worker out of twenty was forced, every two years, to seek employment in a new manufacturing industry, or in a non-manufacturing industry. These conditions placed lighter demands upon industry for the training of new men, but placed much heavier demands upon wage-earners, and enforced a degree of adaptability not required under pre-war conditions'.

When men were discharged from factories owing to the discontinuation of a particular process, two-thirds to three-quarters received lower wages when they found a new job, and most of the remainder were unemployed for a long period. Bakke found that 'apparently the qualities which helped men to rise to skilled jobs and high wages *while at work* are of limited use in helping men to readjust satisfactorily *when the job goes*'.

The growth in total output from 1920 to 1929 was not sufficient to create enough new jobs to absorb the available manpower, and it was to be expected that technological progress would continue to present serious problems of industrial, economic and social readjustment, unless some improved methods of solving them were found.

The American investigators did not halt after they had collected some of the facts of recent development. They discussed how the main lines of future development might be forecast. The history of nineteen major inventions was analysed, and it was found that the average interval between the proposal of the idea and the first patent granted in connection with it was 176 years. The average interval between the first patent and practical use was 24 years. Then from practical use to commercial success 14 years, and to important use 12 more years; or about 50 years from the first serious work on the invention. It is hardly possible to find an invention that became important in less than ten years from the time that it, or some fully equivalent substitute was worked on. These figures provide a guide to prediction, for they show that many inventions that will become of major importance in the future are already in existence, and some of them should be recognizable by intelligent study.

It was found that distinguished scientific and technical men made the best predictions in their own field, but they were liable to overlook the possibility of problems in their own field being solved by innovations in other fields.

There was no reason 'why one should not use science in estimating the future, as in any other business'. The telephone, the motor-car, the aeroplane, the motion picture, rayon, and the radio are now the basis of six major industries which did not exist in 1900, and yet most of the basic inventions had already been made. It should not have been impossible in 1900 to have made a useful forecast of the rise of these industries, and to have prepared social legislation to meet their effects. Wider main roads might easily have been planned. The effects of rayon in undermining class distinction by removing the difference between the styles worn by different classes might have been foreseen. The swift expansion of urban life through the motor-car should have been plainly visible, and suitable laws for regulating it might have been made, before the rise in estate values made improvement prohibitively expensive.

Perfected television would effect enormous changes through propaganda and teaching. The photo-electric cell, or electric eye, sees all that the human eye can see, and more. It does not suffer from fatigue. It brings the automatic factory and the automatic man closer, and it would very probably produce unemployment.

Perhaps the greatest changes were to be expected from the synthesis of substances that have a fundamental rôle in living organisms. Several of the most important natural hormones, such as those which control sexual behaviour, had already been synthesized. These offer the prospects of basic changes in the constitution and nature of man.

Forecasts of the effects of the development of plastics, synthetic rubber, prefabricated houses, facsimile transmission, motor-car trailers, steep-flight aeroplanes and the intensive cultivation of plants in trays under special chemical and physical conditions, would almost certainly provide information of value for far-sighted social legislation.

Some of these inventions, already successful on a small scale, should, according to the experience of the past, be used on a large scale, within twenty-six years. Forecasts of their effects, even if only approximate, would prepare man for their arrival, and help him, while it was still easy, and before the new interests created by the new inventions had crystallized, to avoid unnecessary social disorganization, and draw the maximum benefit from his own achievements.

79

Science Thwarted

UP TO the year 1850, seventy-four per cent of all the children born in London died before reaching the age of five. In 1939, the percentage had been reduced to about twelve. Deaths from typhoid fever in England declined from 5,000 in 1900 to 206 in 1937. In 1871–80, 2,880 out of every hundred thousand English people were killed each year by tuberculosis. This figure had declined to 690 in 1937. Mortality from scarlet fever sank from 720 per 100,000 in 1871–80 to 9 in 1937. The corresponding figures were 380 and 26 for measles; 510 and 43 for whooping cough. In 1922 42·5 per cent of all deaths in Britain occurred before the age of fifty. In 1937, the figure had declined to 27 per cent. In the twenty years 1911–31, the average height and weight of boys of twelve attending elementary schools in Leeds had increased by three inches and 10·9 lb. In 1912, 39·5 per cent of the children in the London elementary schools had parasitic skin infections. By 1937, the figure had declined to 2·6 per cent.

These improvements were extraordinary, but they raised the question of what was happening before they were made. A large part of the improvement was due to the establishment of habits of cleanliness, and another large part, concerning the improvement of physique, to better diet. The better cleanliness and diet were due chiefly to government action and rising wages. The mass of the population succeeded, largely through political pressure, and to a lesser degree through goodwill, in securing a share of the great increase in production that had accompanied the growth of technology. The explanation why this should have had such great effect was elucidated by a century of research led by Liebig, Pasteur, the modern students of nutrition and thousands of medical scientists. Perhaps the most important outcome of their work, besides the large number of individual discoveries, was their confirmation of the common-sense view, that if men have good wages, they and their families will obtain better food, and more soap, fresh air and sunshine, and will be stronger and healthier.

The provision of unanswerable arguments for policies advocated by reformers has been one of the most valuable results of modern medical research. How can it be decided whether sanitary laws or bacteriological knowledge have been the more beneficial to society? But it was certain that modern knowledge of bacteriology and nutrition had greatly strengthened the demand for better food and housing.

For instance, it was found that if schoolboys are given additional milk, and butter instead of margarine, the number of fractures in football matches and accidents declines significantly. A large part of hospital work is occupied in treating fractures, and there was no doubt that the amount of it would decrease if the whole population drank more milk and ate more butter.

In 1937 there were 61,339 cases of diphtheria in England and Wales, causing 2,963 deaths. The average child patient stayed in hospital for six weeks, and the annual cost of the disease to the country was £1,500,000. Yet it had been demonstrated that diphtheria might be eliminated. In the town of Hamilton, Ontario, with a population of 155,000, no case of diphtheria had been diagnosed for five years, owing to the application of modern measures. Nearly all the suffering and waste due to diphtheria might have been eliminated at once by preventive inoculation.

The average height and weight of the sons of prosperous Englishmen at the age of eleven were respectively 55·33 inches and 76·22 lb., while those of the working class were respectively 3 inches and 12 lb. less.

The mortality due to tuberculosis was four times as great in the children of the poor under the age of one, as in those of the prosperous. The mortality rate for bronchitis and pneumonia was six times as great in the infants of the poor under the age of two.

Mellanby wrote that 'the day will probably come when the country will regard it as intolerable that the number of deaths of children under two is related to the amount of money received per week by the father of the family'. He said that the medical scientist complains of 'the great delay which often occurs before many of the teachings, which his investigations have elucidated, are adopted by public authorities and private citizens'. He considered that this was due sometimes to administrative inertia, sometimes to lack of political and social interest, and sometimes to laziness, but 'more often it is due to such economic and social restrictions as prevent people from attaining the nutritional and hygienic conditions necessary for healthy existence'. There was little doubt that it would pay the state to provide milk and other foods free to all schoolchildren. The saving through better health and lower incidence of disease would be greater than the cost.

In spite of the splendid return on medical research, the British Government spent only £195,000 per annum through its Medical Research Council. It was evident that two of the chief forces thwarting medical science were opposition to higher wages and Government expenditure on free foods, and inadequate expenditure on research itself.

The contrast between possibility and actuality in technical science was even greater. The millions of discoveries and inventions registered in the United States had not enabled that country of rich natural resources to eliminate some ten million unemployed, and a vast amount of misery, especially in rural areas.

During prosperous periods corporations tended to invest large sums in plant to supply vigorous demand. When prosperity was followed by depression, there was not enough business to use the expanded plant, so from the corporation's point of view there was no point in modernizing the plant with the new inventions developed since the slump in its research laboratory. Thus a corporation might be piling up discoveries that are not being introduced into practice, and the plant in the country where the new inventions are being developed may fall out of date, while backward countries that did not modernize their plant during the prosperous period may begin to introduce the new inventions first.

The coaxial cable, which will transmit hundreds of messages simultaneously, was first introduced more extensively in England than in the country where it was developed, as the former English equipment was more out of date, and therefore the obsolescence costs were less than they would have been in the United States, which had relatively recently extended its equipment.

Famous inventors have repeatedly asserted that corporations have used their financial power to buy inventions at less than their proper price. Edison said in 1912 that 'the long delays and enormous costs incident to the procedure of the courts have been seized upon by capitalists to enable them to acquire inventions for nominal sums that are entirely inadequate to encourage really valuable inventions. The inventor is now a dependent, a hired person to the corporation'.

Bernard J. Stern contended that the rights of private property, and hence of patents, 'are clearly above the other interests of the community and above the needs of technological progress'.

Much industrial research is concerned with the discovery of methods of evading the patents of competitors. Corporations seek for inventions which might embarrass their competitors. If they are owned by small private firms, they may assist these small firms to withstand legal attacks by competing corporations, and organize them as a sort of guerilla in commercial warfare conducted with the weapon of patents.

Edison described how he invented a relay at Jay Gould's request, based on his discovery that moistened chalk becomes slippery when a current passes through it, to enable the financier to attack on the Stock Exchange the Western Union Company, which held Page's patents covering all forms of electromagnetic relay.

14*

Inventions made in response to such requests have proved of value to science. The Podbielnak apparatus for fractional distillation, which has established a new degree of accuracy in some branches of chemistry, and has been an essential aid to many of recent spectacular triumphs in the synthesis of biologically important substances, was invented in connection with patent litigation.

Fifty per cent of the corporations insisted that their staffs, at the time of hiring, should assign the rights in any relevant inventions made during and subsequent to their employment to them. For instance, in 1935 the Ingersoll-Rand Company required its employees to sign a document which contained the following: 'In consideration of one dollar ($1) paid to me by Ingersoll-Rand Co., the receipt whereof by me is hereby acknowledged, and of my employment by that company during such time as may be mutually agreeable to that company and myself, I agree to assign and hereby do assign to said company, its successors and assigns, all my rights to inventions which I have made or conceived or which I may hereafter make or conceive, either solely or jointly with others, in the course of such employment, or with the use of the time, material, or facilities of said company, or relating to any method, substance, article of manufacture, or improvements therein within the scope of the business of that company.' The agreement stipulated that the inventor must disclose the invention to the company as soon as practicable. In addition to the contents of the agreement, the company printed comments on them on the same form. It explained that without such an agreement it would be impossible to bring new employees 'into free and open relations with those engineers who are regularly assigning inventions to the company'. Though it did not promise additional compensation for these inventions, 'its policy is to recognize all good service of whatever nature, by proper adjustment of the salaries, & cont.' But 'it is obvious that during this employment a man may acquire many records and data and much confidential information which under no circumstances should be used after the termination of the employment'.

The drift of these developments was to make those corporations that control virtually the whole of any industry the sole owners of patents bearing on it, and the sole arbiters of how those patents should be used. As these corporations have, in America, the legal status and rights of a private person, it means that they are not responsible to the American community for the use that they make of their private property in patents, even though those patents may have an essential part in the life of that community. Their rights in their patents are certain, but their services to the American people are determined only by their own will and judgment. This does not necessarily mean that these services are not well performed, but it does mean that the American people have signed away, through their own laws, their control over vital machinery in their social life.

The effect on technological development of corporations that follow their own narrow interests was seen in the events at Jarrow in England. After the First World War British shipbuilding firms could no longer obtain sufficient orders to keep all their shipyards busy. This led to fierce price-cutting competition, so presently many firms combined, and with the support of the Government, the Bank of England, and other banks, a syndicate was formed to buy shipyards, so that a sufficient number could be closed, and those left open could make a satisfactory profit. The capacity of shipyards for construction was reduced by one-third, though the approach of a great naval war was evident to many persons of political judgment. The syndicate chose the yards to be closed mainly according to the degree of their financial difficulties. Consequently, some of the best-equipped yards in England, including Palmer's Shipyard at Jarrow, were dismantled. After this had happened, an attempt was made to purchase the site for the erection of a large modern steel works. This proposal was fiercely opposed by the neighbouring firms, who saw that the new plant would undersell the products from their older obsolescent plants. These firms, through their Iron and Steel Federation, and its connection with the Bank of England, made it virtually impossible for the industrialist to raise funds for his enterprise. They could also virtually prevent him from selling his products, if he had succeeded in making them, owing to the Iron and Steel Federation's connections with the Continental Steel Cartel, and the power given to it by the Government to control prices. The new company would have been compelled to pay into a pool, for the benefit of the older firms, a fine practically equal to the savings effected by its superior equipment. The project was killed, though a much smaller works was ultimately allowed. As a writer in the *New Statesman* remarked: 'That the effect of these methods has been to weaken Great

Britain for war as well as for peace is abundantly clear. For nineteenth-century capitalism it could at any rate be said that, however ruthless it might be about the social consequences of its actions, it did stimulate production and apply new technical inventions with all the speed it could. But this newer capitalism is the enemy of technical progress. Accepting the limitation of markets, it sets out to entrench itself and its obsolescent methods and equipment—to create scarcity, and out of scarcity to maintain profits in the interests of big industrialists and financiers.'

The progress of science and technology was thwarted by many other social influences and traditions. In England, many people excused the small expenditure on scientific research on the ground that there is a lack of scientific ability, and that additions to present expenditure would merely cause money to be wasted on second- and third-rate men, because the first-rate men already have enough. There were instances of English industrial scientists who had conspicuous success in America, after moderate success in England. The chief difference between their conditions in America and in England consisted of much larger subsidies and equipment for research. Some of these men were unable to make great discoveries with small means, but this did not prove that they could not make them with big means. Success in research may depend as much nowadays on the ability to organize a team as on the individual ability of a Faraday, who solved very difficult problems merely by personal effort, without one trained assistant. There was little doubt that a great deal of English scientific ability was being thwarted by lack of means.

Patent agreements between national corporations, covering the whole world, were tending to cause all of their important research to be concentrated in laboratories established in one country. The populations in the other countries had no opportunity for work in this domain, and were unable to acquire the knowledge and experience necessary for original work in it. Such countries must pay royalties on the master patent held by the unofficial world corporation, and have neither the knowledge nor the skill to make the new inventions that will enable them to evade them. This does not apply only to small poor countries. Some of the richest countries prefer to follow this policy, for it is easier to pay royalties than to discover new things, even though the latter policy is the cheaper in the long run.

80

Science, Art and Discontinuity

PLANCK discovered in 1900 that if he assumed that action does not occur in continuously varying amounts, but in multiples of an elemental quantum, he could explain certain puzzling observed properties of radiation. He regarded his quantum theory more or less as a trick for solving certain problems. He did not consider the philosophical contradictions raised by the theory fundamental, and believed they arose from the limitations of the human intellect, and might present no paradoxes to a superhuman intellect.

The acceptance of quantum properties as a fundamental characteristic of nature was due to Bohr. He explained in his *Faraday Lecture* the considerations that prompted him to propose his quantum theory of the atom in 1913. He arrived at Manchester just after Rutherford had proved that the atom behaved as if it consisted of a very small heavy nucleus surrounded by relatively distant revolving electrons, like planets round a sun. This discovery was of immense importance because it showed that the atom might be conceived, not as a virtually formless lump of three-dimensional jelly, but as an assemblage of discrete particles that could be treated as mathematical points. It seemed to Bohr that Rutherford's atomic model had brought the ancient philosophers' dream of reducing the interpretation of the laws of nature to pure numbers within sight of realization, and the prospect seemed thrilling with promise. But the first consideration of the new Rutherford model showed that it could not operate according to the laws of Newtonian mechanics. If the electrons revolved round the nucleus in a manner comparable with the revolution of planets round the sun, they should vary their motion continuously, and emit a continuously varying quantity of associated radiation. Bohr therefore searched for some principle by which the movements of the parts of the Rutherford atom might be limited. He found it in Planck's idea of the quantum of action. He postulated that any well-defined change of state of an atom is an elementary process, consisting in a complete transition of the atom from one state to another. While the atom was in one of these states it was absolutely unchangeable. Further, the number of these possible states was defined in terms of Planck's quantum, and was practically very small. The fewness, and permanence of states while they existed, completely explained the paradoxical stability of matter.

While Bohr was laying down in 1913 his momentous postulate of discontinuity as the basis of the properties of matter, other thinkers in entirely different fields were also invoking discontinuity. T. E. Hulme, who was to have much influence on T. S. Eliot and other literary figures, was compiling notes at about the same time for a critique of humanism. He believed that the fundamental difference between medieval civilization, and civilization since the Renaissance, consisted of a change in human attitude. In the medieval period, human nature was held to be bad, while after the Renaissance it was held to be good. In the first, original sin was held to be real, while in the second it was not. Perfection in the earlier period was therefore sought outside human nature, while in the latter it was sought within human nature. The second attitude was accompanied by the belief in the perfectibility of man, and therefore of a justifiable interest in himself. As man contained the seeds of perfection, he could by attention make himself continuously better. This engendered in him the idea of continuous development and progress. It also made human nature the centre of interest, so that it became the chief subject of literature and art. The first autobiographies were written, and pictorial art became engaged in the description of the human figure and personality.

Hulme followed Weber in the belief that this growth of interest in the human and the self was one of the bases of the capitalist spirit. He thought that this spirit arose first, and that the economic features of capitalistic society were a consequence of it.

As the medieval attitude was not directed towards the human, the subject of its art was not the human figure. It sought perfection not in the living lines of the human figure, but in geometrical shapes. This was seen particularly well in Byzantine art. The angularities of Byzantine figures were not defects in depictions of the human form, because that was not their primary purpose. The Byzantine artists aimed at the construction of abstractly beautiful geometrical shapes, and used the lines of the human figure merely as a foundation for the drawing. The disposition of the lines of the human figure, which were regarded as trivial because human, were distorted into angular and discontinuous shapes intended to suggest geometrical, non-human perfection. A similar aim was seen in ancient Egyptian sculpture.

Hulme believed that the rise of interest in abstract art that began before 1914 was a sign of the collapse of naturalistic art, and of the humanistic attitude associated with it. He thought that it foreshadowed a profound transformation of society, in which the dogma of continuous human perfectibility would be abandoned, and the movement of humanism, which had been the feature of history since the Renaissance, would be ended. It would be succeeded by a revival of the belief in the reality of original sin, and of the absoluteness of the difference between good and evil. The relativity of humanist thought, which, owing to its belief in the continuous perfectibility of human nature, regarded all conduct as differing in degree but not in kind, would be swept away, and replaced by a system based on a hierarchy of values. These would be absolutely discontinuous, and there would be no possibility of transformation by continuous change from one into another.

Hulme forecast that a renewed belief in original sin would lead to the growth of a new social authoritarianism, as the elements of original sin in human nature could not be controlled without external discipline.

It is not difficult to see that given hierarchies of discontinuous absolute values, those who believe they possess the highest of these values will feel compelled to organize society by force, in accordance with their values. As they believe in the reality of original sin, they will also believe in strong external discipline. They will attempt to organize society in a hierarchy of classes, or a hierarchy of groups within one party, with the assistance of a powerful police directed by those in possession of the highest values. Hulme was conscious of a difficulty in his views. He did not wish to lose the results of modern science, and he was aware that these were a product of the humanist period. He therefore said that 'a new anti-humanist ideology could not be a mere revival of mediaevalism. The humanist period has developed an honesty in science, and a certain conception of freedom of thought and action which will remain'.

Hulme became an enthusiastic militarist, and was killed in the First World War.

Bohr, who was more at home with discontinuity and its implications, emphasized the danger of drawing faulty conclusions from misinterpretations of Heisenberg's principle of uncertainty, which he regarded as a triumph of the rational understanding. Bohr lived on, and became President of the Society for the Protection of Science and Learning.

81

The New Interest in the Social Relations of Science

SCIENCE has necessarily been related to social affairs since it came into existence. This is not a new phenomenon, though a new interest in it arose, especially during the 1930s.

Sprat and the founders of the Royal Society knew that their advancement of scientific research was a response to a general movement that had become evident at least as early as Edward VI. Though they acknowledged the stimulus they had received from Bacon, they were aware that Bacon himself had not done more than enhance the expression of a movement that preceded him.

When the Royal Society was founded, only about one-fifth of the fellows were scientists. The rest were men of general learning and intelligence, including some professional men and tradesmen, and statesmen who might assist science through influence. Objections to this mixed membership arose early, and Newton supported in 1674 'the ejection of all useless fellows'. But no effective move to alter the membership was made for nearly two centuries. This occurred during the first half of the nineteenth century. The society contained 662 fellows in 1830, but only 106 had published at least one paper in the Society's journal. The election of the remaining fellows could be justified only by their patronage of science, but from 1662 until 1828, no fellow left any substantial sum for this purpose, and then, the first fellow to do so was not one of the patronal type, but the eminent scientist Wollaston. As Lyons noted, 'It is somewhat remarkable that although the majority of the fellows had been hitherto elected as being men of substance and in a position to be patrons of science, none of them had ever thought of endowing scientific research in any way.'

Wollaston's bequest was a sign of the quickening interest in science, which inspired much criticism of the Royal Society's condition. A new activity arose in all branches of knowledge at the beginning of the nineteenth century. As Lyons said, 'the industrial revolution which had been steadily developing for some years past had fundamentally modified technical industry, and a similar stimulus was deeply influencing many scientific and technical institutions; the Royal Society also had been modifying many of its old ideas and was to do so much more in the years ahead'. The old order in the Society 'was now being seriously challenged by a number of scientific men in the Society who had realized the active part which science should be playing in the promotion of the industrial reorganization which was already in operation'. They believed that the scientific members of the Society should have more control over its administration. The finances of the Society were reorganized between 1831 and 1833 by the treasurer, J. W. Lubbock, who was a banker. W. R. Grove, the inventor of the Grove cell, and an eminent lawyer, proposed that the number of fellows elected annually should be limited to fifteen, with suitable scientific attainments. Lubbock and Grove were gifted members of social classes which were becoming dominant in the nineteenth century. The change in the mode of election was the most important made in the Society since its foundation in 1662. It was passed in 1847. It transformed the Society from an eminent body of men interested in science, containing a minority of research workers, into a body of carefully selected specialists. It was a reflection in scientific affairs of the sub-division of labour and specialization characteristic of the industrial and social development of the time. The annual number of elections was restricted to fifteen from 1848 until 1930, though the number of candidates increased enormously, owing to the expansion of scientific research and the increase in the number of scientists.

Election to the Society had become intensely competitive in the twentieth century. This circumstance stimulated still further the tendency to specialization, as election was secured more easily by those who confined their work to a narrow field. The Society became a highly professionalized body under these conditions, and the attention of its fellows was withdrawn more and more from the wider aspects of science. Presently, attention to these aspects was deprecated, and was regarded rather as a disqualification in young candidates. The new tradition, which was a result of the change of 1847, was different from that of the founders of the Society, who were men of affairs besides being scientists. Owing to it, the Royal Society at the beginning of the twentieth century devoted less attention to the social relations of science than at any previous period in its history.

Thus, in England, interest in the social relations of science passed largely from the professionalized scientists to men outside their organizations. Among the most eminent of these was H. G. Wells. He was never elected a fellow of the Royal Society, which was a striking illustration of the change in its tradition, for if Wells had lived in the second half of the seventeenth century, it is scarcely conceivable that he would not have been one of its most notable members. He first treated the implications of science through the medium of scientific fantasy. He made imaginative extensions of current scientific tendencies, and gave his extrapolations remarkable interest and verisimilitude. Many readers learned from these works a sense of the possibilities of science.

The second medium through which he advanced the study of the social relations of science was his writing on socialism and science. For him 'the fundamental idea upon which Socialism rests is the same fundamental idea as that upon which all real scientific work is carried on'. It is the assertion that things are orderly by nature, and may be computed and foreseen. The Socialist has just the same faith in the existence of this order, and the knowableness of things, and the power of men through cooperation to overcome chance. 'While Science gathers knowledge, Socialism in an entirely harmonious spirit criticizes and develops a general plan of social life. Each seeks to replace disorder by order.'

Science and socialism were further in sympathy in the demand they made on men to become less egotistical and isolated. He believed that the chief difference between science in the Middle Ages and in the present lay in its collective character, in which all experiments and discoveries are published and explained. 'In a sense scientific research is a triumph over natural instinct, over that mean instinct that makes men secretive, that makes a man keep knowledge to himself and use it slyly to his own advantage.' He advocated socialism because it applied to social and economic relationships the 'same high rule of frankness and veracity, the same subordination of purely personal considerations to a common end that science demands in the field of thought and knowledge'. The common enemies of science and socialism are 'secrecy, subterfuge and the private gain'.

The socialist wants 'Constructive Design', he wants a complete organization for all those human affairs that are of collective importance. 'Our ways of manufacturing a great multitude of necessary things, of getting and distributing food, of conducting all sorts of business, of begetting and rearing children, of permitting diseases to engender and spread are chaotic and undisciplined, so badly done that here is enormous hardship, and there enormous waste, here excess and degeneration, and there privation and death.' So, 'in place of disorderly individual effort, each man doing what he pleases, the Socialist wants organized effort and a plan'. Mankind should not follow 'the methods of a mob when it ought to follow the method of an army'. But he does not wish this image of a plan to be misleading. The Socialist does not plan like an architect who 'deals with dead stone and timber' but like a gardener who deals with 'living and striving things', and 'lays out a garden, so that sweet and seemly things may grow, wide and beautiful vistas open and weeds and foulness disappear'.

In such a Socialist state, 'all the reasons the contemporary Trade Unionist finds against extra work and unpaid work will have disappeared'. The great industries such as mining, cotton and iron, would 'differ chiefly in the permanence of employment and the systematic evasion of the social hardship caused nowadays by new inventions and economies of method. There will exist throughout the world an organized economic survey, which will continually prepare and revise estimates of the need of iron, coal, cloth and so forth', and eliminate speculation. If men are unemployed through technological innovation, they will be sent 'not into the casual wards and colonies', but into 'the technical schools to train for some fresh use of their energies'. There was little need any longer of sheer toil, and it would be 'speedily dispensed with at a thousand points were human patience not cheaper than good machinery'. In the Socialist state, 'every man and woman will be a willing and conscious citizen saturated with the spirit of service, in which scientific research will be at a maximum of vigour and efficiency'. It followed without saying from the essential principles of socialism, that if war was necessary, 'then every citizen will, as a matter of course, take his part'.

He believed that socialism should be advanced along three lines. The '*First*, and most important, is the primary intellectual process . . . in its widest sense it includes all science, literature and invention . . . *Secondly*, comes the propaganda', which was to make socialist conceptions the 'common intellectual property of all intelligent people'. Then, '*Thirdly*, there is the actual changing of practical things in the direction of the coming Socialized State'. This was to be done bit by bit, through penetration among statesmen, trades unionists, philanthropists, etc. He said that 'Socialism is a moral and intellectual process . . . only secondarily and incidentally does it sway the world of politics. It is not a political movement . . . it can never become a political movement'. The Socialist movement was greater than the political organizations that attempted to realize its ideas. There was a natural antagonism between 'the thinker and writer who stand by the scheme and seek to develop and expound it, and the politician who attempts to realize it'. The politicians declared that socialism can only be realized through politics, but he answered that socialism 'can never be narrowed down to politics'. Scientific progress, medical organization, education, artistic production and literature were all aspects of socialism, and they lay apart from 'anything one may call—except by sheer violence to language—politics'. As socialism was an intellectual and moral thing, 'it will never tolerate in its adherents the abnegation of individual thought and invention. It demands devotion to an idea, not devotion to a leader. No addicted follower of so-and-so or of so-and-so can be a good Socialist any more than he can be a good investigator. Socialism has produced no great leaders at all. . . . Socialism under a great leader, or as a powerfully organized party would be the end of Socialism'. It will no doubt inspire great leaders and parties in the future, but it will always remain greater than all such things. Socialism was not the movement of a class, but of the best elements in every class. Under existing conditions it would draw most of its driving force from the Labour Party.

These views were advocated by Wells in 1908. His next phase as a social writer was in education. His greatest contribution in this field was the *Outline of History*, published in 1919. It was the first comprehensive history for the general reader in which weight was given to the influence of science and technology, and historical development was not attributed predominantly to the ambition of persons and nations. The history hitherto read by the working classes, and taught in elementary schools, was a popularized form of the history written by scholars in the classical and literary tradition. They found Wells' history, with its flavour of science, a new sort of history, which was not restricted to the actions of statesmen with whom they had no contact, but touched on the industry and modern life with which they were familiar. The book was read avidly, especially by skilled workmen.

At the same time Lenin, who had led the successful socialist revolution of 1917, was preparing plans of the type advocated by Wells in 1908, for the reorganization of social life on an efficient technical basis. A Commission for Elaborating a Plan for the Governmental Electrification of Russia was founded on his initiative in February 1921. Some two hundred scientists and engineers were engaged on it, and by December a first draft had been completed. This was the foundation for all the subsequent plans of development in that country. It aimed not only at the restoration and extension of electrical equipment, but also at a careful state plan for the extension of the national economy on the basis of advanced technique and electrification. Lenin wrote in 1920 that a discussion of this plan had been placed on the agenda of the Congress of the Soviets, 'so that the single economic plan for the restoration of national economy that we have been discussing may be outlined from the technical standpoint. Unless Russia is placed on a different technical level, higher than before, restoration of the national economy and communism are out of the question. Communism is the Soviet power plus the electrification of the whole country, for without electrification progress in industry is impossible'. This first plan, named the Goelro plan, was projected for a term of ten to fifteen years. It provided for a fresh capital investment of 17,000,000,000 roubles in industry, and a production of 180 to 200 per cent of the 1913 level. It involved the construction of big regional power stations, high voltage networks, and a better utilization of the power, peat, coal and shale resources of the country. The Goelro plan was completed within ten years, and was succeeded by the still more ambitious first, second and third Five-Year Plans.

Wells visited Russia in 1921, and Lenin spoke to him enthusiastically on the plan for electrification and development. He returned to England, and described Lenin as 'the dreamer in the Kremlin'. Wells had formerly placed political action as third in importance to intellectual research and propaganda in the achievement of socialism, which prevented him from fully appreciating the work of Lenin and his associates, who put it first. The success of political action in Russia in starting a planned technological economy demonstrated that more weight should be given to it. Wells and Lenin agreed that socialism could come only through combined research, propaganda, and political action, but they held contrary views of their order of importance. As the post-war years passed, Wells laid more and more emphasis on research and propaganda, while the growing power of Russia gave an increasingly impressive demonstration of the importance of political action. Through this development, Wells became more and more isolated, and consequently pessimistic, while the new generation of students of the social relations of science and technology paid increasing attention to Russia.

While this development was in progress, many other events were altering men's perspective on the social relations of science. The world war of 1914–18 had exposed the scientific and technological inadequacies of the English industrial and military system. Scientists were hastily mobilized from wherever they could be found, and the defects in the utilization of science could no longer be ignored. Before the end of the war, scientists began to organize to secure a better treatment of science and themselves. A memorandum signed by some of the ablest of the younger scientists was issued in January 1918, which stated that 'one of the main reasons why science does not occupy its proper place in national life is that scientific workers do not exercise in the political and industrial world an influence commensurate with their importance. It is also widely held that the reason why they do not exercise such influence is that they have not hitherto adopted the form of organization which, in a democratic community, is necessary to obtain it'.

This proposal was no doubt influenced by others for the organization of professional workers that had been made in 1917. It led to the formation of the National Union of Scientific Workers. A branch was immediately formed in Cambridge. It held its first public meeting in the Cavendish Laboratory under the chairmanship of Horace Darwin, and an address was delivered by J. J. Thomson. The first general meeting of the Union, which had already acquired a membership of 600, was held in London in October 1918. A. G. Church was appointed full-time secretary in 1920, and was later elected a member of Parliament. He was able to bring scientific matters to its notice, and largely through his efforts, backed by the Union, the Government's annual grant to the universities was increased, university teachers were given direct contact with the Treasury, and the conditions of employment of scientists in the Colonial Service were improved. Church was appointed to represent the Government on the East Africa Parliamentary Commission of 1924. He convened a conference on educational and cultural films that led to the foundation of the British Film Institute.

The organization had difficulty in surviving in the depression after the First World War. It severed its connection with the Trades Union Congress, and renamed itself the Association of Scientific Workers. Nevertheless, in spite of its weakness the Association played a large part in a movement in 1930 in favour of converting the Science Library at South Kensington into a National Science Library, with a virtually complete collection of world scientific publications.

The Association dissolved its own parliamentary committee after the formation of the general Parliamentary and Scientific Committee in 1933, of which it could claim to be the parent.

The senior membership of the Association fell to 695 in 1935, and then a revival began. This was due to several factors. The economic situation had improved. Many scientists had been shocked by the persecution of scientists in Germany after the Nazis had acquired power in Germany in 1933, and a marked renewal of interest in the social relations of science had begun about 1931. In addition, a new generation of scientists was coming forward, whose views had been formed in the years after the First World War. They had been much more impressed than the pre-war generation by the need for organized action for the protection of their interests. The organization of the Association was overhauled in 1935, largely under the influence of this new generation of scientists. W. A. Wooster of Cambridge became the honorary secretary, and in 1938 the Association appointed a physicist, Mrs. R. Fremlin, as organizing secretary. The membership steadily increased, and by 1939 had reached 1,319.

A foundation had been laid, on which a big expansion during the Second World War was built. The Association became a

trade union. Its membership increased to 18,000, and it had a
fine record of achievement in improving the conditions of its
members and of influencing constructive scientific policy in
England. Already in 1937, J. D. Bernal had drawn up on behalf
of the Association a memorandum on the development of
scientific research, which was transmitted to the Government.
Suggestions were also made for the improvement of the Patent
Office Library, and for rebates of income tax on research
expenditure.

While these developments were in progress, there were other
parallel movements. R. A. Gregory, the editor of *Nature*, who
many years before had been a fellow-student with H. G. Wells
under T. H. Huxley, gave his influential support to all efforts to
encourage the study of the implications of science. He extended
the recognition of science as a cultural study, especially in education. He explained that apart from its vocational value, it contained instruction which was at least as broadening and humane
as any that could be learned from the classics.

Under Gregory's editorship, *Nature* acquired an unrivalled
position in the scientific world. This was due particularly to his
awareness of the implications of science for social affairs. He
never allowed science to be treated as if it were isolated from the
rest of life.

Another movement arose as a reaction against general and
post-war pessimism, such as that of the Bishop of Ripon in 1927,
in a sermon delivered in Leeds, during the meeting of the British
Association for the Advancement of Science. His text was taken
from the Psalms, and read: 'Surely every man walketh in vain, he
heapeth up riches, and knoweth not who shall gather them. And
now, Lord, what wait I for? My hope is in thee.' He said that,
amid far and away the greatest triumphs ever won by Man's
mind over his environment, we were desperately uneasy about
the human future because Man had so little control over himself.
In spite of all his new mastery of nature Man did not seem to be
really advancing his own cause. Development of his resources did
not spell either development or happiness for himself.

These fears for mankind led him to propose a scientific
holiday. 'After all we could get on very happily if aviation, wire-
less, television, and the like advanced no further than at present,
disappointing as it would be for those whose life work has lain in
such fields. Dare I even suggest, at the risk of being lynched by

some of my hearers, that the sum of human happiness outside scientific circles would not necessarily be reduced if for ten years every physical and chemical laboratory were closed and the patient and resourceful energy displayed in them transferred to recovering the lost art of getting on together and finding the formula for making both ends meet in the scale of human life. Much of course we should lose by this unusual scientific holiday. We should possibly miss new forms of comfort and convenience, new means of making more money for the few at the cost of less work for the many, and a right curiosity on many points would go unsatisfied for a time. But human happiness would not necessarily suffer.'

The holiday would give the non-scientific 99 per cent some chance to assimilate the revolutionary knowledge acquired by the 1 per cent and the 1 per cent would have leisure to read up one another's works and all might go meanwhile in tardy quest of that wisdom which was other and greater than knowledge. The remaking of Man was more urgent than the problems of the several sciences. 'In this tragic generation we needed, like the tragic psalmist, to make once more our own the faith in a personal God.' The scientist was accustomed to abandoning hypotheses at the bidding of new facts, and the new facts of modern life had proved once more that salvation could not be found in the extension of science and the mastery of technical organization, but only in individual acts of repentance and faith.

The Bishop of Ripon was then forty-five years old. He had been educated at Harrow School, and had gained a scholarship at Balliol College, and graduated at Oxford with first class honours in classics and philosophy, and had won many prizes. His able restatement of the feudal doctrine, with its emphasis on personality, deprecation of the value of science, and proposals for halting research, nettled even the narrowest specialists, who joined in the protests of scientists with wider views, and began to give more serious consideration to the social implications of science.

Another big stimulus in the English development came from the attendance of a group of Soviet scientists at the International Congress on the History of Science, held in London in 1931. The eight Soviet delegates arrived by aeroplane just before the congress started, without having informed the organizers how much time they would require for their papers. Consequently, they found that they had been allotted ten minutes each. As each had prepared addresses from one to three hours long, there were dynamic consultations as to what could be done. An extra half-day was added to the congress, to be devoted entirely to the Soviet papers. Meanwhile, the delegation, which was led by Bukharin, decided on the heroic task of translating, printing and publishing their papers before the end of the congress, within a week, so that their papers would receive adequate expression, and their visit not be in vain.

Translators and printers were engaged, and after one of the most extraordinary weeks of intellectual activity that ever occurred in an Embassy, the proofs were just ready for the Soviet scientists' session. Philosophers and scientists rushed about in rolled-up sleeves, and the diligent translators and printer's boys running with 'copy' and proofs were working overtime through most of the nights. This enthusiasm for the history of science was unprecedented. The organizers of the congress had been hoping that they could do a little to remove the neglect of their subject. One of the members had pointed out that though science had transformed the modern world, the twelve volumes of the current Cambridge Modern History contained no more than fifty pages on it. They would have been glad if they could have brought the schools to take a little more interest in science and its history, and a little less in kings and statesmen. The members of the congress had assembled from twenty countries. A few were active scholars in the history of science, but the majority were amateurs, or elderly scientists who had taken an antiquarian interest in science after they had retired from specialist studies. They discussed the history of science in a leisurely way, as if it were of secondary importance. This heterogeneous congress was astonished by the Russians, who discussed the history of science as if it were a subject of unsurpassed importance. For them, in fact, it was such a subject, for the Soviet planning of science and technology was built on the foundation of what history had to teach on science and technology. The eight Russians had evidently organized their discourses. Each chose a different theme, but all had decided beforehand the sort of opinions, found in the papers of other delegates, that they would oppose. They criticized mechanistic views, especially when expressed by biologists whose specialist work was of the highest distinction, so that in several instances they criticized most vigorously the philosophical views of scientists whose scientific work they most admired.

The enthusiasm and aims of the Russians were highly per-plexing to the majority of the members of the congress. Rubin-stein had prepared a long address on the Soviet electrical industry, but it was ruled out of order. It dealt with the future rather than the past, and historians were unaccustomed to accepting the future as part of history. The most outstanding paper was delivered by B. Hessen on *The Social and Economic Roots of Newton's 'Principia'*. Hessen gave the first concrete example of how science should be interpreted as a product of the life and tendencies of society. Predecessors who had given consideration to the social significance of science were literary historians who were not at home with science, and were unable to recognize with confidence which points in scientific theories were significant for history, because they were uncertain which scientific ideas were of crucial importance. They were apt to accept too humbly the opinions of scientific specialists who had given no attention at all to historical matters, and were acquainted only with the history of the internal development of their own science. Hessen's demonstration of the depth and range of Newton's dependence on the ideas promulgated by the epoch in which he appeared, made a profound impression on some of the younger members of the congress. It transformed the study of the history of science, and out-moded the former conceptions of the subject, which treated it as governed only by the laws of its internal logical development. Henceforth, no satisfactory history of science could be written without giving adequate attention to the dependence of science on social factors. Hessen's evident technical compe-tence in the handling of scientific ideas subsequently gained for his work the attention of scientists who hitherto had despised historical studies, because they were so often written by men without first-hand scientific knowledge.

None of the amateur and professional students of the history of science could think of any comment for opening a discussion on the Russians' enthusiastic and exciting papers. After a pause, a twenty-year-old youth named David Guest drew attention to the significance of their views, stressing especially the historical element in all their philosophical and scientific concepts, and contrasting this with the non-historical concepts employed by Pearson and Russell in their philosophy of science. No other speaker could think of anything more to say. Guest subsequently graduated with first class honours in philosophy at Cambridge

University, and was killed in Spain in 1938, fighting with the
International Brigade in defence of the Republican Government.

Since Hessen's essay, a number of books in which science was
discussed and expounded in relation to its social background
were published, some with great success. The movement, of
which Hessen's essay was the most stimulating expression,
transformed the history of science from a minor into a major
subject. It showed that a knowledge of the history of science was
not only of entertaining antiquarian interest, but was essential for
the solution of contemporary social problems due to the unor-
ganized growth of a technological society.

This recognition of the social significance of the history of
science strengthened the rising interest in the social relations of
science. An event that occurred two months later in 1931 added
still further to the rising interest. An economic crisis arose,
following the crisis in America in 1929. It was signalized by an
enormous increase in unemployment, and the formation of a
Government which described itself as National.

This break raised new questions of the value of the modern
advances in science and technology. A. Ewing, in his presidential
address to the British Association in 1932, inquired whether the
Association still gave the community reason to support it. In his
youth, some of the spokesmen of science, though not the greatest,
had displayed a cocksureness in notable contrast with the spirit
of contemporary spokesmen. Admiration was now tempered by
criticism, and complacency had given way to doubt, and doubt
was passing into alarm. There was a sense of perplexity and
frustration, as if man had taken the wrong turning. It was impossible to go back, but how should he proceed?'An old exponent
of applied mechanics may be forgiven if he expresses something
of the disillusion with which, now standing aside, he watches the
sweeping pageant of discovery and invention in which he used to
take unbounded delight. It is impossible not to ask:Whither does
this tremendous procession tend? What, after all, is its goal?
What its probable influence upon the future of the human
race?'

The engineer had given man much wealth and comfort, but
his achievements had also produced present burdens, and potential tragedy. 'Man was ethically unprepared for such a bounty.
In the slow evolution of morals he is still unfit for the tremendous
responsibility it entails. The command of Nature has been put

into his hands before he knows how to command himself.'

The development of mechanical production was in great measure depriving man of 'one inestimable blessing, the necessity of toil'. It was destroying the joy in craftsmanship, and when it filled every country with a glut of competitive commodities, every country attempted to secure its home market by tariff walls. Such were the results of the tyranny of the machine.

'Where shall we look for a remedy?' he asked, and said: 'I cannot tell.'

Another distinguished engineer, Miles Walker, one of Cockcroft's teachers, speaking at the same meeting in 1932, had a different outlook. He said that modern technology, if efficiently employed, would make mankind ten times as wealthy as it is today. The majority of inhabitants of Europe and America were very poorly supplied with commodities, and scarcely anything at all had been done for the teeming millions of India and China.

The great difference between what was possible and what had been achieved was due to the incompetence of rulers. They are very seldom men of real ability, and are talkers rather than doers. They have not undergone any test to show whether they can arrive at a logical conclusion from a given set of premises. The muddle of the world contrasted strongly with the efficiency of a management of a great engineering works. He believed that if engineers, among whom he included all scientific men, took a greater part in world management, they would make a greater success of it. 'In this world crisis there is a call to the engineer to manage the world.'

Walker attributed the colossal unemployment, especially in the United States, where food, raw material and capital were abundant, to the desire for excessive and illegitimate profits. Things were usually sold at three or four times the cost of their production. If prices were based exactly and legitimately on the costs of production, the people who made goods would earn sufficient to be able to buy them. They would consequently make more and buy more, and wealth would increase.

He suggested that the British Government should found a self-supporting colony to be run as an experiment by engineers, scientists and economists, to discover how far it is possible for a community, of, say, one hundred thousand persons, to free itself from the restraints and social errors of modern civilization, by the application of the best methods of manufacture and distribution.

Walker desired the British Association to support the application of engineering and scientific methods to social questions, but his proposals were baldly rejected, as involving science and scientists in political affairs.

The presidential address in the following year was delivered by F. G. Hopkins, the co-discoverer of vitamins, who opposed the pessimism of Ewing, and supported renewed proposals that the Association should attend to the social implications of science. Hopkins said it seemed to him that apart from war, 'science and invention have done little to increase opportunities for the display of the more serious of man's irrational impulses. The worst they do perhaps is to give to clever and predatory souls that keep within the law, the whole world for their depredations, instead of a parish or a country as of yore'. It was not within his capacity to say anything of value on the cure of the paradox of poverty amongst plenty, but he confessed that he saw 'more present danger in the case of "Money versus Man" than danger, present or future, in that of the "Machine versus Man" '. He had recently been re-reading Bacon's *New Atlantis*, and he thought that while the organization of Solomon's house had been drafted when its author was too much in the mood of a Lord Chancellor, the conception that the best intellects should be organized for the service of the community contained a valuable suggestion.

The replacement of human labour by machinery was creating the prospect of extended leisure. He was optimistic concerning the probable effects of its increase. He believed that the replacement would impose a new structure on society, though few men of affairs realized that. This new structure could be obtained without revolutionary change if there was 'real planning for the future'. If civilization escaped its other perils, he would have little fear of the final reign of the machine. 'We should not altogether forget the difference in use which can be made of real and ample leisure compared with that possible for very brief leisure associated with fatigue; or the difference between compulsory toil and spontaneous work.' Recent experience had shown that the population of Great Britain, except for a minority, was educable. 'Most of us have had a tendency in the past to fear the gift of leisure to the majority. To believe that it may be a great social benefit requires some mental readjustment.'

Largely under Hopkins's influence, the Association now began to attend to the social implications of science. It would not arrange special discussions on the problem, but it asked speakers to draw attention to the social implications of their special subjects. The economist Josiah Stamp was asked to discuss the question, and he gave a lecture at the same meeting entitled: 'Must Science Ruin Economic Progress?' He said that the innovations of the previous hundred years had been assisted by four agencies: the great elasticity of the demand for old commodities at reduced prices; the rapid introduction of new things, which absorbed labour released in the manufacture of old things by improved processes; the rise in population created by the increase in produce; and industrially backward countries overseas, which could absorb manufactured commodities. The first agency had become less elastic, owing to the rise in the standard of living. A man who has good meals does not buy twice as many if their price is reduced fifty per cent.

The third agency was ineffective, as the rise in the standard of living was being accompanied by a tendency of the population to fall. The fourth agency was ineffective because hitherto backward countries were now becoming producers.

The second agency was working more and more in the direction of introducing things which demanded increased leisure for their proper absorption and use.

Stamp expressed the opinion that a theoretical technique can be worked out for the most profitable rate of absorption of scientific invention, but he did not believe that it could be operated without hopelessly impairing the consumer's individual choice of his demands, and it would require in the operators an exalted view of the perfectibility of social organization and political wisdom. 'In the field of international relations and foreign trade, which alone can give full effect to scientific discovery, it demands qualities far beyond anything yet attainable.'

He believed that economic life in this generation must pay a heavy price for the ultimate gains of science, unless there were large infusions of social direction and internationalism. This did not mean government by scientific technique, technocracy, or any other *transferred* technique, as the aggregate of human wills was not regulated by the principles that were so potent in mathematics, chemistry, physics or even biology. He thought that scientific workers might contribute much by entering the social sciences, and giving a greater proportion of the best minds to this field and planning research in it.

Hopkins was also president of the Royal Society during this period. In his last anniversary address, in 1935, he discussed the increasing interest in the social relations of science, and the social responsibilities of scientists. He said that the contribution of science to higher standards of intellectual honesty was often overlooked, and mentioned how much the researches of Darwin and the teaching of Huxley had contributed to this in the last century. Science had also, more than any other influence, established the belief in progress, and substituted a dynamic for a static view of the world. This undermined the depressing belief that man and the social fabric he had made for himself, while so imperfect, were yet incapable of betterment, and was the one excuse for that particular form 'of professed otherworldliness which from time to time has been an essential part of narrow religious ideals, but which was surely evil in its almost contemptuous indifference to social wrongs and to the urgent problems of this world'.

But the scientist, as scientist, has little opportunity for effective action, and he commonly concludes that he will be most useful to society by continuing his chosen work in its proper environment. It was impossible not to sympathize with this view, as the special endowments needed by the scientist were not those of the politician or missionary. Nevertheless, some method of closing the gap between the outlooks of the publicist and scientist is needed. It was a just claim that in a civilization so largely based on science, the scientist should have more influence on policy than he has hitherto been allowed. He thought that not long ago the gap was wide, but it was lessening now.

The immediate importance of the social relations of science had now been recognized by the highest scientific authorities. The British Association organized a discussion under the chairmanship of Walter Elliot, then Minister of Agriculture, on food and agriculture, and John Boyd Orr published the results of his investigations of the nation's food. He showed that half of the British people suffered some degree of undernourishment. His researches inspired the distribution of free milk to school children by the Government, and reports on nutrition by the League of Nations.

The British Association recognized the new tendencies by electing Stamp as president in 1936. He spoke on 'The Impact of Science upon Society', and elaborated the four points he had made in his earlier address on the question as to whether science must ruin economic progress. The fluidity of invention and the rigidity of society were increasing simultaneously. He thought that the increasing difficulties of innovation might be reduced by psychological research, which would reveal the laws that govern the change of fashion in human demands. He said that he had observed in his business experience that mind-training gained in one speciality was not usually of particular value when applied to general and social problems. He suggested that money and effort should be devoted to biological and psychological research, and estimated that at present the expenditure of the natural sciences is about ten times that on the social sciences.

Stamp's presidential address was followed by some vigorous discussions. Hogben considered that Stamp had shown himself to be an intransigent individualist. Stamp was willing to agree to some slowing down of the rate of innovation, and appealed for the birth control of scientific knowledge rather than sacrifice his individualism. Hogben thought that the younger men of science would prefer to scrap an outworn individualism and offer the alternative of making the business man a ward in chancery.

Daniel Hall said that if scientists did not attend to the degradation of their inventions to use in propaganda and war and other anti-social activities, they would soon discover that they were slaves, and when they had become slaves the motive and the fascination of scientific work would disappear. He suggested that an institute for the investigation of the influence of science on society should be founded.

E. G. Conklin, the president of the American Association for the Advancement of Science, and a delegation of American scientists attended the British Association's meeting of 1936. The British and the Americans decided to explore the possibilities of collaboration.

While these developments were in progress, Ritchie Calder suggested the formation of a World Association for the Advancement of Science, with collaboration between the British and American associations as an embryonic nucleus. Etienne Gilson at the Harvard Tercentenary in 1936 had advocated the international organization of scholars, and in 1937 the International Council of Scientific Unions received a proposal from the Royal Academy of Amsterdam that it should appoint a committee to study what co-ordination can be achieved in the opinions which

15

have been put forward regarding the social responsibilities of science and scientists towards the dangers at present menacing civilization. There were lively differences of opinion as to whether such work lay within the objects of the Council, and the proposal was formally withdrawn, in favour of one for a committee limited strictly to scientific activity, which would report on the most important results and the directions of progress in the physical, chemical and biological sciences, with reference to their interconnections and the development of the scientific picture of the world in general and the social significance of the applications of science.

The committee was formed with J. M. Burgers as secretary, and made its first report in 1938. It aimed at the preparation of a list of outstanding developments and new applications of science, the organization of scientific research, summaries of interpretative work on the world picture given by science, and of thought on the social relations of science, with bibliographies on all these subjects.

The American Association passed resolutions proposing that it should collaborate with the British Association, and all other societies of the same sort throughout the world, to co-operate not only in advancing science, but also in promoting peace among nations and intellectual freedom in order that science may continue to advance and spread more abundantly its benefits to all mankind.

The American Association reaffirmed a resolution by R. A. Millikan and H. N. Russell, that the suppression of independent thought and its free expression is a major crime against civilization. Existing liberties had been won through ages of struggle at enormous cost, and there could be no hope of progress in science, justice or peace, or even of material well-being, if they were seriously impaired or lost. It was their duty to denounce all such actions as intolerable forms of tyranny, and there could be no compromise on this issue, because learning could not endure 'half slave and half free'. 'By our life and training as scientists and by our heritage as Americans we must stand for freedom.'

The Royal Society of London and the United States National Academy of Sciences established exchange lectures for the description of the progress of science, and of new ideas that might bear fruit and give promise of wide expansion in the future. It was hoped that these exchanges would strengthen international contact, and so promote peace. With similar aims, the Royal

Society exchanged lecturers with the Kaiser Wilhelm Gesell-schaft. Under these auspices, Otto Hahn visited London in 1939.

The British Trades Union Congress invited eminent scientists to advise them on industrial problems affected by science. A strong committee was formed.

The British Association in the meanwhile discussed how it might assist the study of the social relations of science more effectively. It studied reports on this subject at its meeting in 1938, which was attended by the secretary of the American Association and one hundred scientists from North America, and by several leading American scientific journalists.

It became evident that if the British Association did not form an organization for the study of the social relations of science, an independent organization for this purpose would be formed. The Association decided to create a new Division for the Social and International Relations of Science. This was done at the Cam-bridge meeting in 1938. No activity of the Association in the present century had inspired so much enthusiasm among diverse personalities. It was hoped that the new division would provide authoritative evidence for the possibility of constructive evidence.

Gregory, who had contributed so much to this development, was elected chairman of the new division, and he visited America in 1938-39 to encourage the formation of a similar division there. The American Association had already organized extensive symposia on Science and Society. It was hoped that correspond-ing divisions would be established in France, Scandinavia and the Netherlands. The British Division began activities in 1939 with meetings on the nutritional and social aspects of improved milk diet, and the impacts of science on society. In June of that year, H. Levy chose for the subject of his Pedler Memorial Lecture 'The Social Relations of Science: A Study of Method'.

The Division encouraged the Political and Economic Planning Society, which, for the first time in English history, had set a full-time research worker to investigate how British science was organized and financed. During the Second World War the Division held outstanding meetings, while other activities of the Association had virtually ceased. The most outstanding was on *Science and World Order*, in 1941. The chairmen of its six sessions were Gregory, J. G. Winant, Maisky, Benes, Wellington Koo, and H. G. Wells. It was a unique demonstration of international unity and collaboration between scientists and statesmen.

82

Science and the Press

SCIENTIFIC JOURNALISTS had done much to stimulate the new interest in the social relations of science. They were founding a new profession, though its principles and status were not yet well-defined.

Before they appeared, the articles on science in the press were written almost entirely by scientists who received their main income from other sources. The majority of these articles fell into the class of entertainment, of which Ray Lankester's articles on 'Science from an Easy Chair' were a famous example.

Another type of article, the systematic production of which started in the 1920s, consisted of anonymous reports of the progress of science, expressed in the perspective of its social implications. In these articles the intrinsic interest and significance of science was placed before the attractions of personal opinion. The new scientific journalists saw that science was a distinguishing feature of modern civilization, and yet its principles and progress were not systematically expounded and followed in the press. This was an extraordinary situation. In England, for instance, the population had risen from ten million in 1800 to forty million in 1900. This huge increase in population was due to the growth of technology and science. Yet most of the population, and especially that section who had a literary and classical education, were ignorant of this factor which had been essential in making it possible for them to exist. It was evident that modern civilization would not survive if this situation continued.

In 1939 the British Parliament contained no working scientist, and there was no adequate machinery for bringing scientific matters to its notice. Public opinion was not dissatisfied, because it did not appreciate science better than the statesmen. It was clear that statesmen would not appreciate science and scientific methods more until the public expected that they should.

Some of those who perceived the situation believed that the better public knowledge of science should come through the improvement of science teaching in schools. This was necessary, but not sufficient. The majority of English children then left school at the age of fourteen, so they could not learn much science. The best mass training for science was in these circumstances given by experience in industrial work, rather than the elementary school. Many persons acquired a rough grasp of scientific ideas through their work as mechanics, electricians and agriculturists. Their grasp could be clarified and extended through systematic explicatory articles in the press, and this would assist its possessors to judge whether the affairs of state were being managed with scientific acumen. In particular, it would enable them to make a not entirely unfounded judgment of a statesman's knowledge of science and technology. It does not need deep knowledge to tell whether proposals advanced under the label of science are genuinely scientific. Joule rightly said that 'the trite proverb that "a little knowledge is a dangerous thing", absurd in other cases, is peculiarly so in this. This doctrine of fools would necessarily discountenance any education whatsoever because in passing from ignorance to the highest state of intellectual acquirement a man must be at one time induced with the dreaded little knowledge. The truth is that a little knowledge is a little good and much knowledge is a great good, while ignorance is an unmitigated evil allying us with the beasts that perish'.

Maynard Keynes explained that he did not expect that his popular expositions of economics would make its principles clear to the non-specialist public. But he thought that they would help people to see what these principles looked like, and be able to tell whether the proposals of statesmen seemed consonant with them.

In an issue of *Nature* in October 1939, it was suggested that the British Government's new Ministry of Information might include a department for scientific information. The Editor said that 'this view may seem strange, even amusing to senior administrators of the old type, trained perhaps thirty years ago in a school of ancient philosophy. It will not seem so strange to their younger colleagues and not at all strange to the large number of skilled working people who are perhaps the most important class in our community. To many of the latter, science is a thing of high repute, and information and advice given in technical and scientific form (provided that is not too dull) carries special conviction. The nation has particular need of their help . . . and it will receive it the more freely if . . . they can be told how and why'.

The English governing classes, as typified by the Cabinet, were non-scientific, whereas, as the Editor of *Nature* explained, the most important part of the population, the skilled artisans, had some grasp of science and technology. This split with regard to science was but one of the social fissures which would destroy the social structure if they were not removed.

The new science writers included in their aims the encouragement of the scientific interests of the skilled masses, to assist them to secure from governments a more scientific treatment of affairs. They conceived scientific journalism as an essential binder in the structure of modern civilization. Thus, as a proper craft, scientific journalism was social. It demanded the steady exposition of the simpler and more important facts, as they were discovered, and avoided the expression of opinions. Yet it gave still more expression to the exposition of the atmosphere of science than of the facts, for the scientific attitude is more important than any particular facts. It described laboratories and interviewed discoverers, so that the public might acquire some idea of the atmosphere and processes of creative scientific discovery, rather than hear the armchair dreams of scientists after dinner or in retirement.

This work, which required the rapid adjustment of the mind to many different subjects, demanded the whole time and intellectual energy of the writer. The scientific journalist of the new type tried by continuous impersonal accounts to create the scientific attitude required to solve contemporary social problems. The work of even the most gifted sporadic writers, who tend to appeal mainly to entertainment, did not contribute very much to this end.

The new scientific journalists found their work difficult, especially in England. In 1939 not one British newspaper employed a writer to give the whole of his time to science.

The low rate of payment for impersonal work that avoided stunts was one of the causes of the difficulty of systematically reporting science. If the scientific journalist was paid by the article, he did well if he received five guineas per thousand words, which was the length of the ordinary newspaper column. It is easy to calculate how much could be earned in a year by a weekly article at this rate. A wide range of subjects would be necessary for variety, and as the newspapers' readers contained experts in every subject, the articles must be reasonably accurate, or they would draw protests. The political journalist had the advantage of dealing with matters of opinion. He could write many articles without palpable errors of fact. In contrast, the facts of science were far more definite, and when the scientific journalist made a mistake he was easily proved wrong. This inhibited his initiative, and prevented him from writing many articles which he would have undertaken if they had been less risky.

The difficulty of writing on fifty different subjects in a year, with a standard of accuracy that does not excite too much annoyance among specialists, is evident. Yet the rate of payment for scientific articles was not higher than for political articles, which may be written with so much more facility. The difficulty of variety increased with time. Many writers could produce a series of interesting articles for a few weeks, but it required a special ability to maintain the standard indefinitely, after stored knowledge had been exhausted.

The sum earned by the scientific journalist paid on space was not net but gross. The information he used for his articles may have been suggested or collected during travel. It was not possible to obtain the freshness and information needed in the new scientific journalism without it. So the gross sum might easily be reduced by one-third on account of expenses.

The sums received by eminent scientists who wrote special articles, or features, were often much smaller than was commonly believed. Sometimes they would write articles of two columns in a famous newspaper for a fee of five guineas. The new scientific journalists regarded the scientists who wrote such articles as 'blacklegs'. If an editor could obtain an article from the leading authority in the world for five guineas, he was tempted to prefer it to one from a regular scientific journalist. It was very desirable that the best scientists in the country should write for the press if they had an aptitude for it, but this should not have been allowed to obstruct the development of science reporting. Many scientists had the specialist's tendency to write down to the public. This disqualified contributions for reputable papers, as it denoted a lack of respect for their readers. Scientists were sometimes heard excusing their newspaper articles by saying that they had dashed them off in a railway carriage.

The commercial press sought big circulation, which was obtained, among other methods, by supplying exciting news that appeals to the emotions rather than the intellect. Evelyn Waugh defined this sort of news when he wrote: 'News is what a chap who doesn't care much about anything wants to read.' It is not a very hopeful medium for communicating the progress of science to the wide public.

But perhaps the other sort of newspaper was in some ways even worse. It had a small circulation. The chief commercial newspapers had a daily circulation of 2,000,000, whereas the others had one of 50,000 to 200,000. They had smaller financial resources. But there was a more serious difficulty. Their editorial staffs consisted mainly of first-class honours graduates in classics or history from the older universities. The majority of this class, though there were notable exceptions, were more stupid about science than the men who drove their cars. The motor-driver has some knowledge of the elements of mechanics and electricity, and it is possible through this to assist him to see what the state must do to make the best use of science. But the first-class classical or historical scholar nearly always believed he *knew* how to manage a scientific civilization before he had begun to *learn* about science and its possibilities. He frequently pushed the consideration of science away from him, with a mock humility, saying that he did not understand such things. The Cabinet minister or editor, who turned his mind away from science was more inimical to progress in a scientific civilization than a population of quarter-educated mechanics who had at least some inkling of the most potent instrument in their civilization. Men with a literary training have much difficulty in appreciating that experiment is more important than theory.

The situation of the new scientific journalist was better in America than in England. The American people had a better general knowledge of science, owing to the traditional use of labour-saving contrivances, and the larger amount of science taught in schools. This knowledge, though often superficial, was widespread, and had created a demand for science news. A considerable service grew up in America since the 1920s to provide it. Several of the most influential newspapers and news agencies already had men who devoted the whole of their time to the reporting of science. These scientific journalists of the new type formed a society named the National Association of Science Writers of America. Its members, defined as those who were 'employed by individual newspaper, newspaper syndicates or press associations and devote more than half their time in this employment in reporting or preparing articles on science in its various aspects'. An Association of British Science Writers was formed in 1947.

Yet even in America, few scientific journalists devoted the whole of their time to science. Nor were the wealthy American newspapers much more generous than the British in their payments.

When it was realized how much modern social and international strife was due to the inability of society to utilize science properly, scientific journalists would become equal in status and resources with political journalists. Their comparative resources and status in 1939 were a measure of the degree of fundamental disorder in contemporary society.

Nevertheless, the history of the new interest in the social relations of science showed that the new scientific journalists accomplished something, in spite of their handicaps. This was owing to the size of the new social forces set in movement through modern science, which they were among the first to express.

They would accomplish much more, if they were given better support. They would gain this mainly through the demands of readers for more science. Progress would arise from initiative in both editors and readers, and reciprocal action between them.

There were two ways of organizing a better service of science news. Those newspaper proprietors who foresaw the possibility and importance of a growing interest in science should appoint full-time science editors and reporters. Other wealthy bodies interested in the dissemination of scientific information should create and encourage organizations such as the American Science News Service. These were particularly useful in big countries such as America, where newspapers had a mainly local sale, and identical copy might be duplicated in the papers in many different states.

Newspapers in a small country such as England did not find such a service so attractive, as many of them had national circulations, and were on sale everywhere. They objected to having articles identical with those of their competitors. But their competitiveness might be an additional stimulus to the appointment of their own full-time science reporters collecting original information.

A science information service would be valuable for the supply of science news to local newspapers.

When a corps of science news writers of high status had been formed, this would attract talented recruits, who in turn would make the reporting of the progress and implications of science still more effective.

15*

83

The Social Responsibilities of Scientists

IN 1939 the Royal Society of London had 7,000 names on its register of British scientists. The British Ministry of Labour had 100,000 names on its register of technicians and engineers. The population of Great Britain was 45,000,000. These figures gave an impression of the small size of the number of scientists compared with the rest of the population, even in an advanced industrial country.

It was evident that the influence scientists could exert in the community through weight of numbers was negligible. The influence of their small number was not multiplied through wealth, as they were rarely paid more than £2,000 per annum. Nevertheless, though their numbers and wealth were small, they were exceedingly important, as they provided the new knowledge which was the seed of progress in a productive system based on science and technology. They alone were in contact with the future as it was unfolded. What should they do if they observed that the community was not making the best use of their essential knowledge, and was moving in directions which would pervert the use of old science, made new science barren, and prevented further discovery?

Loyalty to science, to self-interest, and to the welfare of the community precluded acquiescence in such a drift. Some scientists, when they became aware of such tendencies in modern society, felt tempted to resign from scientific work and enter politics. A few who did this found that they were more effective in their new work, and were thereby justified, but in general good scientists did not become good politicians. Those scientists who became constructive political leaders rarely started their political life voluntarily. They usually found themselves forced into politics against their desire, because they found that political action was necessary to prevent the wastage of their research. The political excursions of eminent experts on nutrition were an example.

If the competent scientist attempted to remedy the obvious abuses that confronted him in the course of his work, he found himself taking political action soon enough, and his political conduct was more reliable because it was based on exact knowledge acquired during his expert work. Few would be qualified to contradict him in his own field.

Many scientists aware of their social duty experienced a desire to drop the tantalizing ardours of hampered research, and devote the whole of their energy to the transformation of a social order that hindered science so much. They felt, with justification, that concentration on research was impossible in the shadow of social catastrophe. But this feeling was to be resisted. Young scientists who abandoned science for politics often proved to be unstable in their views, and after a few years of bohemian agitation became conspicuously disillusioned.

Scientists as a class should be doubly anxious to retain within their ranks those of their members who possessed social insight. If all scientists with political understanding resigned from science, the remainder would be left without any social guidance.

The scientist who abandoned professional work was liable to perform two disservices. He failed to remain at the frontier of knowledge, and lost the capacity to appeal to the technical judgment of his colleagues, and he lost his authority as a scientist with the non-professional public. His colleagues no longer paid so much attention to his political suggestions because they came from an outsider, and the public ignored them because he did not possess conventional scientific authority.

The scientist is confronted with the difficult task of acquiring professional competence and practising political activity. Clerk Maxwell laid down in his inaugural lecture in 1871 as the first Cavendish professor of experimental physics at Cambridge, that the creation of a sound spirit of criticism should be one of the first duties of the new professor and his colleagues. 'We are daily receiving fresh proofs that the popularization of scientific doctrines is producing as great an alteration in the mental state of society as the material applications of science are effecting in its outward life.' He noted that the inculcation of 'sound dynamical ideas has already effected a great change in the language and thoughts even of those who make no pretensions to science', and he feared that the public might be converted to the most absurd opinions if 'expressed in language, the sound of which recalls some well-known scientific phrase'.

As Clerk Maxwell foresaw, one of the tasks of the scientist was to see that the non-scientific public was not misled in the name of science. The scientist who wished to be of social use could perform an important service by keeping his scientific knowledge up to date and authoritative, so that he could instantly expose pseudo-scientific doctrines that recall the phrases which describe established scientific truths.

Assuming that a scientist is competent in his own work, how should he engage as such in social affairs? he might do so in several ways. He should join a professional union for the protection of his interests and working conditions. The medical profession had created powerful organizations of this sort, which especially in the earlier part of their history performed valuable social services, such as propaganda for the establishment by law of qualifications for practice. In England, the Association of Scientific Workers had made some progress, and would probably make more. Scientists have difficulty in organizing because their interests and working conditions are exceptionally varied. For example, the problems and conditions that affect physicists, bacteriologists and plant geneticists are often widely different.

In 1939, the relative comfort of scientists in academic work was another factor that inhibited organization. In Britain, a scientist who had just qualified would receive a salary of about £200 per annum, if he secured an academic appointment. His hours of work were flexible, he usually had superiors of definite ability, and he could find some congenial colleagues. His conditions were frequently better than the corresponding ones in industrial research, where he might easily have started at a lower salary, have to keep regular hours from 9 a.m. to 5.30 p.m., and work under a director who might have owed his position to pliability, favouritism, or even nepotism. Academic appointments were, on the whole, made more objectively than business appointments.

Scientists who transferred from academic to industrial work, or from the research to the selling side of a business, were often struck by the lower tone. The relatively attractive conditions of research work disposed many scientists towards conservatism and indifference. They were apt to ignore external affairs because discovery could not be made without intense concentration. These circumstances exposed the scientist to dangerous influences. His work trained him in orderly thought and action, and his isolation, comparative comfort, and concentration tended to restrict his experience of affairs. He was apt to be attracted by social proposals that appealed to his habits of orderliness and at the same time promised to preserve his superior status and comfort. The immediate economic and class interests of scientists tended to make them fall in with authority. But this was not true of their ultimate interests.

The scientist uses foresight as part of his technique. He is in the habit of imagining consequences in the process of planning experiments. It is possible to appeal to him through this habit, and to consider the prospects of his work and himself. He might be comparatively satisfied at present, but what will happen in the future? Are international affairs drifting into war? Will war be good for science, and if he is already engaged in war, are his services being employed to the best advantage, either for military or civil research? Do the authorities know how to make the best use of science?

Apart from the appeal to the scientist to take social action on behalf of science and himself, there is the appeal to him as an ordinary good citizen. Some scientists will feel moved to support constructive social policies from general humanitarian motives. They will call for the organization of a better life because they are disgusted by unnecessary suffering and inefficiency.

But however scientists took part in social affairs, influence would not flow from their numbers and wealth. They might try to secure more power through their special knowledge. If the tens of thousands of scientists in England went on strike, the life of the country would ultimately be strangled; but the effects would be slow. That large part of science, the application of which had already been reduced to routine, would remain in use. Months would pass before the effects became serious, and in that time the majority of scientists would have returned to work under threats. As Lea had shown in his history of the Inquisition, the resistance of intellectual workers to persecution had not been notably high.

For these reasons, scientists could not achieve much by independent action. Their most effective policy would be to study the general movement of social affairs, and attach themselves to the most constructive major social forces. They could discover these only from political study and experience, so they would have to take part in social affairs, in order to discover whom they should support.

They should advocate the dissemination of a better knowledge of science throughout the population, so that politicians must acquire a grounding of scientific knowledge before they can satisfy the electorate. They should not propose government by scientists. As soon as a scientist became a politician, under the contemporary conditions, he ceased to be a working scientist, and his methods became indistinguishable from those of any other politician. When a politician was pursuing political aims, he would not give much attention to science unless he perceived that this was demanded by a powerful section of the population.

The social responsibilities of scientists seemed, then, to include the following:

1. The exposure of errors in science, such as racialist theories, and the exposure of scientific errors in the ideas of destructive social movements.

2. The organization of such intellectual criticism by co-operative effort, so that sober fact should not be borne down by blatancy and persistence.

3. Solid demonstrations of the relations between science and social affairs, so that scientists may be convinced of the need for their taking part collectively in social affairs, for the sake of science.

4. Descriptions of what social improvements are desirable for the advancement of science, and explanations of how science is thwarted in bad social systems, and how this thwarting is liable to produce still worse social systems. This would include accounts of how science had declined in Fascist countries.

5. The persuasion of scientists who keep their scientific and political ideas in separate compartments to support constructive movements on the ordinary political grounds of economic interest and social justice.

6. They should collectively establish contact with Cabinets and centres of governments, so that no major political decision could be taken in ignorance of relevant scientific knowledge. They should destroy the conception of scientists as the servants of politicians, but they should not become politicians. They should see only that politicians and the electorate are permeated by science, so that action contrary to the indications of scientific knowledge would become difficult or impossible.

7. In peace, to co-operate with all constructive social and intellectual movements, expand science, and remove the causes of war.

8. In war, to consider which side was the less inimical to science, and then to do what was possible to see that it was not defeated. Scientists, like others, cannot be above the battle, either in politics or war.

References used in the First Edition

SECTIONS 1–11

Man Makes Himself: V. Gordon Childe, 1936
Science in Antiquity: Benjamin Farrington, 1936
Origins and Development of Applied Chemistry: J. R. Partington, 1935
'The Oriental Background of Modern Science': V. Gordon Childe, *The Modern Quarterly*, 2, Vol. 1, 1938
'Vesalius on the Ruin of Ancient Medicine': Benjamin Farrington, *The Modern Quarterly*, 1, Vol. 1, 1938
Vorgriechische Mathematik: Otto Neugebauer, 1934
A History of Mechanical Inventions: A. P. Usher, 1929
Mathematics for the Million: Lancelot Hogben, 1936
Science for the Citizen: Lancelot Hogben, 1938
The Golden Bough, Part I, 'The Magic Art': J. G. Frazer, 2 vols., 1907
Makers of Chemistry: E. J. Holmyard, 1931

SECTIONS 12–30

Science in Antiquity: Benjamin Farrington, 1936
The Civilization of Greece and Rome: Benjamin Farrington, 1938
Science and Politics in the Ancient World: Benjamin Farrington, 1939
Introduction to the History of Science: G. Sarton, Vol. I, 1927
A Short History of Biology: Charles Singer, 1931
A Short History of Science: F. Sherwood Taylor, 1939
A Short Account of the History of Mathematics: W. W. Rouse Ball, 1915
The Technical Arts and Sciences of the Ancients: A. Neuburger, 1930
Legal Status of Labour in the New Testament: F. S. Granger, 1933
On Architecture: P. Vitruvius, translated by F. Granger, 2 vols., 1931–4
A History of Mechanical Inventions: A. P. Usher, 1929
Slavery in the Roman Empire: R. H. Barrow, 1928
Physical Science in the Time of Nero: being a translation of the Quaestiones Naturales of Seneca, by John Clarke, with notes by A. Geikie, 1910
The Pneumatics of Hero of Alexandria: edited by B. Woodcraft, 1851
From Magic to Science: Charles Singer, 1928
'L'Attelage: Le Cheval de Selle à travers les âges': Lefebvre de Noëttes. Contribution à *l'Histoire de l'Esclavage*, 2 vols., 1931

A History of Magic and Experimental Science during the first thirteen centuries of our era: Lynn Thorndike, Vol. I, 1923
A History of Slavery and Serfdom: J. K. Ingram, 1895

SECTIONS 31–35

The Legacy of Islam: edited by Thomas Arnold and Alfred Guillaume, 1931
A History of Europe: H. Pirenne, 1939
Makers of Chemistry: E. J. Holmyard, 1931
The Algebra of Muhammed Ben Musa (Al-Khwarizmi): edited and translated by F. Rosen, 1831
The Cambridge Medieval History, Vol. II, Chaps. XI–XII: A.A. Bevan, C. H. Becker
Introduction to the History of Science: G. Sarton, Vol. II, 1931

SECTIONS 36–46

A History of Magic and Experimental Science: Lynn Thorndike, Vol. II–IV, 1924–34
The Place of Magic in the Intellectual History of Europe: Lynn Thorndike, 1905
Mont-Saint-Michel and Chartres: Henry Adams, 1919
Anselm: *Encyclopaedia Britannica*, 14th edition
Facsimile of the Sketch-book of Wilars de Honecourt with commentaries & cont: translated and edited by R. W. Willis, 1859
Byzantine Civilization: Steven Runciman, 1933
The Summa Theologica of St. Thomas Aquinas: literally translated by Fathers of the English Dominican Province, 22 vols.
Saint Thomas Aquinas as a Philosopher: A. E. Taylor, 1924
Saint Thomas Aquinas: Etienne Gilson, 1935
The Philosophy of St. Thomas Aquinas: E. Gilson, 1929
Medieval People: Eileen Power
Studies in the History of Medieval Science: C. H. Haskins, 1924
The Legacy of the Middle Ages: edited by C. G. Crump and E. F. Jacob (including C. R. S. Harris on 'Medieval Philosophy'), 1926
Inquisition and Liberty: G. G. Coulton, 1938
The Renaissance of the Twelfth Century: C. H. Haskins, 1927
Rashdall's Medieval Universities: edited by F. M. Powicke and A. B. Emden, 1936
The Universities of Europe in the Middle Ages: H. H. Rashdall, 1895
A History of Europe: H. Pirenne
Medieval Contributions to Modern Civilization: ed. F. J. C. Hearnshaw: 'Science': Charles Singer, 1921
A History of the Inquisition of the Middle Ages: H. C. Lea, 1887

454   *References used in the First Edition*

The Opus Majus of Roger Bacon: A translation by Robert Belle Burke, 1928
Studies in the History and Method of Science: Roger Bacon and the State of Science in the 13th Century: Robert Steele, 1921
The Origin and Influence of the Thoroughbred Horse: W. Ridgway, 1905
Natural Science in the Middle Ages: L. Thorndike, 1915
Die Technik der Antike und des Mittelalters: F. M. Feldhaus, 1931
The Inquisition: G. G. Coulton, 1929
The Rise of Universities: C. H. Haskins, 1923
Le Système du Monde: P. Duhem, 5 vols., 1913–7
A History of Mechanical Inventions: A. P. Usher, 1929

SECTIONS 47–48

The Place of Science in Modern Civilization: T. Veblen, 1919
Science and Thought in the 15th Century: Lynn Thorndike, 1929
The Civilization of the Renaissance in Italy: Jacob Burckhardt
The Renaissance: F. Funck-Brentano
Capital and Finance in the Age of the Renaissance: Richard Ehrenberg, translated by H. M. Lucas, 1928
Luxus und Kapitalismus: Werner Sombart, 1913
Krieg und Kapitalismus: Werner Sombart, 1913
Speculations: T. E. Hulme, 1936
The Fifteenth Century: E. F. Jacob, 1930
The Renaissance: E. F. Jacob, 1930
The Ethic of Free Thought: Karl Pearson, 1888

SECTIONS 49–50

The Notebooks of Leonardo da Vinci: E. MacCurdy, 1938
The Literary Works of Leonardo da Vinci: J. P. Richter, 2 vols., 1883
The Mind of Leonardo da Vinci: E. MacCurdy, 1928
Leonardo da Vinci: O. Siren, 1916
Leonardo da Vinci: A Psycho-sexual study of an Infantile Reminiscence: S. Freud, 1916
A Treatise on Painting: by Leonardo da Vinci, English edition, 1802
Leonardo der Techniker und Erfinder: F. M. Feldhaus, 1913
Quaderni d'Anatomia Christiania: 1911–6
Introduction to the Method of Leonardo da Vinci: Paul Valéry, translated by Thomas McGreevy, 1929
The Mechanical Investigations of Leonardo da Vinci: I. B. Hart, 1925
Etudes sur Leonard de Vinci: P. Duhem, 1906
'Leonardo da Vinci': Sidney Colvin, *Encyclopaedia Britannica*, 11th Edition
Vasari on Technique: translated by Louisa S. Maclehose, edited by G. Baldwin Brown, 1907

Lives of the most Eminent Painters: Vasari, 10 vols., 1912
Sciences Physico–Mathematiques: Leonardo da Vinci, 1901
A History of Mechanical Inventions: A. P. Usher, 1929

SECTION 51

A History of Europe: Henri Pirenne, 1939
Capital and Finance in the Age of the Renaissance: Richard Ehrenberg, translated by H. M. Lucas, 1928
Prince Henry the Navigator: C. R. Beazley, 1895
The Dawn of Modern Geography: C. R. Beazley, 1897–1906
The Renaissance: F. Funck-Brentano
Tudor Geography: E. G. R. Taylor
'Christopher Columbus': C. R. Beazley, *Encyclopaedia Britannica*, 11th edition

SECTION 52

De Re Metallica: Georgius Agricola, translated from the first Latin edition of 1556, by H. C. Hoover and L. H. Hoover, 1912
A History of Science, Technology and Philosophy in the XVIth & XVIIth Centuries: A. Wolf, 1935

SECTIONS 53–54

The Cambridge Modern History: William Cunningham, Vol. I
The Renaissance: F. Funck-Brentano
Disme: The Art of Tenths; or, Decimall Arithmetike Invented by the excellent Mathematician Simon Steven: Published in English with some Additions by Robert Norton, Gent., 1608
Galileo and the Freedom of Thought: F. Sherwood Taylor
Source Book of Mathematics: edited by D. E. Smith, 1929
The Science of Mechanics: E. Mach, translated by Thomas J. McCormack, 1919

SECTIONS 55–57

Dialogues Concerning Two New Sciences: Galileo Galilei, translated by H. Crew and A. de Salvio, 1914
The Sidereal Messenger of Galileo Galilei: translated by E. S. Carlos, 1880
Military and Maritime Discipline in Three Books: Captain Thomas Venn, 1672; 'The Compleat Gunner', Galileo
Galileo and the Freedom of Thought: F. Sherwood Taylor, 1938
Galileo: *Encyclopaedia Britannica*, 11th edition
The Private Life of Galileo: Allan-Olney, 1870
Mathematical Collections and Translations in two tomes: Thomas

Salusbury, 1661; "The System of the World', Galileo; in four dialogues

Dante :The Divine Comedy : translated by H. F. Cary, 1897

The Science of Mechanics : E. Mach, translated by Thomas J. Mc-Cormack, 1919

A History of Science, Technology and Philosophy in the XVIth & XVIIth Centuries : A. Wolf, 1935

The Social Function of Science : J. D. Bernal, 1939

SECTIONS 58–59

The Cambridge Modern History : 'Economic Change': William Cunningham, Vol. I, Chap. XV

The Works of Francis Bacon : edited by J. Spedding and R. L. Ellis, 14 vols., 1857–74

The Two Bookes of Francis Bacon : Of the Proficience and Advancement of Learning, 1605

'A True Discourse of the late voyages of discouerie': George Best, 1578; quoted in *Isis,* May, 1939

'Description of a Natural and Experimental History: such as may serve for the foundation of a true philosophy': *Works,* Vol. IV

'Valerius Terminus: of the Interpretation of Nature': Harleian MS 6463, *circa* 1603

'Of the Interpretation of Nature': F. Bacon; edition of *Works,* 1826

'New Atlantis': F. Bacon; edition of *Works,* Vol. II, 1826

'The Great Instauration: The New Organon': *The Works of Francis Bacon,* edited by J. Spedding and R. L. Ellis, Vol. IV

The Dictionary of National Biography : 'Francis Bacon': S. R. Gardiner and T. Fowler

SECTION 60

Otto von Guericke's Neue 'Magdeburgische' Versuche über den leeren Raum : edited by F. Dannemann; Ostwald's Klassiker, Nr. 59

Otto von Guericke : F. W. Hoffmann, 1874

Great Men of Science : P. Lenard, translated by H. S. Hatfield, 1933

Historica civitatis magdeburgensis occupatae et combustae : O. von Guericke, translated by W. Hoffmann

'Otto von Guerickes Forschungswege': W. Kossel; *Die Naturwissenschaften,* 15 Mai 1936

SECTION 61

The Works of the Honourable Robert Boyle in Five Volumes : edited with a life by Thomas Birch, 1744

SECTION 62

The History of the Royal Society : Thomas Sprat, 1667

The Rôle of Scientific Societies in the Seventeenth Century: Martha
  Ornstein, 1928
'Science, Technology and Society in Seventeenth Century England':
  Robert K. Merton; *Osiris*, Vol. IV, part 2, 1938
*A History of Science, Technology and Philosophy in the XVIth & XVIIth
  Centuries:* A. Wolf, 1935

SECTION 63

The Theory and Practice of Finding the Longitude at Sea or Land:
  Andrew Mackay, 2 vols., 1810
The Marine Chronometer: Its History and Development: R. T. Gould,
  with a foreword by F. W. Dyson, F.R.S., 1923
'Navigation': *Encyclopaedia Britannica*, 11th edition
Correspondence and Papers of Edmond Halley: edited by E. F. MacPike,
  1932
Science for the Citizen: Lancelot Hogben, 1938
*A History of Science, Technology and Philosophy in the Sixteenth,
  Seventeenth and Eighteenth Centuries:* A. Wolf, 2 vols., 1935 and 1938

SECTION 64

A Short History of the Steam Engine: H. W. Dickinson, 1939
A History of Mechanical Inventions: A. P. Usher, 1929
'Science, Technology and Society in Seventeenth Century England':
  R. K. Merton; *Osiris*, Vol. IV, part 2, 1938
*A History of Science, Technology and Philosophy in the Eighteenth
  Century:* A. Wolf, 1938
The Social Function of Science: J. D. Bernal, 1939
British Scientists of the Nineteenth Century: J. G. Crowther, 1935
Famous American Men of Science: J. G. Crowther, 1937
'Logic and Probability in Physics': C. G. Darwin; presidential address
  to Section A, British Association, Cambridge, 1938

SECTION 65

The Lunar Society: H. C. Bolton; New York Academy of Sciences, 1888
Life of Mary Anne Schimmelpenninck: 2 vols., 1858
Scientific Correspondence of Joseph Priestley: edited by H. C. Bolton, 1892
*Remarks on the Explanation & cont. concerning the letters of John H.
  Stone:* Peter Porcupine, 1799
Collected Works: Joseph Priestley, 25 vols.
A Short History of Chemistry: J. R. Partington, 1937
Makers of Chemistry: E. J. Holmyard, 1931
*A History of Science, Technology and Philosophy in the Eighteenth
  Century:* A. Wolf, 1938
Science for the Citizen, Lancelot Hogben, 1938

Famous American Men of Science: J. G. Crowther, 1937
James Watt, Craftsman and Engineer: H. W. Dickinson, 1936

SECTION 66

Modern France: edited by A. Tilley, 1922
A History of the French People: Charles Seignobos, 1933
Antoine Lavoisier: Douglas McKie, 1935
Letters Concerning the English Nation: F. M. A. de Voltaire, 1741
A Short History of Chemistry: J. R. Partington, 1937
Makers of Chemistry: E. J. Holmyard, 1931
A History of Science, Technology and Philosophy in the Eighteenth Century: A. Wolf, 1938
Encyclopédie, ou Dictionnaire raisonné des Sciences, des Arts et des Métiers: edited by M. Diderot and M. D'Alembert, 1751, and cont.
'The Plan of the French Encyclopaedia . . .': translated from the Preface of the French Editors, London, 1752

SECTION 67

Science and Life: J. G. Crowther, 1938
Famous American Men of Science: J. G. Crowther, 1937
British Scientists of the Nineteenth Century: J. G. Crowther, 1935
'Science, Technology and Society in Seventeenth Century England': R. K. Merton; *Osiris,* Vol. IV, Part 2, 1938
A History of Science, Technology and Philosophy in the Eighteenth Century: A. Wolf, 1938
Makers of Science, Electricity and Magnetism: D. M. Turner, 1927

SECTION 68

'Industrial Research Laboratories': A List compiled by the Association of Scientific Workers, 1936
Year Book of the Universities of the Empire, 1938

SECTION 69

The Telephone in America: American Telephone and Telegraph Company, 1937
Pictures from the Bell Telephone Laboratories
Bell Telephone System: Technical Publications
Manchester Guardian, 25.7.36, 7.10.38

SECTION 70

The Cambridge University Calendar: 1816, 1840, 1874, 1900
The Universities Year Book, 1938
A History of the Cavendish Laboratory, 1910

The Science of Petroleum, 'Apiezon Oils': C. R. Burch, p. 2594, Vol. IV, 1938
Manchester Guardian, 28.4.37, 21.11.38

SECTIONS 71–72

The Kaiser Wilhelm Gesellschaft for the Promotion of Science : Friedrich Glum, 1930
Aus Leben und Beruf : Fritz Haber, 1927
'Haber Memorial Lecture': J. E. Coates, *Journal* of the Chemical Society, November 1939
Imperial Germany and the Industrial Revolution : Thorstein Veblen, 1915

SECTION 73

On the Encouragement of Fundamental Research : National Union of Scientific Workers, 1924
'Rights and Duties of Science': M. Polanyi, *The Manchester School*, October 1939
The Social Function of Science : J. D. Bernal, 1939
The Craft of Experimental Physics : P. M. S. Blackett, Cambridge University Studies, 1933
T. H. Huxley's Diary of the Voyage of 'H.M.S. Rattlesnake' : Edited by Julian Huxley, 1935
Charles Darwin's Diary of the Voyage of 'H.M.S. Beagle': edited from the MS. by Nora Barlow, 1933
Charles Darwin: The Fragmentary Man : Geoffrey West, 1937
Isaac Newton: A Biography : Louis Trenchard More, 1934
The Search : C. P. Snow
'The Social Implications of Scientific Discovery: Karl T. Compton, Jayne Memorial Lecture, 1938
British Scientists of the 19th Century : J. G. Crowther, 1935

SECTION 74

The Place of Research in Industry : F. B. Jewett, Bell Telephone System Technical Publications, March 1932
The Romance of Research in the Telephone Industry : F. B. Jewett, Bell Telephone System Technical Publications, May 1929

SECTION 75

Committee of the Privy Council for Scientific and Industrial Research: *Report*, 1916
Medical Research Council: *Report*, 1915
National Research Council of the National Academy of Sciences: *Bulletin*, Vol. I, Part I, 1919–21

SECTION 76

Science and Life: J. G. Crowther, 1938
The Scientific Worker: Vol. X, No. 4, 1938
The Social Function of Science: J. D. Bernal, 1939
Science and Civilization: Bernard Lovell, 1939
Annual *Reports* of the Department of Scientific and Industrial Research, the Medical and the Agricultural Research Councils
'Jayne Memorial Lecture': Karl T. Compton, 1938
The Manchester Guardian, 7.6.37, 9.1.39

SECTION 77

Soviet Science: J. G. Crowther, 1936
The Social Function of Science: J. D. Bernal, 1939
Capital: Karl Marx, translated from the third German edition by Samuel Moore and Edward Aveling; seventeenth edition, 1920
Modern Science: H. Levy, 1939

SECTION 78

Recent Social Trends in the United States: 2 vols., 1933
Technological Trends and National Policy: United States Government Printing Office, 1937

SECTION 79

Recent Advances in Medical Science: A Study of their Social and Economic Implications: E. Mellanby, 1939
Technological Trends and National Policy: 1937
The Frustration of Science: 1935
Social Factors in Medical Progress: Bernhard J. Stern, 1927
'Frustration of Technology': Bernhard J. Stern, *Science and Society*, Vol. II, No. 1, 1937
'Restraints Upon the Utilization of Inventions': Bernhard J. Stern, *Annals of the American Academy of Political and Social Science*, November 1938
The Social Function of Science: J. D. Bernal, 1939
Science and Civilization: Bernard Lovell, 1939
The Town that was Murdered: Ellen Wilkinson, 1939
The New Statesman and Nation: 30 September 1939

SECTION 80

'Chemistry and the Quantum Theory': Niels Bohr, *Journal* of Chem. Soc., p. 349, 1932
The Physical Principles of the Quantum Theory: W. Heisenberg, 1930
Speculations: T. E. Hulme, 2nd ed., 1936
The Progress of Science: J. G. Crowther, 1934

SECTION 81

Notes and Records: Royal Society of London, 1938, 1939
The Scientific Worker, Vol. XI, No. 3, 1939
New Worlds for Old: H. G. Wells, 1908
Electric Power Development in the U.S.S.R.: Prepared under the guidance of Benjamin I. Weitz, translated by Leonard E. Mins, 1936
Science at the Cross Roads, 'The Social and Economic Roots of Newton's *Principia*': B. Hessen, 1931
David Guest: A Memoir, edited by Carmel Haden Guest, 1939
'Presidential Address to the British Association': A. Ewing, *Nature,* Supplement, 3 September 1932
'Presidential Address to the British Association': F. G. Hopkins, *Nature,* Supplement, 6 September 1933
'Must Science Ruin Economic Progress?': J. Stamp, *Nature,* 16 September 1933
'Science in Modern Life': F. G. Hopkins, *Nature,* 7 December 1935
'A World Brains Trust': Ritchie Calder, *New Statesman,* 3 September 1938
'International Council of Scientific Unions': *Nature,* 24 April 1937, 22 May 1937
'The Advancement of Science and Society: Proposed World Association': *Nature,* 22 January 1938
Report of 'Committee on Science and its Social Relations', instituted by the International Council of Scientific Unions, 1938
Manchester Guardian, 11.9.36, 10.9.36, 25.8.38
'Science's Magna Charta': *New York Times,* 28 December 1937

SECTION 82

Science for You: J. G. Crowther, 1928
An Outline of the Universe: J. G. Crowther, 1931
British Scientists of the Nineteenth Century: J. G. Crowther, 1935
'A Directorate of Scientific Information': *Nature,* 14 October 1939

SECTION 83

'The Social Responsibilities of Scientists': J. G. Crowther, *The Scientific Worker,* October 1936
'The Frustration of Science': P. M. S. Blackett, *The Frustration of Science,* 1935
The Social Function of Science: J. D. Bernal, 1939
Science and Civilization: Bernard Lovell, 1939

New References

For work bearing on the period of this book, and published since 1939, *Science and Civilization in China* (Cambridge), by Joseph Needham, in course of publication since 1954 in seven volumes, is of major importance.

A guide to recent researches on the History of Science with a similar bearing will be found in the bibliographies in *A General History of the Sciences* (London), published in four volumes, under the editorship of René Taton, from 1963 onwards.

Index